BEE COUNTY COLLEGE
DATE DUE

| AUG 3 1978 | | |
|---|---|---|
| | | |
| | | |
| | | |
| | | |

15199

HD
20.5
.L4

Levin
Linear programming
for management
decisions

AUG 3 1978

15199

HD
20.5
.L4

Levin
Linear programming for
management decisions

# Linear Programming
## for
## Management Decisions

RICHARD I. LEVIN, Ph.D.
*Graduate School of Business Administration*
*University of North Carolina*

RUDOLPH P. LAMONE, Ph.D.
*College of Business and Public Administration*
*University of Maryland*

1969

RICHARD D. IRWIN, INC., Homewood, Illinois
Irwin-Dorsey Limited, Georgetown, Ontario

*Library of Congress Catalog Card No. 68–54729*

*Printed in the United States of America*

This book is dedicated to
Minerva F. Levin
Mary Lamone
Dominic Lamone, Sr.

# *Preface*

This is a book on linear programming, one of the newer quantitative tools available to management today. It was not written for, nor will it have any appeal to, the professional mathematician. Instead it was prepared for students and managers with modest mathematical backgrounds who want to learn more about this valuable technique and its possible applications without having to struggle through complicated notation and proofs on the one hand or to accept rote learning methods on the other.

It contains none of the notation usually found in other linear programming books, nor does it resort to complex mathematical proofs of the linear programming theorems. Instead, it develops linear programming by using representative problems from managerial situations familiar to everyone from their personal experience. It assumes the reader has a modest competence in elementary algebra; the entire presentation is developed from this foundation. There are no mathematical appendices, nor is the term "it can be shown" used anywhere in the book.

In this book we shall not ask the reader to accept and apply any procedure which is not first proven. Our proofs shall be heuristic ones; i.e., extensions and refinements of the way in which most people approach any problem they face. Our objective is to bring the non-mathematical reader to the point where he can solve linear programming problems of modest complexity and completely understand *why* each step of his solution method is necessary, *what* it does, and *why* it works. It is our opinion that any presentation which falls short of these criteria represents dangerous learning for any individual.

Chapter 1 is a customary opening unit. It presents a short history of linear programming and develops the few elementary economic ideas requisite for complete understanding of the possible application areas of this tool.

Chapter 2 explains graphic methods for the solution to linear programming problems; while these are not used in business today because of their inability to handle larger problems, they furnish an excellent foundation on which to develop the several other methods available for solution to operational problems.

Chapter 3 concerns algebraic solution methods for linear programming problems. It uses simple methods of simultaneous equations to solve problems involving no more than three variables.

The fourth and fifth chapters describe the logic and methodology of the simplex solution method in linear programming. This is the operational method most often used for solution of actual operating problems. Methods for both maximizing and minimizing an objective function are treated.

Chapter 6 is devoted to special purpose linear programming methods; here we discuss certain specialized methods useful for a limited class of problems. These are all variants of the general linear programming solution method, each with its special usefulness for a particular class of problem.

Chapter 7 treats operational problems, that is, the practical kinds of problems one runs into in applying linear programming. Special instruction in how to obtain and define input data is given. Helpful operational techniques for treating the problems one encounters in actual solutions are also discussed.

Chapter 8 discusses the economic significance of linear programming to the operating organization. Its relationship to capital budgeting, managerial planning, and evaluation of alternatives is explored in detail.

Applications are the subject of Chapter 9; problems using linear programming selected from the experiences of the authors and others in the field are illustrated and explained. The fields covered include product mix situations, advertising allocations, production-sales balancing, and capital budgeting.

The final chapter concerns the relationship of linear programming and computers. A survey of the computer programs available for the solution of linear programming problems is made, along with suggestions concerning their cost and use.

Our reviewers have been most helpful with their suggestions. In particular we want to thank Mr. Ömer Yağız of Middle East Technical University, Ankara, Turkey; Mr. Morris Slonim of the Bureau of the Census, Washington, D.C.; Charles A. Taff of the University of Maryland; Robert E. Schellenberger of Southern Illinois University; and John Kottas of the University of North Carolina. Our graduate students Frank Budnick and Harry Richardson have been helpful with their comments. Special thanks is also due to Tülin Tanrıkut and Linda Hefler, who prepared the manuscript. We earnestly hope this book will help those people who are interested in developing themselves to better serve the aims of their organizations in today's dynamic decision-making environment.

*December, 1968*                                    RICHARD I. LEVIN
                                                   RUDOLPH P. LAMONE

# Table of contents

**10.   Linear programming and electronic computers**   .   .   276

The computer and its basic units. Basic computer units: *Input.
Memory. Arithmetic. Output. Control.* The stored program. Linear
programming codes: *A sample of linear programming codes.* Using the
codes: *Formulating the problem. Choosing the code. Preparing the unit.
Output.* Computer applications of linear programming problems.

## chapter 1

# *Introduction*

### History

Something less than three quarters of a century ago Frederick W. Taylor and Carl Barth did the pioneering work for a book which they later published under the title *The Art of Cutting Metals*. While the modern student of management and particularly operations research might tend to scoff at their primitive methods of optimization, they did achieve the remarkable feat of isolating and treating with reasonable operating success 13 variables, each of which influenced decision making in that particular field. This early period of management research and discovery did not produce the spectacular quantitative breakthroughs that we know today, but it did demonstrate that certain management problems could be treated using the principles of scientific observation and research.

The serious student of operations research today will remember that as early as 1915, L. W. Harris had derived and used operationally an early model for minimizing the cost of acquiring and storing inventory, a model which often appears with little or no alteration in most operations research books even today. Nor are these two early examples exhaustive of the success which was achieved by these pioneers in management. The concept of Shewhart charts in quality control dates from 1930, and has become the foundation for much of the material currently employed in statistical quality control in industry today.

Contributions to the field of management in the period beginning with World War II, when compared with previous developments seem to differ in two main respects: (1) writers and researchers in the field increased their emphasis on the study of the firm as a whole, i.e., an integrated unit where each decision made takes into effect the total operating environment instead of concentrating in a specific functional field, and (2) the increased development of mathematical tools to aid management in decision making. Combined with the corresponding development of high-speed computers, this approach has given the post-World War II development of management technology a characteristic or personality all its own.

Originally developed to aid in the solution of large tactical and strategic military problems, many of these newer approaches to decision making have carried over into the postwar period with considerable success in nonmilitary endeavors. This body of tools, integrating ideas, and quantitative approaches to decision making have come to be known as operations research. The subject of this book, linear programming, is one of the quantitative tools which falls under this general category of management aids.

## Operations research

There are probably as many definitions of operations research as there are writers in the field. To pick one and label it as the best may perhaps be too presumptuous; however, for a working definition— one which both describes the scope of the field and yet leaves room for the flexibility so desperately needed in management decision making—the authors offer the definition by Professors Miller and Starr, found in *Executive Decisions and Operations Research*. "Operations Research is applied decision theory. It uses any scientific, mathematical, or logical means to attempt to cope with the problems that confront the executive when he tries to achieve a thoroughgoing rationality in dealing with his decision problems." Linear programming is one of the mathematical tools which fits this definition. It has certain specific uses in business decision making which shall of course be discussed in more detail later in this chapter. It is designed to allow the businessman to cope more successfully, if not optimally, with a certain class of problem often encountered in many phases of business operation.

## Linear programming

Linear programming can be defined as a mathematical method of allocating scarce resources to achieve a stated objective when both the objective and the environmental constraints which limit the degree of achievement of the objective can be stated in the form of linear equations and inequalities. Linear programming helps management to determine how it can best use the resources of a business to achieve a specific objective such as maximum profit or minimum cost when the resources have alternate uses. The term *linear* has a specific meaning in this context which shall be treated in some detail shortly. Suffice it to say at this early point that linear implies a fixed, definable relationship between the variables in the problem to be solved. The term *programming* simply refers to the orderly process by which this type of problem is solved; programming in this context means much the same as any orderly problem-solving process in general use today. For instance, it would be completely logical and sound in this context to refer to the process by which one solves a simple algebraic equation as a program, if some orderly, definable approach is used. Again in this sense, one could legitimately refer to the method for the proper lubrication of an automobile as a program without committing any semantic error. Thus linear programming can be thought of as an orderly process for solving a particular kind of problem when the variables in the problem are related in a particular way.

## Linear programming and computer programming

Unfortunately there is some confusion between linear programming and computer programming among people who do not specialize in these fields and a word of clarification may be in order. Linear programming has no specific relationship to computers or computer programming. It is a mathematical procedure which, but for the restraints of time and human endurance, could be worked (solved) entirely by hand. Persons who use linear programming often make use of computers but only to perform the "arithmetic" involved in obtaining the solution.

The decision as to whether a computer should be used in linear programming problems is one based on economic considerations, i.e., the comparison of personnel costs involved in hand solution methods (and the time available) with the expense of using a high-speed computer for the calculations. In this context, the authors have installed linear programming as the solution method for complex yarn balancing problems in textile operations where hand-computed solutions are accomplished weekly by two high school girls, using step-by-step procedures; neither girl has any knowledge of the mathematical principles involved in linear programming. The actual computation time for the weekly yarn schedule involves about 12 hours' time for each girl, but when compared with the cost of programming and operating a computer for constantly changing problems, the management feels this minimum labor cost (and flexibility they gain) is indeed a worthwhile tradeoff. To be more specific, the estimated weekly savings between previously estimated yarn schedules and the optimum schedules achieved by these two young ladies involves a return of over a thousand percent on their investment of labor time.

## History of linear programming

Linear programming is a child of modern mathematics; it is now about 20 years old as an operational tool for problem solving, but its origins go back beyond this in the scientific literature of both mathematics and economics. The first paper on a workable programmed solution method for linear programming (called the simplex method) was published by Dr. George B. Dantzig in 1947. Dr. Dantzig collaborated with Marshall Wood, Alex Orden, and certain other scientists while working on research projects for the U.S. Air Force. The results of this early work form the foundation for procedures to be explained in this book.

The early applications were primarily those in military operations but in a few short years the scientific journals have become full of innovations of Dr. Dantzig's early work. The carry-over from early military applications to business uses of linear programming has been rapid and today thousands of firms make use of this managerial tool. Its uses range from determining the best possible way to saw up logs for lumber to the efficient scheduling of equipment by airlines for different routes to minimize unfilled seats. Later in this chapter we will discuss in more detail several of the uses of linear programming in business today.

### The use of linear programming as a solution method

The need for linear programming as a solution method can be illustrated by a simple problem, common to most businesses today. Let us think of this firm as being small enough to own just one production machine with a capacity of eight hours of work daily. Let us further suppose that the list of possible products this firm can manufacture and successfully sell is shown by the table in Figure 1–1; each product has a known requirement of machine time and a known contribution to the overall profit of the firm.[1]

FIGURE 1–1

| *Possible Products* | | | *The Manufacturing Process* |
|---|---|---|---|
| *Hours per Unit* | *Profit per Unit* | | |
| A........ 2 | $3 | → | |
| B........ 4 | $7 | → | *Machine 1* |
| C........ 1 | $2 | → | *Available* |
| | | | *8* |
| D........ 5 | $6 | → | *hours per day* |
| E........ 3 | $4 | → | |

The decision process concerning the most profitable production schedule for this simulated firm is a simple one. First we would divide the hour requirements of each of the five possible products into the eight hours available on the machine to determine how many of each of the products could be manufactured. Then we would multiply each of these possible production amounts by the profit contribution of each. This has been accomplished in Figure 1–2.

---

[1] The term profit is used here for illustrative purposes only; the concept of the use of contribution to fixed costs and profits as a decision criterion will be developed later in this chapter.

FIGURE 1–2

| Product | Possible Production | Profit Expected |
|---------|--------------------|-----------------|
| A........ | 8/2 =   4 units | 4 × $3 = $12.00 |
| B........ | 8/4 =   2 units | 2 × $7 = $14.00 |
| C........ | 8/1 =   8 units | 8 × $2 = $16.00 |
| D........ | 8/5 = 1.6 units | 1.6 × $6 =  $9.60 |
| E........ | 8/3 = 2.7 units | 2.7 × $4 = $10.80 |

The results of our calculations are obvious. The most profitable production schedule for the company to follow would be to produce eight units of product C, requiring an hour of machine time each, and contributing a total profit to the company of $16 daily. In a problem of this complexity, operationally sound solutions can be found without resorting to involved decision methods, and linear programming  has no value to the decision maker.

Let us now alter the problem such that the products must each

FIGURE 1–3

| Possible Products | Production Hours per Unit | | Profit per Unit |
|-------------------|--------------|--------------|-----------------|
|  | Machine 1 | Machine 2 |  |
| A........ | 2 | $\frac{1}{2}$ | $3 |
| B........ | 4 | 3 | $7 |
| C........ | 1 | 4 | $2 |
| D........ | 5 | 1 | $6 |
| E........ | 3 | 2 | $4 |

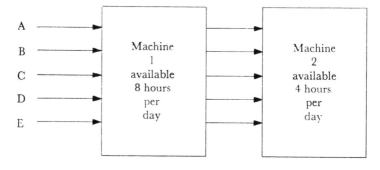

pass through two production processes in the factory. The requirements of each of the products in each of the production processes and the availability of hours in each machine are given in Figure 1–3 along with a schematic diagram of the entire production process.

Let us begin the solution to this expanded problem by taking what we found to be the most profitable solution to the simpler problem and testing it under the new restraint (the addition of a second production process). Eight units of product C which made us a profit of $16, in the first example, could not possibly be produced in the factory since each unit of C requires four hours on the second machine and we have only four hours available on that machine. In fact only one unit of product C could be run through both machines and thus be considered a finished unit. But one unit of C returns only $2, an obviously poor solution. What about other products?

FIGURE 1–4

| Prod-uct | Hours per Unit | | Maximum Production | | Profit per Unit | Total Profit |
|---|---|---|---|---|---|---|
| | Machine 1 | Machine 2 | Machine 1 | Machine 2 | | |
| A.... | 2 | $\frac{1}{2}$ | $8/2 =$ ④ | $4\frac{1}{2} = 8$ | $3 | $12.00 |
| B.... | 4 | 3 | $8/4 = 2$ | $4/3 =$ ①.3 | $7 | $9.10 |
| C.... | 1 | 4 | $8/1 = 8$ | $4/4 =$ ① | $2 | $2.00 |
| D.... | 5 | 1 | $8/5 =$ ①.6 | $4/1 = 4$ | $6 | $9.60 |
| E.... | 3 | 2 | $8/3 = 2.7$ | $4/2 =$ ② | $4 | $8.00 |

If we begin in an orderly fashion with all of the products and calculate the number of each which could be processed through both machines, we first divide the hours available in each of the two machines by the time required for a unit of each product to be manufactured on that machine; then we multiply the maximum number of units of each product which can be produced through both machines by its profit contribution per unit to obtain total possible profit. This has been accomplished in Figure 1–4. The circled figure is the maximum production of each product which can successfully pass through both machines.

Our new solution is to manufacture four units of product A with a total profit contribution of $12. But are we sure with this solution that we have achieved the maximum possible profit contribution?

Have we overlooked the possibility of making various combinations of two products, or various combinations of three, four, or even a combination of all five products? Perhaps some of these combinations will produce a profit higher than that which we could realize by manufacturing just one product.

Without going into the mathematics of just how many combinations of two, three, four, or five products it is possible to make in this simple example, one can see that the total number is quite large, and that if we attempt to solve this problem by enumeration (listing each of the possible combinations and calculating its profit), we are apt to be at it for many hours, if not days. To further complicate even this simple two-machine problem, we must not forget that a solution by enumeration of the possible combinations would have to allow for decimal units of finished product. For example, it is possible to manufacture 1.33 units of a product per day by manufacturing 4 units every three days.

A quick calculation by the authors has established that if we limit the definition of units of product to one decimal place, (1.2, 4.3, etc.) there are enough possible combinations of products which can be made to keep a clerk busy for over 200 hours solving this simple example. Finally we must remember that we have a factory consisting of two machines and a limit of five products. With a more realistic definition of a production process (say 20 processes) and a product line of 50 products, one can see the enormous number of combinations of possible products which results.

### A realistic example from industry

Let us move for a moment from our simple contrived two-machine problem to one in which the authors have been personally involved. This particular manufacturing firm "finishes" textile material, that is, they take cloth from the weaving mills and send it through various chemical and physical processes until it is ready for the market in various patterns, finishes, colors, and so on. In a typical week, the finishing mill has orders for as many as 70 different styles of finished cloth. On the average, unfinished cloth (known as grège goods) must go through at least 12 processes to be finished. Each type of goods requires different chemical treatment, different speeds on the finishing machinery, and different labor requirements for its completion. Also, each type of cloth contributes a certain profit per yard to the company operation. The problem of the production scheduling department in this plant is identical to the contrived two-machine problem, that is, what particular combination (to the nearest yard) of the thousands of possible combinations of the marketable products they produce will return the highest total profit to the company.

In an actual operating situation the highest total profit combination cannot be found by enumeration (calculating every possible combination and comparing them), because by that time the need for the solution would have passed. It is just these sorts of problems involving choice from among thousands, even millions of alternatives that provide a fruitful area of application of the principles of linear programming. Linear programming offers a systematic method of determining in reasonable time, what alternative among a huge number of possible alternatives will best achieve the goals of the company. For this reason, it finds an increasing use in industry today, particularly where cost finding techniques and industrial engineering standards have been intelligently prepared.

## Areas of application of linear programming

The illustrative problems we have discussed so far have concerned the possible use of linear programming to determine the maximum profit combination of products when manufacturing facilities are limited. Aside from this application of the technique, there are many other examples of successful use of linear programming. Here are a few of the many applications.

*1. Petroleum industry.* The typical refinery receives each week large amounts of crude oil to be made into a variety of possible products. The production requirements of each of these products together with its contribution to the total profitability of the refinery are known, as well as the marketing conditions, i.e., price and market demand for each product. Each time a certain product is produced, say gasoline, another series of petroleum products is also produced as a residue of the gasoline cracking process; the number of combinations of products is enormous. Thus the problem of allocation of crude oil among refineries and the determination of the optimum total production schedule in a refinery have furnished a fruitful area for the application of the techniques of linear programming.

*2. Production control.* Because of the seasonal demand for certain products, it is usually necessary for the manufacturing firm to produce for inventory in their off-season and then store the finished goods until the period in which the demand for the items increases; in this manner they utilize the productive facilities to a greater extent and reduce the probability of running out of the item when demand is highest. When storage costs are known, when price fluctuations can be estimated in advance, and with a reasonable sales forecast, linear programming can be of value in determining what product to produce in what period of the manufacturing year to minimize the total cost of storage, overtime, and production costs.

3. *Blending.*   Animal feeds are made from various ingredients each of which contributes a certain number of units of the required nutritional content of the finished mix. Identical nutritional values may be obtained from many different ingredients, the prices of which vary daily. The problem of how to furnish the required nutritional content with the minimum total expenditure for raw materials has provided another operational area for the principles of linear programming. This problem is also common to other blending industries such as fertilizer and pharmaceuticals.

4. *Transportation.*   Many manufacturing firms have multiple plants each of which produces the same items for distribution. It is quite normal for the firm to distribute the finished products from these several manufacturing points to hundreds, even thousands of wholesale or retail points. Transportation costs from each of the manufacturing points to each of the final distribution points are different. Stocks of each of the products which are available at each manufacturing point vary from time to time and the requirements of each final distribution point are different. Thus it is possible to arrange an almost infinite number of distribution schedules, each with its own total cost. Linear programming methods have been designed which make this particular problem routine and which yield the lowest total cost of distribution as long as costs are accurately known.

5. *Waste and trim application.*   Many manufacturing processes produce finished material in large sizes which is later cut to fit individual customer orders. The corrugated board industry is a good example of this procedure. When an order for a small item is to be cut from a roll or sheet of a larger board paper, considerable trim waste results. The problem of how to cut the board or paper so that customer requirements, inventory stocks, and production capabilities are coordinated to yield the least possible waste due to trimming is one that can often be solved with the aid of linear programming.

*6. Agricultural applications.* Most field crops have specific requirements as to soil type, water, drainage, location, capital inputs required, and labor requirements. One of the significant agricultural problems particularly where tillable or irrigable acreage is in limited supply is the allocation of crops to specific fields so that the maximum production (measured in some financial terms) results. The choice of which crops should be planted in which fields to achieve the optimum results is a problem often solved by linear programming techniques. The authors are acquainted with one such application in Turkey which is proceeding with highly satisfying results.

*7. Military applications.* The military establishment, with the aid of certain contract research organizations such as the RAND Corporation, has made considerable use of linear programming. The scheduling of airplanes for the Berlin airlift was one of the more successful applications. Other work goes on today in the use of linear programming for troop and weapons deployment and aircraft deployment. Other uses of this technique are concerned with establishing bomb patterns to achieve specific objectives, and the deployment of facilities to minimize damage from enemy attack.

*8. Government applications.* In countries where criteria other than the marketplace and market-determined prices are used for the allocation of resources, linear programming has provided a significant policy decision-making aid. When the objectives to be attained are stated and the resources at the disposal of the planning organization are definable, the optimum allocation of these resources to the society can often be aided with the use of linear programming. An interesting example of the application of this technique has been made in Turkey, where both government-controlled enterprise (State Economic Enterprises) and privately controlled firms operate.

No single list could possibly exhaust the applications field of linear programming. The items cited are to give the reader a general idea of the scope of the use of this technique, and to introduce the requirements and characteristics common to linear programming problems.

## Requirements for a linear programming problem

In order for linear programming to be used effectively in the solution of certain business problems, there are several requirements that must be met by the problem and the problem environment. Like any other quantitative tool, linear programming cannot be used indiscriminantly but must be utilized under certain definable conditions and with certain limitations each of which will be discussed in some detail.

1. Management must have a definite objective in mind which must be defined or stated mathematically: Like most other mathematical tools linear programming requires a certain preciseness of definition of objective. It is one thing to state that the objective in a particular problem is to maximize the total profit contribution of a group of products, when the per unit contribution of each is known with some precision. It is clearly another to state in general terms that the objective is to "do something about the manner in which products are scheduled through a manufacturing plant," without even a cost accounting system to measure the cost and profit contribution of each. In the first example, we have stated the objective in precise enough terms to allow us to use linear programming; in the second example we have not. In terms of an application of linear programming to the area of personnel management (assignment of personnel to vacant position), it would not be sufficient to have as our objective "better assignment of men to jobs." What would normally be required for the successful use of linear programming in this type of problem would be some quantitative measures of the abilities of each of the men to be assigned (with respect to their probable performance in each of the open positions) and some quantitative measures indicating the job requirements of each of the positions to be filled. Then and only then could some optimum "matching" be made with the use of linear programming.

As one final example of the requirement that objectives be stated with mathematical precision, let us turn a moment to the problem of getting the maximum benefit from an advertising program when there are multiple media in which advertisement may take place. The statement of the objective in this particular case cannot simply be "to get better advertising for less money," but must be made more specific. An objective of an advertising program when state mathematically would have to pinpoint exactly what was to be maximized (or minimized). For example, we might state that the objective was to reach the greatest number of readers, or quite possibly to present the advertising in the largest number of different media, or even to advertise so as to reach the fewest number of readers under 21 years. Whatever form the objective may take, it must be stated in quantitative not qualitative terms. When the objective satisfies this requirement, then and only then can linear programming be employed as an effective aid to managerial decision making.

2. The resources involved in the problem must be in limited supply and must be statable in quantitative terms: Since linear programming determines in precise mathematical fashion what alternative is best under constraining conditions, it is only logical that as a problem requirement, those constraints which affect the decision-making process be stated in precise terms also. Secondly, if there are unlimited resources there is obviously no problem at all. In the sample problems presented earlier in this chapter which involved scheduling products through machines, it would not be sufficient to say for example that we are busy in the machine shop this week. What would be required as a mathematical statement of a restraint would be the number of available hours on each machine for the week. Other such restraints to decision making must also be stated in terms at least this precise.

The authors participated in a linear programming installation where the question of undertime (hours worked less than 40 per week) was involved. It became necessary for the management of this concern to state exactly how few hours per week they were willing for the employees to work *before* linear programming could be applied. Had this not been done, it is quite possible that the final solution to the problem would have occasionally scheduled one department to work as few as five hours weekly, especially when inventories rose considerably. Thus linear programming does not substitute for quality input data but only aids in making better decisions when environmental conditions can be stated with some certainty.

One final example of resource or restraint definition will amplify this point. Production scheduling by linear programming in manufacturing operations is usually done within the constraints of a 40-hour week; however the authors participated in one such installation where the management was willing to schedule production for overtime hours if it could be shown that such was profitable action. To define the restraints necessary for this problem, management had to state the number of hours of overtime per week the employees would accept over an extended period of time, and also furnish the increased cost figures for both labor and direct factory overhead which would be occasioned by overtime work. Such precise statements of the restraining conditions would obviously be a great help to decision making even where linear programming is *not* employed.

3. There must be alternative courses of action too numerous for solution by other methods: Though this requirement may seem a little ridiculous, it is included as a further delineation of those problem areas where linear programming will be of benefit. It should be obvi-

ous that when the possible alternatives are small in number and are easily recognized, linear programming has nothing to offer as a solution method. Only when the possible number of alternatives is large does this systematic search method generate a payoff. For simple problems with few alternatives, there are much less sophisticated techniques available such as graphics, and enumeration of the possibilities. The major value of presenting this requirement is to illustrate that linear programming like any other management investment must have a payoff, and that it should be reserved for those problems which will produce just that.

FIGURE 1–5

| When the Value of X Is | The Value of Y Is |
| --- | --- |
| 2 | 4 |
| 4 | 8 |
| 6 | 12 |
| 8 | 16 |
| 10 | 20 |

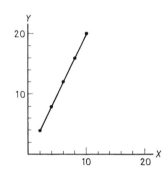

4. The variables in the problem must be linearly related: The term *linear* imposes certain strict requirements on problem solving and for that reason should be thoroughly understood. When two variables are linearly related, this means that a change in one causes an exactly proportionate change in the other. An example of this is shown in Figure 1–5. Suppose that we are observing the behavior of two related variables $X$ and $Y$, and we find they take on the values shown in Figure 1–5. When we plot the values of $Y$ related to corresponding values of $X$ on a graph such as that in Figure 1–5, we notice that the resulting line of relationship is straight, an indication that the relationship between those two variables is linear. A change in one causes an exactly proportionate change in the other. In this case, when $X$ changes one unit, $Y$ changes two units. This relationship is constant (linear) throughout the entire table.

An example of a nonlinear relationship is given by the variables $R$ and $S$ shown in Figure 1–6. When we plot the values of $S$ corresponding to the values of $R$ on a graph we find that they do not take the form of a straight line and therefore are not considered linear. The resulting line of relationship plotted through the points is not straight because a change in $R$ causes a differentially increasing change in $S$. A problem involving this type of relationship would not be suitable for solution by linear programming. There are other solution methods suitable for these types of problems (for example, nonlinear programming).

FIGURE 1-6

| When the Value of R Is | The Value of S Is |
|:---:|:---:|
| 1 | 4 |
| 5 | 10 |
| 10 | 20 |
| 15 | 32 |
| 20 | 60 |

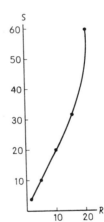

Suppose we look now at a more typical relationship between two variables, specifically volume (in units) and profit per unit for a manufacturing firm. These are the variables we will have to deal with in the typical linear programming problem involving the optimum mix of products. Let us design a mythical company which has fixed overhead per year of $100, and direct costs for labor and materials per unit of $10; the company sells its output at $20 per unit. In Figure 1-7, we have prepared a table showing volume, overhead cost, direct cost, income, and profit per unit for various operating levels. The relationship between volume and profit per unit has also been expressed graphically in the same figure.

It is obvious from the graph in Figure 1-7 that profit per unit and volume are not linearly related. This of course derives from the spread of fixed overhead over greater production volume causing the profit

FIGURE 1–7

| Volume (Units) | Overhead | Direct Cost | Sales | Profit | Profit per Unit |
|---|---|---|---|---|---|
| 1 | $100 | $ 10 | $ 20 | − $ 90 | − $90 |
| 2 | 100 | 20 | 40 | − 80 | − 40 |
| 3 | 100 | 30 | 60 | − 70 | − 20.33 |
| 4 | 100 | 40 | 80 | − 60 | − 15 |
| 5 | 100 | 50 | 100 | − 50 | − 10 |
| 10 | 100 | 100 | 200 | 0 | 0 |
| 20 | 100 | 200 | 400 | 100 | 5 |
| 50 | 100 | 500 | 1,000 | 400 | 8 |
| 100 | 100 | 1,000 | 2,000 | 900 | 9 |

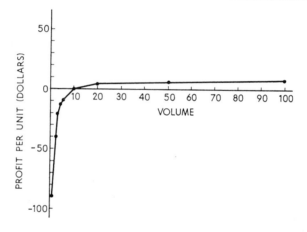

per unit to rise much faster proportionally than volume rises; thus the relationship between volume and profit is not linear. This may seem to present a problem in many linear programming problems which involve volume and profit. Fortunately, however, there is an accounting concept which is used as a surrogate for profit which *does* relate linearly to volume and which will yield the same economic effect as profit in our decision making.

This concept is called *contribution* to fixed costs and profits per unit and is expressed in Figure 1–8. Here we illustrate the same data for the company in Figure 1–7, except that instead of calculating profit per unit we calculate contribution per unit. Just to show that the answers mean the same thing managerially, we have included a profit column at the extreme right of the example so it can be compared with Figure 1–7. Contribution per unit is nothing more than price less direct cost. It does not mean profit; it simply means "here is what is left after we pay labor and materials to cover the fixed overhead and contribute to the eventual profit." Thus a company which maximizes total contribution as a decision-making criterion (and whose overhead is fixed, at least in the short run) accomplishes the same effect as a company which maximizes profit; the only difference is that using contribution per unit (which is linearly related to volume) allows us to employ linear programming, a tool which makes such a requirement upon its variables.

FIGURE 1–8

| Volume | Sales | Direct Cost | | Contribution | Contribution per Unit | Profit |
|--------|-------|-------------|---|--------------|----------------------|--------|
| 1.... | \$ 20— | \$ 10 | = | \$ 10 | \$10 | \$ −90 |
| 2.... | 40— | 20 | = | 20 | 10 | −80 |
| 3.... | 60— | 30 | = | 30 | 10 | −70 |
| 4.... | 80— | 40 | = | 40 | 10 | −60 |
| 5.... | 100— | 50 | = | 50 | 10 | −50 |
| 10.... | 200— | 100 | = | 100 | 10 | 0 |
| 20.... | 400— | 200 | = | 200 | 10 | 100 |
| 50.... | 1,000— | 500 | = | 500 | 10 | 400 |
| 100.... | 2,000— | 1,000 | = | 1,000 | 10 | 900 |

NOTE: Fixed overhead, $100; direct cost, $10 per unit; price, $20.

Without graphing contribution one can ascertain directly from Figure 1–8 that it is constant per unit regardless of sales volume, and that if one graphs total contribution it is easily seen that it rises exactly proportionally to sales volume. The concept of contribution is related to a cost accounting system known as "direct costing," in use since about 1936. An alternate method of illustrating this same point would be simply to subtract the direct cost of $10 per unit for labor and materials from the price of $20 per unit and see that no matter what the production volume is, the contribution of each unit produced to the payment of fixed overhead and the eventual creation of profit is still $20 − $10 or $10. Thus a correct statement of the objective in product mix problems is: "find that particular mix which maximizes the total contribution to fixed costs and eventual profits" as opposed to saying incorrectly "maximize profits." The net result for the company is the same; however using contribution allows the variables to be linearly related at all levels of volume. The logic of this system is simple. No matter what your product mix solution is, the fixed overhead will still be incurred (at least in the short run) so why let it become a part of the problem?

FIGURE 1-9

| Volume | Fixed Cost | Direct Cost | Total Cost | Total Cost per Unit | Direct Cost per Unit |
|---|---|---|---|---|---|
| 1.... | $1,000 | $ 20 | $1,020 | $1,020 | $20 |
| 2.... | 1,000 | 40 | 1,040 | 520 | 20 |
| 3.... | 1,000 | 60 | 1,060 | 393 | 20 |
| 4.... | 1,000 | 80 | 1,080 | 270 | 20 |
| 5.... | 1,000 | 100 | 1,100 | 220 | 20 |
| 10.... | 1,000 | 200 | 1,200 | 120 | 20 |
| 20.... | 1,000 | 400 | 1,400 | 70 | 20 |
| 50.... | 1,000 | 1,000 | 2,000 | 40 | 20 |
| 100.... | 1,000 | 2,000 | 3,000 | 30 | 20 |

In problems involving minimization of cost, we encounter much the same situation, i.e., which cost to minimize. A look at another simulated company shown in Figure 1-9 will demonstrate that total cost per unit is different at different levels of production, and thus is not linearly related to volume. On the other hand, when direct cost is observed, it is seen to be constant per unit. Thus when a company minimizes its total direct cost (labor and materials) it is pursuing the best possible course of action, because in the short run its fixed overhead will not change and thus in fact total costs are being minimized.

### Linear programming and management functions

Used as an integral part of business decision making, linear programming can play a part in each of the basic management functions. In the simplest possible ordering of managerial duties, we find that the efforts of decision makers are directed at four distinct phases of business operations, *Planning, Organization, Direction,* and *Control.*

There are many recorded examples where linear programming has been made an integral part of each of these four functions.

The fact that optimum production plans can be formulated with the help of linear programming makes the obvious case for its use as a planning tool. When production allocations are made with the preciseness inherent in linear programming there is more reason to believe that realization of planned objectives will be achieved. The fact that a definition of objectives and restraints is called for gives greater certainty to the final realization of objectives. Even when we agree that business conditions will produce deviations from planned objectives which will render them incorrect, we must also grant that defining the problem in precise terms, stating the objectives in clear language, and recognizing and treating the restraints with objectivity all combine to help ensure that the results will be at least near to the planned goals.

The contribution of linear programming to the function of organization has not been as comprehensive as its contribution to the other functions. However there are some significant instances where the use of linear programming has produced workable results in the assignment of personnel within an organization to the vacant positions which exist. In this respect, it has been able to match job requirements with individual skills to an extent not possible with other methods (when the number of alternatives is quite large).

As an aid to the day-to-day direction of activities, linear programming has found wide acceptance. Not only can it aid in the solution to the daily problems involving allocation and the other uses previously mentioned, but it can also guarantee to a greater extent that operating level decisions are being made with reasonable precision. It can relieve certain operating officials from the tedium of calculating and evaluating alternatives by enumeration, and can put day-to-day decision making on a more objective basis.

The process of control involves comparison of actual achievements with planned achievements and the initiation of corrective action. When an executive knows that he has been able to define optimality (in terms of the best possible alternative open to him at the present time), he has established a goal toward which he can work. We may calculate a production mix in a plant, for example, which for many operating reasons may never be realized; however, knowing what the optimum mix is may help operating level officials make more reasonable day-to-day decisions since they at least have the major objective clearly in mind in quantitative terms. Evaluations of operations and personnel can be put on a factual basis when the standard is defined to the extent it is when linear programming is employed. An interesting example of the application of linear programming as a control tool was observed by the authors in a textile operation. After the optimum assignment of orders to departments had been determined by the use of linear programming, there were the usual rearrangements necessary in any operating organization. These were due to customers' last minute calls, temporary labor shortages, and the like. These factors necessitated minor deviations from the optimum production plan in the actual day-to-day operation of the plant. Periodically, these deviations were put back into the original linear programming solution as actual mathematical restraints and the "next-most-optimum" schedule programmed. Then this was used as a control on the ability of the production planning group to adjust to operating deviations using intuitive methods.

### Company requirement for linear programming

Linear programming is no substitute for good management but in fact depends for its success on good management. Precise cost data, so necessary for linear programming success can be generated only by an adequate cost accounting department, or cost analyst. The production data concerning unit capacity requirements, productivity measures, and labor content usually come from the industrial-engineering function. Measures and data concerning the financial restraints under which the company must operate emanate directly from the financial officer of the firm. Data concerning what the market will provide in the way of demand, and what our near term marketing needs are, come from the marketing research department. And finally, the statement and quantification of the objective is a function of the top management of the firm. Without each of these important ingredients, linear programming cannot be used by the operating concern. With the aid of each of these contributing factors it can be an effective tool for the solution of management problems.

# chapter 2

# *The graphical method*

In the previous chapter, we found that linear programming is concerned with the problem of allocating resources to achieve a specific objective such as maximizing profit or minimizing cost when the resources have alternate uses. Three methods for solving such linear programming problems will be presented: the graphical method, the algebraic method, and the simplex method. The same problem will be used to demonstrate each method. In this way, the relationships among the different methods can be grasped more readily.

This chapter is devoted to the graphical method. Since this method can be used only where no more than three variables (products, in this case) are involved, the graphical method is not generally used to solve real-world linear programming problems. However, the method is very effective in providing a conceptual understanding of the solution process itself. Familiarity with the problems which can occur in the simple cases involving only two or three variables provides a great deal of insight into what can happen in the more realistic case with many variables. Finally, an examination of both the graphical and algebraic methods will enable the reader to grasp the mechanics and rationale of the more general method of solution known as the simplex method, discussed in Chapter 4.

### Inequalities and equations

Before presenting and solving the sample problem, it may be help-ful to review briefly two types of mathematical statements. Although less familiar than the equation, the inequality is an important rela-tionship in linear programming. How are the two different? The equation is a very specific statement expressed in mathematical form; it is a mathematical sentence. For example, the statement that the cost of five cabinets must be exactly $50 is, when expressed as an equation, $5X = $50$. The solution, of course, is $10. Why? Because if we substitute $10 for $X$ in the equation, we find that the equation is "satisfied," meaning that the two sides of the equation are equal.

However, since many business problems cannot be expressed in the form of nice, neat equations, the ability to use inequalities is ex-tremely important to the decision maker. Instead of being precise, specifications may provide only that minimum or maximum require-ments be met. For example, the manufacturer of the cabinets is more likely to say that the cost of five cabinets must not exceed $50. And if the cost is less than $50, he certainly will not be unhappy. To express the above statements in mathematical form requires the following *inequality:* $5X \leq $50$. The sign $\leq$ means "is equal to or less than." In this case any total cost equal to or less than $50 satisfies the in-equality. Thus, many solutions are possible. In the equation $5X = $50$ only one solution is possible—$10, no more, no less. An equation, therefore, is much more restrictive than a corresponding inequality.

Let us look at another type of inequality. Suppose that the cabinet manufacturer said that he could sell *at least* 100 cabinets. Expressed as an inequality, this statement is $X \geq 100$. The sign $\geq$ means "is equal to or greater than." Any value equal to or greater than 100 would satisfy this inequality.

Familiar name tags have been given to the terms in an equation or inequality. For review, these are identified in the following equa-tion:

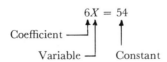

A restriction common to all linear programming problems is that the variables must not be negative, i.e., take on negative values. The absence of such a restriction in solving real-world problems would yield nonsense results. For example, producing a negative number of cabinets is meaningless. In the graphical method this means that the solution must lie in the top right quadrant of the familiar rectangular coordinate system shown in Figure 2–1. In this quadrant both $X$ and $Y$ are positive.

FIGURE 2–1

The Rectangular Coordinate System

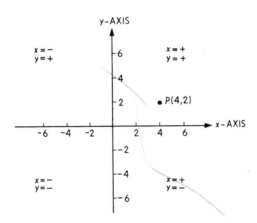

Any point may be located by identifying the coordinates of the point. For example, point $P$ in Figure 2–1 has the coordinates (4, 2). Recalling that the $X$ coordinate is always read before the $Y$ coordinate, point $P$ lies four units along the x-axis to the right of the y-axis and two units along the y-axis, measured upward from the x-axis.

## The sample problem

The graphical method is best demonstrated when applied to a manufacturer who wants to determine the most profitable combination of products to make and sell.

Assume that our manufacturer produces two products, automobile engine pistons and connecting rod pins. Production of each product requires processing in two departments, the lathe department (1), and the drill press department (2). Department 1 has up to 32 hours available. Department 2 can handle up to 34 hours of work. Manufacturing one piston requires three hours in department 1 and one hour in department 2. Each pin requires two hours in department 1 and four hours in department 2.

The profit contribution is $5 per piston and $6 per pin. The company has no difficulty selling all the pistons and pins it can produce. The manufacturer's problem is to determine the best possible combination of pistons and pins to produce in order to maximize profits. The possible profit, however, is limited by the time constraints in each department, since there are only 32 hours available in department 1 and 34 hours available in department 2. Thus, in choosing the best combination of products, the manufacturer must allocate the limited resources of each department in a way which will yield the highest possible profit.

FIGURE 2–2

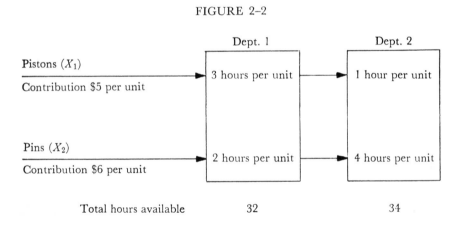

Let us use $X_1$ to represent the optimum number of pistons to be produced and $X_2$ to represent the optimum number of pins to be made. The information needed to solve the problem is summarized in Figure 2–2.

### Step 1.  *Formulate the problem mathematically*

To begin solving the problem, we must restate the information in mathematical form. Our manufacturer realizes a profit contribution of $6 per piston and $5 per pin. His objective is to make as much profit as possible on all the pistons and pins produced. We can express the objective as an equation

$$P = \$5X_1 + \$6X_2$$

where

$$P = \text{Profit}$$
$$\$5X_1 = \text{Total profit from sale of pistons}$$
$$\$6X_2 = \text{Total profit from sale of pins.}$$

This equation is referred to as the *objective function* which shows the relationship of output to profit.

We have two constraints which will limit the extent to which profit can be maximized: (1) the time available in department 1, and (2) the time available in department 2. The time used in producing pistons and pins must certainly not exceed the total time available in the departments. In other words, the hours required to make one piston times the number of pistons produced, plus the hours necessary to make one pin times the number of pins produced must be equal to or less than the time available in each department. From the data given in Figure 2-2, we can express these constraints as inequalities.

$$3X_1 + 2X_2 \leq 32 \qquad \text{(dept. 1)}$$
$$X_1 + 4X_2 \leq 34 \qquad \text{(dept. 2)}$$

The first inequality above states that the hours required to produce one piston (3 hours) times the number of pistons produced ($X_1$), plus the hours necessary to make one pin (2 hours) times the number of pins made ($X_2$), must be equal to or less than the 32 hours available in department 1. A similar explanation applies to the second inequality.

For reasons already given, all values of the variables in the solution of any linear programming problem must be positive. In our problem, this means that the variables must be greater than or equal to zero ($X_1 \geq 0$, $X_2 \geq 0$).

The mathematical formulation of the problem can now be summarized.

Maximize:

$$P = \$5X_1 + \$6X_2$$

Subject to these constraints:

$$3X_1 + 2X_2 \leq 32$$
$$X_1 + 4X_2 \leq 34$$
$$X_1 \geq 0$$
$$X_2 \geq 0.$$

### Step 2.    Graph the constraints

Our next step is to plot the constraints in the problem on a graph, with $X_1$ shown on the $x$-axis and $X_2$ shown on the $y$-axis. Figure 2–3 shows the $X_1$ and $X_2$ axes.

FIGURE 2–3

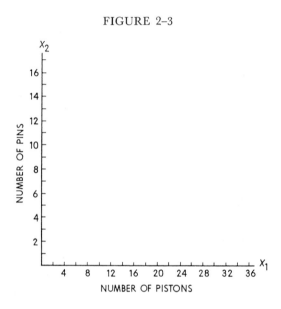

Before graphing the first inequality, $3X_1 + 2X_2 \leq 32$, let us note that it consists of two parts: an equality part and an inequality part. Thus the possible combinations of pistons and pins that can be processed in department 1 will be all points which satisfy either

$$3X_1 + 2X_2 = 32$$

or

$$3X_1 + 2X_2 < 32.$$

Now the equality, $3X_1 + 2X_2 = 32$, may be plotted on the graph by first locating its two terminal points and joining these points by a straight line. To locate these points we proceed as follows:

a) If we assume that *all* the time available in department 1 is used in processing pins—that production of pistons is zero—then 16 pins could be made. Thus, if we let $X_1 = 0$, then $X_2 = 16$.

Proof:

$$3X_1 + 2X_2 = 32$$
$$3(0) + 2X_2 = 32$$
$$X_2 = 16 \text{ pins.}$$

Our first point then, is $(0, 16)$, meaning the production of 0 pistons and 16 pins.

   *b*)  To find the second point we now assume that all the time available in department 1 is used in making pistons—that the production of pins is zero. Under this assumption we could produce $10\frac{2}{3}$ pistons. Thus, if we let $X_2 = 0$, then $X_1 = 10\frac{2}{3}$.

   Proof:

$$3X_1 + 2X_2 = 32$$
$$3X_1 + 2(0) = 32$$
$$X_1 = 10\frac{2}{3} \text{ pistons.}$$

Our second point, therefore, is $(10\frac{2}{3}, 0)$, meaning the production of $10\frac{2}{3}$ pistons and 0 pins. Locating these two points $(0, 16)$ and $(10\frac{2}{3}, 0)$ and joining them gives us the straight line shown in Figure 2–4.

   The inequality part of our first constraint, $3X_1 + 2X_2 < 32$ is the entire shaded area to the left of the line $BC$. Thus the graph of the inequation, $3X_1 + 2X_2 \leq 32$, including both parts, is the entire area $ABC$ which lies *on* or *to the left* of the line $BC$. To graph the inequality,

FIGURE 2–4

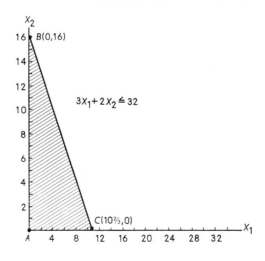

therefore, we simply graph the equality. The resulting line forms the upper boundary of the area represented by the inequality.

Let us now examine several combinations of pistons and pins shown as points in Figure 2–5.

FIGURE 2–5

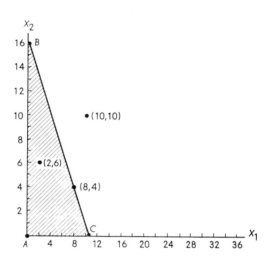

*Any* combination of pistons and pins on line *BC* will use up all the 32 hours available in department 1. For example, producing 8 pistons and 4 pins, point (8, 4) on the graph, will require all of the available 32 hours: 8(3 hours) + 4(2 hours) = 32 hours. Any point to the left of the line will result in unused capacity, i.e., all the hours will not be used. If, for example, we produced 2 pistons and 6 pins, point (2, 6), the total required time would be 18 hours:

$$2(3 \text{ hours}) + 6(2 \text{ hours}) = 18 \text{ hours.}$$

Thus 14 hours (32 − 18) are left unused. Can we produce 10 pistons and 10 pins, point (10, 10)? This would require 50 hours:

$$10(3 \text{ hours}) + 10(2 \text{ hours}) = 50 \text{ hours.}$$

The answer is therefore no, because the hours needed exceed the hours available. This point (10, 10) or indeed, *any* combination of pistons and pins which lies to the right of the line *BC cannot* be produced without violating the constraint, i.e., exceeding the 32 hours available. We can produce *only* those combinations of pistons and pins which lie within the area $ABC$.

A similar explanation applies to the graph of the second constraint for department 2 represented by the inequality $X_1 + 4X_2 = 34$. Using the same procedure explained above, the terminal points are located as follows:

   *a*) Let

$$X_1 = 0;$$

then

$$X_2 = 34/4 = 8\tfrac{1}{2}$$

First point: $(0, 8\tfrac{1}{2})$.

   *b*) Let

$$X_2 = 0;$$

then

$$X_1 = 34$$

Second point: $(34, 0)$.

Joining these two points gives the line $EF$ in Figure 2–6, representing all combinations of pistons and pins which use up exactly 34 hours $(X_1 + 4X_2 = 34)$. The shaded area $AEF$ contains *all* possible combinations which may use less than or up to the 34 hours available $(X_1 + 4X_2 \leq 34)$. Thus any point—any combination of pistons and pins falling within the shaded area $AEF$—will satisfy the time restric-

FIGURE 2–6
Capacity Restriction in Department 2

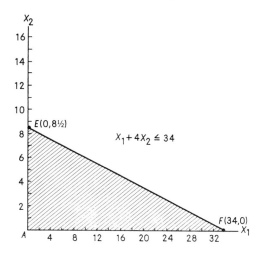

FIGURE 2–7
Graphical Representation of Problem Constraints

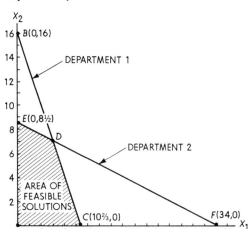

tion in department 2. Conversely, any point outside the shaded area will violate the time restriction in department 2.

In graphing the two constraints, we have found the combinations of pistons and pins which may be processed in each department without violating the time restrictions. However, in order to *complete* a piston or pin, *both* departments must be used. Our task, then, is to find an area which is common to both areas described by the separate graphs for each department so that the best combination of *completed* pistons and pins will not exceed the available time in either department. To find this common area we simply plot the two original inequalities (see Figures 2–4 and 2–6) on the same $X_1$ and $X_2$ axes. This we have done in Figure 2–7.

The area that does not exceed the time constraints in either department—the shaded area *AEDC* in Figure 2–7—contains all possible combinations of pistons and pins satisfying the inequalities

$$3X_1 + 2X_2 \leq 32$$

$$X_1 + 4X_2 \leq 34.$$

To illustrate, three combinations have been located as points in Figure 2–8.

FIGURE 2–8

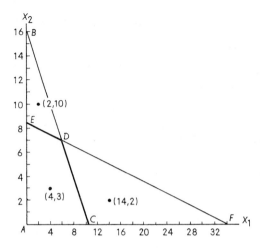

*Example (a).*    Four pistons and three pins

Dept. 1    $3X_1 + 2X_2 \leq 32$ hours available

$3(4) + 2(3) = 18$ hours required

Dept. 2    $X_1 + 4X_2 \leq 34$ hours available

$(4) + 4(3) = 16$ hours required.

The time required to make four pistons and three pins falls within the time available in both departments. The reader may verify that any point within the common area *AEDC*, referred to as the area of feasible solutions, will use less than or up to the time available in both departments.

*Example (b).*    Two pistons and 10 pins

Dept. 1    $3X_1 + 2X_2 \leq 32$ hours available

$3(2) + 2(10) = 26$ hours required

Dept. 2    $X_1 + 4X_2 \leq 34$ hours available

$(2) + 4(10) = 42$ hours required.

In the above example we find that the time required to make two pistons and 10 pins falls within the time available in department 1 but *exceeds* the time available in department 2. Thus this combination is not possible, since it falls outside the area of feasible solutions.

*Example (c).*    Fourteen pistons and two pins

Dept. 1    $3X_1 + 2X_2 \leq 32$ hours available

$3(14) + 2(2) = 46$ hours required

Dept. 2    $X_1 + 4X_2 \leq 34$ hours available

$(14) + 4(2) = 22$ hours required.

In this example, the time required to make 14 pistons and 2 pins falls within the time available in department 2 but *exceeds* the time available in department 1. Thus it would be impossible to produce this combination given the present time constraints.

### Step 3.    Test the corner points of the feasible solutions area

Our goal is to choose that combination of pistons and pins which will maximize profit given the time restrictions in each department. For reasons to be explained later, the optimum combination in the graphical solution to *any* linear programming problem will be found at one of the corner points of the area of feasible solutions; in our problem, this is the area *AEDC*. We already have three of the four corner points (see Figure 2–7):

$$A \ (0, 0)$$
$$E \ (0, 8\tfrac{1}{2})$$
$$C \ (10\tfrac{2}{3}, 0).$$

How can we locate point *D*? Reading its location from a precisely drawn graph is one possibility. Another method is to solve simultaneously the equations of the two lines which intersect at point *D*, the only point common to both equations. To solve these two equations

$$3X_1 + 2X_2 = 32$$
$$X_1 + 4X_2 = 34$$

we proceed as follows:

a) Multiply the first equation by $(-2)$:

$$-2(3X_1 + 2X_2 = 32) = -6X_1 - 4X_2 = -64.$$

Add the second equation:

$$\begin{array}{rcr} X_1 + 4X_2 = & 34 \\ \hline -5X_1 \quad\quad = & -30 \\ X_1 \quad\quad = & 6 \end{array}$$

*b*) Now substitute 6 for $X_1$ in the second equation:

$$X_1 + 4X_2 = 34$$
$$6 + 4X_2 = 34$$
$$4X_2 = 28$$
$$X_2 = 7.$$

Point *D*, thus, is (6, 7).

We can now test the four corner points of the area of feasible solutions by substituting the values of each point in the objective function $(P = \$5X_1 + \$6X_2)$.

Point *A* (0, 0): $\$5(0) + \$6(0) = 0$

Point *E* $(0, 8\frac{1}{2})$: $\$5(0) + 6(8\frac{1}{2}) = \$51$

Point *C* $(10\frac{2}{3}, 0)$: $\$5(10\frac{2}{3}) + \$6(0) = \$53\frac{1}{3}$

Point *D* (6, 7): $\$5(6) + \$6(7) = \$72.$

The optimum combination, six pistons and seven pins, located at point *D* yields a maximum profit of $72. Substituting 6 for *X*, and 7 for $X_2$ in the constraints, we find that the optimum solution uses up the time available in each department.

Dept. 1    $3X_1 + 2X_2 \leq 32$ hours available

$3(6) + 2(7) = 32$ hours required

Dept. 2    $X_1 + 4X_2 \leq 34$ hours available

$(6) + 4(7) = 34$ hours required.

As will be shown in another section, there may be cases where the optimum solution will result in unused capacity.

Let us now examine why the most profitable combination of pistons and pins occurs at corner point *D*(6, 7). To do this, we must plot the objective function $(P = \$5X_1 + \$6X_2)$ directly on the graph of the feasible solutions area.

In order to graph the objective function, we first let profit equal some dollar figure that we can attain without violating a restriction. We have arbitrarily chosen to let profit equal $30, a profit easily attainable. Then the objective function is $\$30 = \$5X_1 + \$6X_2$. We now locate the two terminal points:

when

$$X_1 = 0$$
$$\$30 = \$5(0) + \$6X_2$$
$$X_2 = \$5$$

and when

$$X_2 = 0$$
$$\$30 = \$5X_1 + \$6(0)$$
$$X_1 = \$6.$$

Joining these two points gives the line shown in Figure 2–9.

FIGURE 2–9
Objective Function Plotted

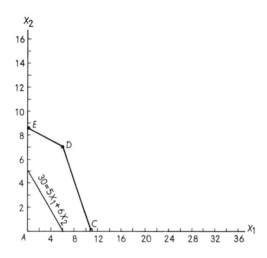

The objection function ($30 = $5X_1 + $6X_2$) graphed in Figure 2–9 represents all the possible combinations of pistons and pins which would yield a total profit of \$30. For example the point $(3, 2\frac{1}{2})$ is located on this line.

$$\$5(3) + \$6(2\tfrac{1}{2}) = \$30.$$

Suppose we graph another line representing all combinations of pistons and pins which would result in a profit of \$45. In other words, we will graph a line represented by the profit equation, $\$45 = \$5X_1 + \$6X_2$. This line is illustrated in Figure 2–10 together with the line of the previous profit equation, $\$30 = \$5X_1 + \$6X_2$.

Let us examine the significance of these parallel profit lines. The second profit line ($\$45 = \$5X_1 + \$6X_2$) represents all combinations which would yield a \$45 profit. The second profit line, then, generated more profit than the first line, ($45 versus $30). Furthermore,

FIGURE 2–10
Two Profit Lines Plotted

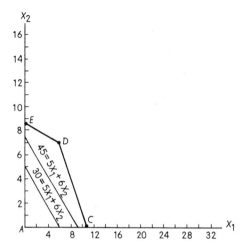

it is parallel to the first line, but farther from the origin, point $A$ (0, 0). In order to maximize profit, therefore, we need to find a profit line which is as far as possible from the origin, but has one point in common with the area of feasible solutions. This line, represented by the profit equation $\$72 = \$5X_1 + \$6X_2$, is shown in Figure 2–11 together with the first two profit lines.

FIGURE 2–11
Three Profit Lines Plotted

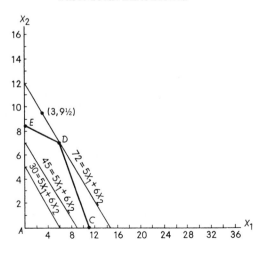

Obviously, the third profit line in Figure 2–11 passes through point *D* which we know to be the optimum combination. Now look at point $(3, 9\frac{1}{2})$ on the line. This combination also results in a profit of \$72 $[5(3) + \$6(9\frac{1}{2}) = \$72]$. However, since it falls outside the feasible solutions area, producing this combination would not be possible given the constraints in our problem. On the other hand, point *D* lies on profit line 3 and is still within the area of feasible solutions; thus it represents the most profitable combination of pistons and pins.

## Exchange rates

The fact that the most profitable combination is found at point *D* can be further amplified by observing what happens to profit as we move from one corner point to another in the feasible solutions area. For convenience, they are repeated below:

Point *A* $(0, 0)$

Point *C* $(10\frac{2}{3}, 0)$

Point *E* $(0, 8\frac{1}{2})$

Point *D* $(6, 7)$.

Moving from point *A* $(0, 0)$, producing no pistons and no pins, to point *C* $(10\frac{2}{3}, 0)$ results in a profit of \$53.33 $[\$5(10\frac{2}{3}) + \$6(0) = \$53.33]$. Referring to Figure 2–7, we find that $10\frac{2}{3}X_1$ represents the maximum number of pistons that can be processed in department 1; all 32 hours are utilized. This means that moving from point *C* to point *D* will require giving up the production of some pistons. Let us examine the effect of giving up the production of one $X_1$ (piston), i.e., produce $9\frac{2}{3}X_1$ in department 1: To do this we simply substitute $9\frac{2}{3}$ for $X_1$ in the equation representing department 1 and solve for $X_2$:

$$3X_1 + 2X_2 = 32$$
$$3(9\frac{2}{3}) + 2X_2 = 32$$
$$29 + 2X_2 = 32$$
$$2X_2 = 3$$
$$X_2 = 1\frac{1}{2}.$$

By giving up the production of one piston, we can make $1\frac{1}{2}$ pins. This is as expected, since processing one piston requires three hours and one pin only two hours in department 1. What effect does this change have on profit? The profit contribution for pistons and pins is \$5 and \$6 respectively. The net effect of giving up one piston to make $1\frac{1}{2}$ pins is shown below.

| | |
|---|---:|
| Profit gained by making $1\frac{1}{2}$ pins...... | $6(1\frac{1}{2}) = \$9$ |
| Profit lost by giving up 1 piston...... | 5 |
| Net profit gained............ | \$4 |

Obviously, giving up one piston to make $1\frac{1}{2}$ pins is a profitable move. At point $C$ $(10\frac{2}{3}, 0)$ total profit is \$53.33. But moving up to the point $(9\frac{2}{3}, 1\frac{1}{2})$ on the $DC$ line segment would give a total profit of \$57.33 (\$53.33 + \$4). Furthermore, the tradeoff or *exchange rate* between pistons $(X_1)$ and pins $(X_2)$ will be the same for all of line $BC$ representing the capacity restriction in department 1. Why? In Chapter 1 we found that the relationship between two variables is *linear* when a change in one causes an exactly proportionate change in the other. In other words, the exchange rate between pistons and pins in department 1 $(3X_1 + 2X_2 = 32)$ is constant, as shown in the example below:

| Pistons $(X_1)$ | Pins $(X_2)$ |
|:---:|:---:|

$$
\begin{array}{ccccc}
 & 10\frac{2}{3} & & 0 & \\
1\left[\phantom{x}\right. & & & \left.\phantom{x}\right] & 1\frac{1}{2}* \\
 & 9\frac{2}{3} & & 1\frac{1}{2} & \\
1\left[\phantom{x}\right. & & & \left.\phantom{x}\right] & 1\frac{1}{2} \\
 & 8\frac{2}{3} & & 3 & \\
1\left[\phantom{x}\right. & & & \left.\phantom{x}\right] & 1\frac{1}{2} \\
 & 7\frac{2}{3} & & 4\frac{1}{2} & \\
1\left[\phantom{x}\right. & & & \left.\phantom{x}\right] & 1\frac{1}{2} \\
 & 6\frac{2}{3} & & 6 &
\end{array}
$$

\* Increase in $X_2$ for every one unit decrease in $X_1$

We have already shown that the tradeoff between $X_1$ and $X_2$ was a profitable one. Moving from point $C$ to $D$, we give up $4\frac{2}{3}$ pistons $(10\frac{2}{3} - 6)$ and make 7 pins $(0 + 7)$. The *total* net gain is:

| | | |
|---|---:|---|
| Make 7 pins $(7)(\$6)$ | = \$42.00 | Gain |
| Give up $4\frac{2}{3}$ pistons $(4\frac{2}{3})(\$5) =$ | 23.33 | Loss |
| Total net gain | \$18.67 | |
| Profit at point $C$ $(10\frac{2}{3})(\$6)$ = | 53.33 | |
| Total profit at point $D$ | \$72.00 | |

Conversely, if we move from point $D$ to point $C$, total profit would decrease.

A similar explanation applies to the move from point $D$ to point $E$.

In this case however, total profit would decrease. First note that line segment $ED$ is on line $EF$ representing the capacity restriction in department 2 ($X_1 + 4X_2 = 34$). Processing one piston ($X_1$) requires one hour and processing one pin requires four hours. Thus if we give up one piston we can make $\frac{1}{4}$ pin. As shown in the following example this is not a very profitable exchange.

$$\begin{array}{lcrl}
\text{Make } \tfrac{1}{4} \text{ pin } (\tfrac{1}{4})(\$6) & = & \$1.50 & \text{Gain} \\
\text{Give up 1 piston } (1)(\$5) & = & \underline{\phantom{0}5.00} & \text{Loss} \\
\text{Net loss on exchange} & & \$-3.50 &
\end{array}$$

Conversely, moving from point $E$ to point $D$ is profitable. At point $E$ we are producing the maximum number of pins ($X_2$), i.e., $X_1 = 0$. For every pin we give up we can make four pistons, the result being a profitable exchange.

$$\begin{array}{lcrl}
\text{Make 4 pistons } (4)(\$5) & = & \$20 & \text{Gain} \\
\text{Give up 1 pin } (1)(\$6) & = & \underline{\phantom{0}6} & \text{Loss} \\
\text{Net gain on exchange} & & \$14 &
\end{array}$$

Summarizing, the moves from $E$ to $D$ and $C$ to $D$ are profitable. Any move away from point $D$ ($D$ to $E$ or $D$ to $C$) is not profitable. Using the concept of exchange rates, we have shown why point $D$ is indeed the most profitable combination. Exchange rates and their significance to the decision maker will be discussed in more detail in Chapter 4.

### Alternate optima

By delineating the feasible solutions area, we have solved the manufacturer's problem. What effect would a change in the profit contribution of each product have on the feasible solutions area? Since the objective function played no part in defining the area of feasible solutions, the answer is that a change in the objective function will have no effect on the feasible solutions area. It will, however, result in a new optimum combination of pistons and pins.

For example, suppose the profit contribution is $3 per piston and $12 per pin. In this case a new objective function must be maximized.

Maximize:

$$P = \$3X_1 + \$12X_2$$

Subject to:

$$3X_1 + 2X_2 \leq 32 \qquad \text{(Dept. 1)}$$
$$X_1 + 4X_2 \leq 34 \qquad \text{(Dept. 2)}$$
$$X_1 \geq 0$$
$$X_2 \geq 0$$

Since the inequalities are the same as those in the original problem, the feasible solutions area will be the same; only the objective function has changed. Testing the corner points of the feasible solutions area in this new objective function $(P = \$3X_1 + \$12X_2)$ gives the following results:

Point $A$ (0, 0): $\$3(0) + \$12(0) = 0$
Point $E$ (0, $8\frac{1}{2}$): $\$3(0) + \$12(8\frac{1}{2}) = \$102$
Point $C$ ($10\frac{2}{3}$, 0): $\$3(10\frac{2}{3}) = \$12(0) = \$32$
Point $D$ (6, 7): $\$3(6) + \$12(7) = \$102$

We now have *two* different combinations of pistons and pins that yield a maximum profit of $102, points $D$ and $E$. In fact if we plot the new objection function on the graph of the original feasible solutions area, we will find that there are not two but many different combinations of pistons and pins which yield the *same* maximum

FIGURE 2–12
Alternate Optima

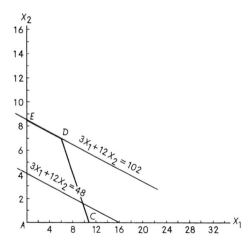

profit, hence the term *alternate optima*. Using the same procedure previously explained, we have plotted two profit lines in Figure 2–12.

Note that the profit lines are parallel to line *ED* which forms part of the boundary of the feasible solutions area. Hence, as we shift the profit line away from the origin, it will coincide with the line segment *ED*. Each point on this line *ED*, including the corner points *E* and *D*, represents a different combination of pistons and pins which can be produced giving the same profit of $102. If we were to shift the second profit line further from the origin, then there would be no point in common with the area of feasible solutions.

Previously we stated that the optimum solution to *any* linear programming problem would be found at one of the corner points of the feasible solutions area. In some cases, as the example above shows, the solution may consist of a whole line segment, but even then there is at least one corner point solution, i.e., points *E* and *D*.

### Optimum solution with unused capacity

In the solution to the sample problem, we used up all the hours available in each department. Assume that the pistons and pins had to be processed in a third department, having 60 hours available. A piston requires two hours and a pin requires four hours in this third department. The problem is shown as follows.

Maximize:

$$P = \$5X_1 + \$6X_2$$

Subject to:

$$3X_1 + 2X_2 \le 32 \qquad \text{(Dept. 1)}$$
$$X_1 + 4X_2 \le 34 \qquad \text{(Dept. 2)}$$
$$2X_1 + 4X_2 \le 60 \qquad \text{(Dept. 3)}$$
$$X_1, X_2 \ge 0.$$

What effect will the addition of the new third constraint have on the feasible solutions area? In Figure 2–13, the graph of the third inequality is shown together with the feasible solutions area defined by the original two constraints, departments 1 and 2.

The line representing the capacity restriction of department 3 falls completely above the area of feasible solutions. Thus, the original set of feasible solutions is not changed and the optimum solution is the same as before—point *D*. Department 3 is not as restrictive as

FIGURE 2–13
Redundant Constraint

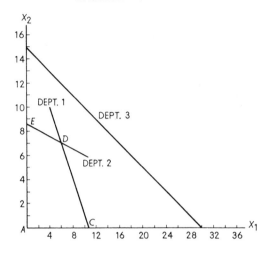

departments 1 and 2. Expressed another way, the manufacturer has more than enough time in department 3 to make any of the possible combinations in the area *AEDC*. For example, the optimum combination, six pistons and seven pins, would require only 40 of the 60 hours available in this department, leaving 20 hours unused time.

$$2X_1 + 4X_2 = 60 \text{ hours available}$$
$$2(6) + 4(7) = 40 \text{ hours required.}$$

In this case, departments 1 and 2 are the limiting departments; all available time has been used. Although we have 20 hours unused capacity in department 3, no more pistons and pins can be made until capacity is expanded in departments 1 and 2. Thus, the third constraint is redundant; it is not a key factor in this problem and can be ignored. Redundant constraints will be discussed further in Chapter 7.

## A minimization problem

We turn now to a different type of problem where the objective is to *minimize* costs subject to certain restraints. Suppose an animal feed company has developed a new dog food consisting of two ingredients, A and B, which cost $3 and $5 per pound respectively. Each pound of ingredient A contains six units of protein, two units of fat, and two units of carbohydrates. Each pound of ingredient B contains 2 units of protein, 4 units of fat, and 10 units of carbohydrates. Each bag of the dog food should contain at least 18 units of protein, 16 units of fat, and 20 units of carbohydrates. The company's problem is to find the best combination of ingredients A and B which will meet the minimum requirements of protein, fats, and carbohydrate at the least cost. The problem information is summarized in Figure 2–14.

FIGURE 2–14
Data for Minimization Problem

| | Units of Nutrients in Ingredient | | Minimum Units of Nutrient Required |
| --- | --- | --- | --- |
| | A ($3/lb.) | B ($5/lb.) | |
| Protein............. | 6 | 2 | 18 units |
| Fats.............. | 2 | 4 | 16 units |
| Carbohydrates...... | 2 | 10 | 20 units |

To solve this minimization problem, we follow the same procedure used in solving the maximization problem: First, we express the problem in mathematical form. Suppose we let $X_1$ equal the number of pounds of ingredient A and $X_2$ the number of pounds of ingredient B. Given the cost per pound for each ingredient, the objective function is

Minimize cost:

$$C = \$3X_1 + \$5X_2.$$

There are three constraints representing the minimum requirements for each nutrient.

$$6X_1 + 2X_2 \geq 18 \text{ units (protein)}$$
$$2X_1 + 4X_2 \geq 16 \text{ units (fats)}$$
$$2X_1 + 10X_2 \geq 20 \text{ units (carbohydrates).}$$

Note that these constraints represent a different type of inequality ($\geq$). This type of inequality is used to represent minimum require-

FIGURE 2–15

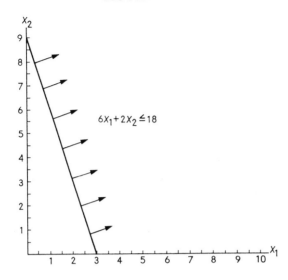

$6X_1 + 2X_2 \leq 18$

ments; for example, in this problem, each nutrient must be *at least* of a certain value.

The first constraint states that the number of units of protein in ingredient A (6) times the number of pounds of ingredient A ($X_1$), plus the units of protein in ingredient B (2) times the number of pounds in ingredient B ($X_2$), must be greater than or equal to 18 units of protein. A similar explanation applies to the second and third constraints.

The next step is to graph the three constraints, using the same procedure previously explained. In Figure 2–15 we have graphed the first constraint.

Note that all combinations of $X_1$ and $X_2$ which satisfy this type of inequality ($\geq$) fall on and to the *right* of the line in Figure 2–15. This type of inequality ($\geq$) represents a lower boundary for the feasible solutions. Compare this to the less-than-or-equal-to type which provides the upper boundary for the feasible solutions in a given constraint. All three constraints are shown in Figure 2–16.

The area of feasible solutions consists of all points falling on and to the right of the line segments *AB*, *BC*, and *CD*, area *ABCD*.

Finally to find the least cost combination, we test each corner point of the feasible solutions area. The points for *B* and *C* given in

FIGURE 2-16

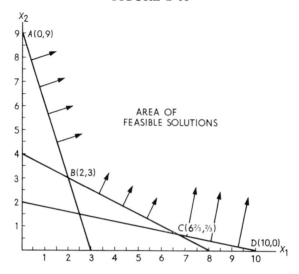

Figure 2-16 were obtained by solving simultaneously the equations of the lines which intersect at those points. Given the objective function, $C = \$3X_1 + \$5X_2$, we can find the least cost combination.

> Point $A$ (0, 9): $\$3(0) + \$5(9) = \$45$
> Point $B$ (2, 3): $\$3(2) + \$5(3) = \$21$
> Point $C$ ($6\frac{2}{3}$, $\frac{2}{3}$): $\$3(6\frac{2}{3}) + \$5(\frac{2}{3}) = \$23.33$
> Point $D$ (10, 0): $\$3(10) + \$5(0) = \$30.$

The optimum solution is at point $B$ (2, 3). This means that the specified requirements of protein, fats, and carbohydrates will be met at a minimum cost of $21 if we mix 2 pounds of ingredient A ($X_1$) and 3 pounds of ingredient B ($X_2$). Thus, each bag of dog food will weigh a total of 5 pounds. The cost per pound will be $4.20 ($21/5 lbs.), obviously a dog food developed only for the "kings" and "queens" of the dog world.

Substituting 2 for $X_1$ and 3 for $X_2$ in the constraints, we find that the minimum requirements have been met.

$$6X_1 + 2X_2 \geq 18 \text{ units (Protein)}$$
$$6(2) + 2(3) = 18 \text{ units per 5 lb. bag}$$
$$2X_1 + 4X_2 \geq 16 \text{ units (Fats)}$$
$$2(2) + 4(3) = 16 \text{ units per 5 lb. bag}$$

$2X_1 + 10X_2 \geq 20$ units (Carbohydrates)

$2(2) + 10(3) = 34$ units per 5 lb. bag

Note that this combination provides more than the minimum requirements specified by the inequality for carbohydrates, $2X_1 + 10X_2 \geq 20$. The company required a minimum of 20 units, but will actually obtain 34 units. In fact, it would actually increase its total cost if the company were to reduce this excess. This demonstrates the importance of inequalities in linear programming problems. If the company insisted on *exactly* 18 units of protein, 16 units of fats, and 20 units of carbohydrates, there would be no possible solution to the problem; but given the possibility of exceeding the minimum requirements, we can find a solution.

In Figure 2–17 we have plotted three cost lines ($C = \$3X_1 + \$5X_2$). The first cost line, $C = \$40$, is the farthest from the origin. As the cost line moves *toward* the origin, total costs decrease (see second cost line). Finally, at the optimum point $B$ (2, 3), the third cost line, $C = \$21$, has one point in common with the feasible solutions area.

FIGURE 2–17

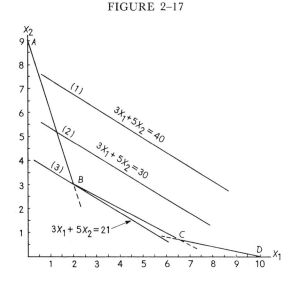

## Other graphical interpretations

Let us now examine a problem which has both types of inequalities ($\leq$ and $\geq$). The problem is

Maximize:

$$P = \$2X_1 + \$1X_2$$

Subject to:

$$4X_1 + 6X_2 \geq 24 \tag{1}$$
$$3X_1 + 4X_2 \leq 21 \tag{2}$$
$$6X_1 + 5X_2 \leq 30. \tag{3}$$

The three constraints are graphed in Figure 2–18.

FIGURE 2–18
Problem with Two Types of Inequalities ($\leq$ and $\geq$)

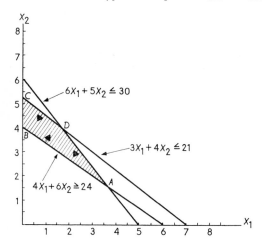

The shaded area in Figure 2–18 represents the area of feasible solutions with the optimum solution at point $A$ ($3\frac{3}{4}$, $1\frac{1}{2}$). Note that the lower boundary of feasible solutions area is represented by the greater-than-or-equal-to type of inequality. Any point below line segment $BA$ is not a feasible solution. Similarly, the upper boundary of the area of feasible solutions is represented by the greater-than-or-equal-to type. Any point above line segments $CD$ and $DA$ is not a feasible solution. Thus, the two types of inequalities are often referred to as lower bound ($\geq$) and upper bound ($\leq$) constraints.

If one of the constraints in a problem is represented by an equality, the optimum solution must lie *on it* rather than *on or to one side of it*. For example, if we add to the above problem the constraint, $7X_1 +$

FIGURE 2–19
The Effect of an Equality Constraint on Feasible Solutions Area

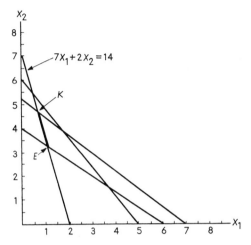

$2X_2 = 14$, we get the new feasible solutions area shown in Figure 2–19. In this case, the area of feasible solutions has been reduced to the heavy portion $KE$ on the line for the new constraint, the optimum solution being at point $K$ $(7/11, 4\frac{17}{22})$.

FIGURE 2–20
Problem with No Feasible Solutions

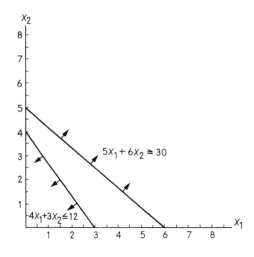

In some cases, there is no feasible solutions area. That is, there are no points that satisfy all of the constraints; hence no feasible solutions are possible. For example, if we graph the following constraints

$$4X_1 + 3X_2 \leq 12$$
$$5X_1 + 6X_2 \geq 30$$

we get the configuration in Figure 2–20, where there is no area common to both constraints, therefore, no area of feasible solutions.

## A three-dimensional problem

Suppose a company manufactures three products, $X_1$, $X_2$, and $X_3$, each of which must be processed through three departments. The problem, in mathematical form, is

Maximize:

$$P = \$5X_1 + 6X_2 + \$7X_3$$

Subject to:

$$X_1 + 2X_2 + 3X_3 \leq 11 \qquad \text{(Dept. 1)}$$
$$3X_1 + X_2 + X_3 \leq 10 \qquad \text{(Dept. 2)}$$
$$X_1 + 4X_2 + X_3 \leq 15 \qquad \text{(Dept. 3)}$$
$$X_1, X_2, X_3 \geq 0.$$

FIGURE 2–21

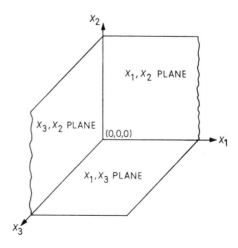

To present this problem graphically, a three-dimensional space is needed. Another axis is necessary to represent the third product $X_3$. Because of the obvious difficulties encountered in presenting such a three-dimensional space on the page of a book, the reader must use his imagination to form in his mind the correct impression of the object depicted. In three-dimensional space, three coordinates are required to locate a point $(X_1, X_2, X_3)$. We can visualize these points in three-dimensional space by looking at a windowless corner of a room, the origin $(0, 0, 0)$ being at the lower left corner of the room (see Figure 2–21).

The plotting procedure is the same as in the case of a two-dimensional problem. For example, to find the three terminal points of the constraint for department 1, $X_1 + 2X_2 + 3X_3 = 11$, we proceed as follows.

1. If

$$X_2, X_3 = 0$$

then

$$X_1 + 2(0) + 3(0) = 11$$
$$X_1 = 11$$

First point: $(11, 0, 0)$.

2. If

$$X_1, X_3 = 0$$

then

$$(0) + 2X_2 + 3(0) = 11$$
$$X_2 = 5\tfrac{1}{2}$$

Second point: $(0, 5\tfrac{1}{2}, 0)$.

3. If

$$X_1, X_2 = 0$$

then

$$(0) + 2(0) + 3X_3 = 11$$
$$X_3 = 3\tfrac{2}{3}$$

Third point: $(0, 0, 3\tfrac{2}{3})$.

Connecting these three points with straight lines, we obtain the triangle shown in Figure 2–22. The points on or beneath this plane represent all possible combinations of $X_1$, $X_2$, and $X_3$ that satisfy the inequality $X_1 + 2X_2 + 3X_3 \leq 11$. The terminal points for the con-

FIGURE 2–22

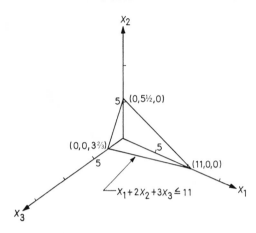

straints representing departments 2 and 3 are obtained in the same manner. The terminal points for each of these constraints are given below for the reader to verify.

$$3X_1 + X_2 + X_3 = 10 \qquad \text{(Dept. 2)}$$

Points: $(3\frac{1}{3}, 0, 0)$, $(0, 10, 0)$, $(0, 0, 10)$

$$X_1 + 4X_2 + X_3 = 15 \qquad \text{(Dept. 3)}$$

Points: $(15, 0, 0)$, $(0, 3\frac{3}{4}, 0)$, $(0, 0, 15)$.

FIGURE 2–23

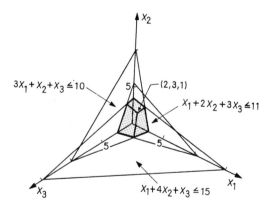

The three constraints are shown in Figure 2–23. The shaded solid represents the feasible solutions to the problem. Each point inside or on the surface of the shaded solid satisfies the three constraints of the problem. Point $(2, 3, 1)$ is the optimum point giving a profit of \$35.

Similar to the two-dimensional problem, we can plot the objective function. In a three-dimensional problem, the objective function will be a plane. Three profit planes have been plotted in Figure 2–24. The reader can visualize that as we move away from the origin, profits increase; the profit plane where $P = \$35$ will just "touch" the remote corner of the shaded solid at point $(2, 3, 1)$.

FIGURE 2-24

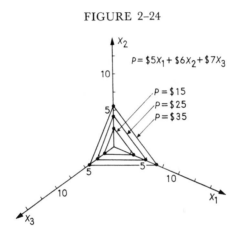

Although we cannot visualize the geometry of a problem with more than three variables, we are not prevented from extending the concepts developed for two and three dimensions to any number of dimensions.

The reader is cautioned once again that the use of the term "profit" throughout the examples in this chapter actually refers to "contribution to fixed costs and profits." The requirement in a linear programming problem for linearly related variables makes this distinction necessary.

## Problems

1.  Maximize $Z = 3X_1 + 2X_2$
    Subject to:  $X_1 + 3X_2 \leq 12$
    $$3X_1 + 4X_2 \leq 30$$
    $$X_1, X_2 \geq 0.$$

2.  Minimize $Z = 14X_1 + 12X_2$
    Subject to: $12X_1 + 20X_2 \geq 240$
    $$25X_1 + 5X_2 \geq 150$$
    $$X_1, X_2 \geq 0.$$

3.  Maximize $Z = 24.5X_1 + 18X_2$
    Subject to:  $X_1 + X_2 \geq 4$
    $$2X_1 + 5X_2 \leq 50$$
    $$X_1 \leq 15$$
    $$X_2 \geq 2.$$

4.  Minimize $Z = 4X_1 + 4X_2$
    Subject to: $5X_1 + 3X_2 \leq 45$
    $$2X_1 + 2X_2 \geq 16$$
    $$X_1 \geq 4$$
    $$X_2 \geq 0.$$

5.  Minimize $Z = 100X_1 + 150X_2$
    Subject to: $2.5X_1 + X_2 \geq 15$
    $$X_1 + 2.5X_2 \geq 25$$
    $$X_1 \geq 10$$
    $$X_2 \leq 15.$$

6.  Maximize $Z = 3X_1 + 4X_2$
    Subject to: $15X_1 + 18X_2 \leq 90$
    $$3X_1 + X_2 \leq 15$$
    $$20X_1 + 5X_2 \geq 130$$
    $$X_1, X_2 \geq 0.$$

7.  The ABC Company manufactures two products, A and B. Both products must be processed in each of the four departments of ABC. The following table lists the time requirements for each product in each of the departments.

|  | Product | |
| --- | --- | --- |
| Dept. | A | B |
| 1........ | 3 | 4 |
| 2........ | 2 | 1 |
| 3........ | 5 | 3 |
| 4........ | 4 | 5 |

The total number of hours available each week are as follows: department 1 = 50, department 2 = 45, department 3 = 55, and department 4 = 60. Product A contributes $5 to revenues and is manufactured at a cost of $3.50, whereas Product B contributes $5.50 to revenues at a cost of $3.75 per unit. Determine the weekly production mix which will maximize profit contribution.

8. The XYZ Company manufactures widgets and gidgets. Widgets and gidgets require processing in three departments. In department 1, widgets require two hours of direct labor, whereas gidgets require 2.25 hours. In department 2, widgets require 4.5 hours and gidgets require 2.75 hours. And in department 3, widgets require 3.25 hours whereas gidgets require five hours of direct labor for each unit. Direct material costs for widgets are estimated at $10 per unit and for gidgets $9 per unit. Overhead costs are estimated at $1 per unit for widgets and $0.75 per unit for gidgets. The cost for direct labor is $2.50 per hour.

Although the firm is assured of selling all it produces, it is essential that it produces 40 widgets and 30 gidgets each week to meet the needs of its regular customers. The number of hours available per day in each department are:

$$
\begin{aligned}
\text{Dept. 1} & \ldots \ldots \ 32 \\
\text{Dept. 2} & \ldots \ldots \ 64 \\
\text{Dept. 3} & \ldots \ldots \ 60
\end{aligned}
$$

What is the weekly production mix of widgets and gidgets which maximizes profits while satisfying the above conditions? Determine this optimum mix by the graphic method. (Assume a five-day work week for the company and selling prices for widgets and gidgets $25 and $22.75, respectively.)

# chapter 3

# The algebraic method

Although the graphical method is very effective in providing a conceptual understanding of linear programming solutions, it becomes impractical as the dimensions of a problem are expanded. For example, in problems involving more than three products (three dimensions) the graphical method is inadequate as a solution procedure. Furthermore, testing each corner point in the area of feasible solutions, while practical in simple cases, becomes very time-consuming as problems become more complex.

The algebraic method is a more efficient technique for searching out and identifying the corner points which represent the optimal solutions to problems. Although the algebraic method is not generally used for solving real-world linear programming problems, it does introduce the basic terminology and process of the computationally more efficient simplex method to be discussed in the next chapter.

**Formulating the problem**

To demonstrate the algebraic method, the simple machine-shop problem of Chapter 2 will be used. For convenience, it is repeated below:

Maximize:

$$Z = \$5X_1 + \$6X_2$$

Subject to:

$$3X_1 + 2X_2 \leq 32 \qquad \text{(Dept. 1)}$$
$$X_1 + 4X_2 \leq 34 \qquad \text{(Dept. 2)}$$

In formulating the problem for the algebraic method, the first step is to convert the inequalities into equations. In the previous chapter, we showed that the optimum solution may not necessarily use all the time available in each department. To take care of this possibility, we must add to each inequality a variable which will take up the slack—the time not used in each department. This variable is called a *slack variable*. For example, let

$$S_1 = \text{Slack variable (unused time)} \qquad \text{(Dept. 1)}$$
$$S_2 = \text{Slack variable (unused time)} \qquad \text{(Dept. 2)}$$

Adding these slack variables to the appropriate constraint inequalities in our sample problem, we have

$$3X_1 + 2X_2 + S_1 = 32$$
$$X_1 + 4X_2 + S_2 = 34.$$

Notice that by adding the slack variables, we have converted the constraint inequalities to equations. The slack variable in each department takes on whatever value is required to make the equation relationship hold. Two examples will clarify this point.

*Example 1.*   Assume that in department 1 we process two pistons $(X_1)$ and four connecting rod pins $(X_2)$.

$$3X_1 + 2X_2 + S_1 = 32$$
$$3(2) + 2(4) + S_1 = 32$$
$$S_1 = 18 \text{ hours unused time} \qquad \text{(Dept. 1)}$$

*Example 2.*   Assume that in department 2 we process three pistons and five connecting rod pins.

$$X_1 + 4X_2 + S_2 = 34$$
$$3 + 4(5) + S_2 = 34$$
$$S_2 = 11 \text{ hours unused time} \qquad \text{(Dept. 2)}$$

Assuming that these slack variables have no money value (no profit or loss is charged against idle time in the departments), the profit function can be written to include the slack variables with zero profit contributions as follows:

$$\text{Profit} = \$5X_1 + \$6X_2 + \$0S_1 + \$0S_2.$$

Finally, in a complete mathematical formulation of the problem using the algebraic method, any unknown that occurs in one equation must appear in all equations. For example, since $S_1$ represents the unused time in department 1 only, it is added to the constraint equation representing department 2 with a zero coefficient ($0S_1$). Similarly, $0S_2$ is added to the constraint equation representing department 1. Thus the equations in a complete mathematical formulation are

Maximize:
$$Z \text{ (Profit)} = \$5X_1 + \$6X_2 + \$0S_1 + \$0S_2$$

Subject to:
$$3X_1 + 2X_2 + \ S_1 + 0S_2 = 32 \text{ hours}$$
$$X_1 + 4X_2 + 0S_1 + \ S_2 = 34 \text{ hours.}$$

Notice that the addition of $S_2$ to the first constraint equation and $S_1$ to the second constraint equation does not in any way affect the equality relationship, since the coefficient of each is zero.

## Setting up the initial solution

In the graphical solution to our sample problem we found that the points in the feasible solutions area represented various combinations of pistons and pins (product mixes). We also found that one possible combination, although not very profitable, was to produce no pistons and pins. This combination occurred at the origin $(0, 0)$, which reflects only unused capacity and, hence, a zero profit. In the algebraic method, we will use this feasible (but zero-profit) solution as a starting point. In other words, the initial solution in the algebraic method will be the worst possible solution: to have idle time in both departments and hence receive no profit.

We can illustrate this feasible solution in the algebraic method by rewriting the constraint equations as follows:

$$S_1 = 32 - 3X_1 - 2X_2 - 0S_2 \qquad (1)$$
$$S_2 = 34 - \ X_1 - 4X_2 - 0S_1. \qquad (2)$$

In this form, these equations show the relationship between the variables in the first solution ($S_1$ and $S_2$) representing idle time, and the other variables in the problem. Equation (1) states that $S_1$ is equal to the total amount of time available in department 1 (32 hours) less any hours used there in processing pistons and pins. Equation (2) states that $S_2$ is equal to the total number of hours available in department 2 (34 hours) less any hours used there in processing pistons and pins.

As a beginning point, we decided to make no pistons and pins. Thus the first solution is:

$$X_1 = 0$$
$$X_2 = 0$$
$$S_1 = 32 - 3(0) - 2(0) - 0S_2 = 32 \text{ hours unused}$$
$$S_2 = 34 - \phantom{0} 0 \phantom{0} - 4(0) - 0S_1 = 34 \text{ hours unused.}$$

To determine the profit from this first solution, we substitute the values of $X_1$, $X_2$, $S_1$, and $S_2$ in the profit function. Thus

$$\text{Profit} = \$5X_1 + \$6X_2 + \$0S_1 \phantom{xx} + \$0S_2$$
$$= \$5(0) + \$6(0) + \$0(32) + \$0(34)$$
$$= \$0. \tag{3}$$

This zero profit points to one of the features of this algebraic method, namely, that the initial solution shows a zero profit. This technically possible but financially unattractive solution provides a starting point from which improved solutions can be obtained.

### Developing an improved solution

To determine whether an improved solution is possible, we begin by examining the profit function. Clearly, improvement is possible by manufacturing some pistons ($X_1$) or pins ($X_2$) in exchange for the idle time ($S_1$ or $S_2$) which contributes nothing to profit. To progress toward the optimum solution—the one best product mix, we first consider manufacturing only that product which contributes the highest profit per unit. In our problem, this would be the connecting rod pins which contribute \$6 per unit.

Having decided which product will enter our next solution, the next step is to determine the maximum number of pins that can be manufactured. To do this, we examine the previous constraint equations (1) and (2). Now assume that all the time available in each department is used to produce pins ($X_2$); hence, the production of rods ($X_1$) will be zero. Constraint equation (1), $S_1 = 32 - 3X_1 - 2X_2 - 0S_2$, shows that 32 hours are available in department 1 and that 2 hours are required to process one pin. Thus the number of pins which can be processed in department 1 is

$$\frac{32 \text{ hours available}}{2 \text{ hours per pin}} = 16 \text{ pins.}$$

Constraint equation (2), $S_2 = 34 - X_1 - 4X_2 - 0S_1$, shows that 34 hours are available in department 2 and that 4 hours are necessary to process one pin in this department. Thus the maximum number of pins which can be processed in department 2 is

$$\frac{34 \text{ hours available}}{4 \text{ hours per pin}} = 8\frac{1}{2} \text{ pins.}$$

Since manufacturing a *complete* pin requires processing in both departments, the maximum number of pins that can be produced without violating the constraints is $8\frac{1}{2}$. For example, processing 16 pins in department 2 would require 64 hours, but the total time available there is only 34 hours. Department 2, therefore, may be referred to as the *limiting department;* it limits the production of pins to $8\frac{1}{2}$ units. Producing $8\frac{1}{2}$ pins requires 34 hours in department 2 and 17 hours in department 1. In this case, production is within the time restrictions in both departments.

We now substitute the values $X_1 = 0$ and $X_2 = 8\frac{1}{2}$ in equations (1) and (2).

$$S_1 = 32 - 3(0) - 2(8\tfrac{1}{2}) - 0S_2 = 15$$
$$S_2 = 34 - 1(0) - 4(8\tfrac{1}{2}) - 0S_1 = 0.$$

The second solution, therefore, is

$$X_1 = 0 \quad \text{pistons}$$
$$X_2 = 8\tfrac{1}{2} \quad \text{pins}$$
$$S_1 = 15 \quad \text{unused hours} \qquad \text{(Dept. 1)}$$
$$S_2 = 0 \quad \text{unused hours} \qquad \text{(Dept. 2)}$$

To determine the profit from this second solution we substitute the new values for $X_1$, $X_2$, $S_1$ and $S_2$ in the profit function. Thus

$$\text{Profit} = \$5X_1 + \$6X_2 + \$0S_1 + \$0S_2$$
$$= \$5(0) + \$6(8\tfrac{1}{2}) + \$0(0) + \$0(0)$$
$$= \$51.$$

Clearly, this solution is better than the zero profit of the first solution.

### Determine whether further improvement is possible

By producing $8\frac{1}{2}$ pins, the amount of unused time in department 2 $(S_2)$ was reduced to zero. In other words, pins $(X_2)$ will replace $S_2$ in our improved product mix. Consequently, the constraint equations (1) and (2) must be changed to reflect this fact. They are repeated below before the change:

$$S_1 = 32 - 3X_1 - 2X_2 - 0S_2. \tag{1}$$

$$S_2 = 34 - X_1 - 4X_2 - 0S_1. \tag{2}$$

Recall that the left side of the above equations represent the variables in the initial product mix, while the right side shows the relationship between the variables in the initial product mix and the other variables in the problem. Since $X_2$ is now going to replace $S_2$, we first solve for $X_2$ in equation (2).

$$4X_2 = 34 - X_1 - S_2 - 0S_1.$$

Dividing through by 4 yields

$$X_2 = 8\frac{1}{2} - \tfrac{1}{4}X_1 - \tfrac{1}{4}S_2 - 0S_1. \tag{2.1}$$

Substituting this value for $X_2$ into equation (1) will result in a new equation (1.1)

$$S_1 = 32 - 3X_1 - 2X_2 - 0S_2. \tag{1}$$
$$S_1 = 32 - 3X_1 - 2(8\tfrac{1}{2} - \tfrac{1}{4}X_1 - \tfrac{1}{4}S_2 - 0S_1)$$
$$S_1 = 15 - 2\tfrac{1}{2}X_1 + \tfrac{1}{2}S_2. \tag{1.1}$$

The two new constraint equations which reflect the new product mix and the new relationship among all the variables in the second solution now are

$$S_1 = 15 - 2\tfrac{1}{2}X_1 + \tfrac{1}{2}S_2. \tag{1.1}$$

$$X_2 = 8\tfrac{1}{2} - \tfrac{1}{4}X_1 - \tfrac{1}{4}S_2. \tag{2.1}$$

The changes made in the second solution and reflected in the new constraint equations will also bring about changes in the profit function. In order to determine whether further improvement is possible, a new profit function must be determined. To make this change, we substitute the new values for $S_1$ and $X_2$, given in constraint equations (1.1) and (2.1), into the profit function.

$$\text{Profit} = \$5X_1 + \$6X_2 + \$0S_1 + \$0S_2 \tag{3}$$
$$= \$5X_1 + \$6(8\tfrac{1}{2} - \tfrac{1}{4}X_1 - \tfrac{1}{4}S_2)$$
$$+ \$0(15 - 2\tfrac{1}{2}X_1 + \tfrac{1}{2}S_2) + \$0S_2$$
$$= \$5X_1 + \$51 - \$1\tfrac{1}{2}X_1 - \$1\tfrac{1}{2}S_2$$
$$= \$51 + \$3\tfrac{1}{2}X_1 - \$1\tfrac{1}{2}S_2 \tag{3.1}$$

At this point, it would be helpful to examine the meaning of this new expression of the profit function (profit = $\$51 + 3\tfrac{1}{2}X_1 - \$1\tfrac{1}{2}S_2$). It shows that by bringing pistons ($X_1$) into the solution, we will make an additional profit of $3.50 for each piston produced. This may be somewhat confusing, since the original statement of the problem indicated that each piston contributed $5 to profit.

Recall, however, that all the hours in department 2 have been committed to the production of pins. This means that pistons can be made only by giving up some of the pins now being made. In department 2, a piston requires one hour and a pin requires four hours. Therefore, to make a piston we must give up the production of $\tfrac{1}{4}$ of a pin. Giving up $\tfrac{1}{4}$ of a pin will reduce profit by $\tfrac{1}{4}$ ($6), but we gain $5 from each piston produced. Thus a gain of $5 and a loss of $1.50 yields a net gain of $3.50. This explains why the revised profit function shows a contribution of $3.50 for pistons.

Now, how can we explain the $-1\tfrac{1}{2}S_2$ in the revised profit function? This means that if we were to give up 1 hour of the 34 hours in department 2 for some other purpose, profit would be reduced by $1.50. Why? Each of the $8\tfrac{1}{2}$ pins we are now producing requires four hours in department 2. To free up one hour for some other purpose would require giving up $\tfrac{1}{4}$ of a pin, the result being a reduction in profit of $\tfrac{1}{4}$ of $6 or $1.50.

Notice also that $X_2$ (pins) is not in the revised profit function. This means that pins contribute $0 to profit. The explanation is that we are already producing as many pins as possible under the time restrictions in department 2. If we were to add a pin, we would have to give up a pin. Adding one unit of $X_2$ would increase profit by $6, but giving up one unit of $X_2$ would decrease profit by $6. Thus the net contribution is $0.

The revised profit function, then, is an expression of the *net* effect of the changes made in the new product mix. To determine whether improvement is possible, the revised profit function is examined. A positive coefficient indicates the amount of increase in total profit possible if one unit of the variable were added to the solution. In our problem, the revised profit function shows that the coefficient of the variable $X_1$ (pistons) is positive, indicating that total profits can be increased by adding pistons to the next solution. A negative coefficient indicates the amount of decrease in total profit if one unit of the variable were added to the solution. For reasons already explained, adding one unit of $S_2$ with a negative coefficient of $-1\frac{1}{2}$ will decrease profits by $1.50. Hence, the optimum solution will be obtained when there are no positive coefficients in the revised profit function.

## The third solution

Using the same procedures discussed under the section "Developing an Improved Solution," we will develop a new solution. The new revised profit function (Profit $= \$51 + \$3\frac{1}{2}X_1 - \$1\frac{1}{2}S_2$) indicates that if we bring pistons ($X_1$) into the solution, we will make an additional profit of $3.50 for each piston we produce. How many pistons can we make?

The number of pistons that can be produced is determined by examining the revised constraint equations (1.1 and 2.1). First, we note that the production of $8\frac{1}{2}$ pins requires all the hours available in department 2. To make a piston, however, we need some time in that department. In other words, we must sacrifice some pins in order to produce pistons. As previously explained, for each pin that we give up, we can process $\frac{1}{4}$ of a piston. Thus if we were to give up all $8\frac{1}{2}$ pins, we could process 34 pistons in department 2:

$$\frac{8\frac{1}{2} \text{ pins now being made}}{\frac{1}{4} \text{ piston given up for 1 pin}} = 34 \text{ pistons.}$$

But pins must also be processed in department 1. What is the maximum number of pins that can be processed in department 1? The revised constraint equation (1.1) for department 1 shows that there are 15 hours now available and that $2\frac{1}{2}$ hours are required to process a piston. The original constraint equation (1) showed that a piston required three hours processing in department 1. How can we justify this apparent inconsistency? We have already shown that to process 1 piston in department 2 would require giving up $\frac{1}{4}$ of a pin. When pin production is reduced by $\frac{1}{4}$ of a pin, one result is to free or release $\frac{1}{4}$ of the two hours required for processing a pin in department 1. Now the three hours required for each piston less the $\frac{1}{2}$ hour

($\frac{1}{4}$ × 2) released or freed by cutting production back by $\frac{1}{4}$ pin equals a *net* requirement of $2\frac{1}{2}$ hours per piston in department 1. Hence, the maximum number of pistons that can be processed in department 1 is:

$$\frac{15 \text{ hours available in department 1}}{2\frac{1}{2} \text{ net hours required per piston}} = 6 \text{ pistons.}$$

A general rule for finding the quantity to be added to the product mix is as follows:

1. Divide the constant in each constraint equation by the coefficient of the variable being added.
2. Choose the smallest positive quotient in step 1 as the quantity to be added.

For example, the constant in equation (1.1) is 15; the coefficient of the variable to be added ($X_1$) is $2\frac{1}{2}$ and $15 \div 2\frac{1}{2} = 6$. Likewise the constant in equation (2.1) is $8\frac{1}{2}$; the coefficient of the variable to be added is $\frac{1}{4}$ and $8\frac{1}{2} \div \frac{1}{4} = 34$. We choose 6 as the quantity of pistons to be added to the next solution. A number larger than 6 would violate equation (1.1); that is, a value greater than 6 would require more time in department 1 than the available 15 hours.

Having decided to add six pistons to the next product mix, we must examine the effects of this decision on the production of pins, the availability of hours, and the generation of profit. The constraint equations calculated after the second solution can help here.

$$S_1 = 15 - 2\frac{1}{2}X_1 + \frac{1}{2}S_2. \tag{1.1}$$
$$X_2 = 8\frac{1}{2} - \frac{1}{4}X_1 - \frac{1}{4}S_2. \tag{2.1}$$

Substituting 6 for $X_1$ and 0 for $S_2$ yields

$$S_1 = 15 - 2\frac{1}{2}(6) + \frac{1}{2}(0) = 0 \text{ unused hours}$$
$$X_2 = 8\frac{1}{2} - \frac{1}{4}(6) - \frac{1}{4}(0) = 7 \text{ pins.}$$

We see that the production of six pistons reduces the production of pins to seven and that all of the available hours in both departments are used.

The third solution, therefore, is

$$X_1 = 6$$
$$X_2 = 7$$
$$S_1 = 0$$
$$S_2 = 0.$$

Substituting these values in the profit function gives the following profit:

$$\text{Profit} = \$5X_1 + \$6X_2 + \$0S_1 + \$0S_2$$
$$= \$5(6) + \$6(7) + \$0(0) + \$0(0)$$
$$= \$72.$$

We can show that all available hours in both departments have been utilized:

| Products | Department 1 (32 Hours Available) | Department 2 (34 Hours Available) |
|---|---|---|
| $X_1$ (pistons)...... | 6 × 3 hours = 18 | 6 × 1 hour  =  6 |
| $X_2$ (pins) ........ | 7 × 2 hours = 14 | 7 × 4 hours = 28 |
| | 32 | 34 |

We must now see if there is a solution which generates a profit greater than the $72 obtained from our third solution. To do this, we proceed exactly as we did in going from the second solution to the third solution, using the procedures discussed under the section, "Determine Whether Further Improvement Is Possible."

First we repeat the constraint equations which showed the product mix just prior to the third solution:

$$S_1 = 15 - 2\tfrac{1}{2}X_1 + \tfrac{1}{2}S_2. \tag{1.1}$$
$$X_2 = 8\tfrac{1}{2} - \tfrac{1}{4}X_1 - \tfrac{1}{4}S_2. \tag{2.1}$$

In the third solution we replaced $S_1$ with $X_1$ to obtain the new product mix. To reflect this change, we solve for $X_1$ in equation (1.1):

$$S_1 = 15 - 2\tfrac{1}{2}X_1 + \tfrac{1}{2}S_2 \tag{1.1}$$
$$2\tfrac{1}{2}X_1 = 15 - S_1 + \tfrac{1}{2}S_2.$$

Dividing through by $2\tfrac{1}{2}$ yields

$$X_1 = 6 - \tfrac{2}{5}S_1 + \tfrac{1}{5}S_2. \tag{1.2}$$

Now substituting $(6 - \tfrac{2}{5}S_1 + \tfrac{1}{5}S_2)$ for $X_1$ in equation (2.1) we have

$$X_2 = 8\tfrac{1}{2} - \tfrac{1}{4}X_1 - \tfrac{1}{4}S_2 \tag{2.1}$$
$$= 8\tfrac{1}{2} - \tfrac{1}{4}(6 - \tfrac{2}{5}S_1 + \tfrac{1}{5}S_2) - \tfrac{1}{4}S_2$$
$$= 8\tfrac{1}{2} - 1\tfrac{1}{2} + \tfrac{2}{20}S_1 - \tfrac{1}{20}S_2 - \tfrac{1}{4}S_2$$
$$= 7 + \tfrac{1}{10}S_1 - \tfrac{3}{10}S_2. \tag{2.2}$$

The revised constraint equations for the third solution are then

$$X_1 = 6 - \tfrac{2}{5}S_1 + \tfrac{1}{5}S_2. \tag{1.2}$$

$$X_2 = 7 - \tfrac{1}{10}S_1 - \tfrac{3}{10}S_2. \tag{2.2}$$

Now to determine if further improvement is possible, we simply substitute the values for $X_1$ and $X_2$ [equations (1.2) and (2.2)] into the profit function:

$$\text{Profit} = \$5X_1 + \$6X_2 + \$0S_1 + \$0S_2 \tag{3}$$

$$= 5(6 - \tfrac{2}{5}S_1 + \tfrac{1}{5}S_2) + 6(7 - \tfrac{1}{10}S_1 - \tfrac{3}{10}S_2) + 0 + 0$$

$$= 30 - 2S_1 + S_2 + 42 - \tfrac{6}{10}S_1 - \tfrac{18}{10}S_2$$

$$= \$72 - \$\tfrac{7}{5}S_1 - \$\tfrac{4}{5}S_2 \tag{3.2}$$

FIGURE 3–1

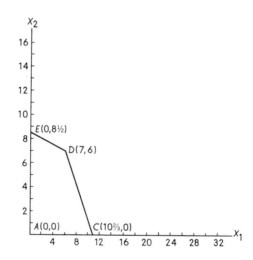

Since no positive coefficients are in the revised profit function, further improvement is not possible; the optimal solution has been obtained.

To see what we have accomplished by using the algebraic method, let us refer to a graph of the previous chapter repeated here as Figure 3–1.

In the initial solution, the product mix contained all unused time. Since no pistons and pins were produced ($X_1 = 0$, $X_2 = 0$), profit was zero. This solution corresponds to the point $A$ in our graph. In the second solution, we entered $8\frac{1}{2}X_2$ (pins) and produced no pistons ($X_1 = 0$). Thus we moved from point $A$ to point $E$. Our third and final solution, $X_1 = 6$ and $X_2 = 7$, corresponds to point $D$. If, in the second solution, we had entered $X_1$ instead of $X_2$, we would have reached point $D$ by way of point $C$.

The algebraic method, therefore, consists of starting at the zero point of the area of feasible solutions and systematically moving along the boundary, from one corner point to another, until the optimal solution has been obtained.

With the basic concepts of linear programming solutions discussed in the graphic and algebraic chapters, we can now turn to the general computational method known as the simplex method.

## Problems

1. Maximize $Z = 200X_1 + 250X_2$
   Subject to: $10X_1 + 40X_2 \leq 560$
   $\phantom{Subject to: }20X_1 + \phantom{4}5X_2 \leq 400.$

2. Maximize $Z = 3X_1 + 5X_2$
   Where $X_1 = $ No. of pins produced
   $\phantom{Where }X_2 = $ No. of pistons produced
   Subject to: $4X_1 + 3X_2 \leq 120$           (Dept. 1)
   $\phantom{Subject to: }5X_1 + 7X_2 \leq 290.$          (Dept. 2)

3. Maximize $Z = 3X_1 + 4X_2 + 2X_3$
   Subject to: $\phantom{0}2X_1 + \phantom{0}X_2 + \phantom{0}X_3 \leq 48$
   $\phantom{Subject to: 00}3X_1 + 6X_2 + \phantom{0}3X_3 \leq 66$
   $\phantom{Subject to: 0}10X_1 + 5X_2 + 10X_3 \leq 130.$

4. A small electronics firm produces two different electrical units utilized in airborne radar systems. The firm is not highly automated and it relies upon labor as its main factor of production. Both products are basically printed-circuit boards with attached electrical components such as transistors, resistors, and modules. Both products begin the production process in the assembly department. Here the electrical components are attached to the printed-circuit board. Labor involved in this department amounts to 15 minutes per board A and 20 minutes per board B. Finally the boards are sent to the soldering department where components are soldered to the printed-circuit boards. Soldering time for each board A is 2 minutes, and for each board B—2.5 minutes. Labor and material costs for board A are $7.50 per unit, and for board B—$8.50. Given that board A is sold for $11.50 and board B for $12.50, and that the hours

available each day in the two departments are 64 and 8, respectively, find the product mix which maximizes profit.

5. The Dumb-Bell Company has among its line of products weighted plates which may be attached to barbells. Their three most popular plates are the 25-pound, 10-pound, and 5-pound plates. These plates are manufactured by casting, grinding, and polishing processes. The times necessary for processing each size plate are given below.

| | Casting | Grinding | Polishing |
|---|---|---|---|
| 5-lb.................... | 5 min. | 5 min. | 10 min. |
| 10-lb.................... | 8 min. | 7 min. | 12 min. |
| 25-lb.................... | 10 min. | 12 min. | 16 min. |
| Total man-hours available per day....... | 16 hrs. | 24 hrs. | 32 hrs. |

Given that the contribution of the three products to profits are:

$$5\text{-lb}.......... \$1.25$$
$$10\text{-lb}.......... \$2.50$$
$$25\text{-lb}.......... \$4.00$$

Determine the product mix which maximizes profit contribution.

# chapter 4

# The simplex method of linear programming—maximization

The graphical method of linear programming introduced in Chapter 2, and the algebraic method of linear programming introduced in Chapter 3 are both workable methods. Experience has shown however that as computational devices, they involve excessive time. For this reason they are normally not employed in the operational solution of linear programming problems. Instead, other more efficient algorithms (logical procedures) have been developed. The best known of these procedures is called the simplex method.

### Simplex method

The simplex method of linear programming was developed by George B. Dantzig in 1947. Since that time it has been further developed as a rapid computational technique by Dr. Dantzig as well as by other contributors to the field. It is a method which can be easily mastered, and which can be applied to problems involving large numbers of variables with great success.

The simplex method, while quite easy to apply, has a theoretical background which is far beyond the scope of a book such as this. When explaining the simplex procedure it is often a temptation to reduce the explanation to a level where the reader is told only "what to do" and not "what he is doing." The theory of the simplex method has been fully developed in the literature of mathematics and economics, and it is a part of accepted mathematical doctrine. However, this argument is of little value to the nonmathematician who is attempting to understand "what he is doing" and "why."

Fortunately there is an alternate method of explanation which, although it avoids use of certain mathematical tools (vectors and matrix algebra, for example), allows the explanation to be made without resorting to the too familiar words "it can be shown," or "it therefore follows." This method employs a commonsense description of the logic of the simplex method using nothing more complicated than the notion of machines processing units of product through a factory. In this book each step in the simplex process will thus be related to a practical business problem, no more baffling than those solved by most businessmen every day. In order that the reader can relate the simplex procedure to the graphic method and the algebraic method, we shall use the same problems described in Chapters 2 and 3.

## Formulating the problem

At the risk of some repetition, we shall briefly summarize the problem first proposed in Chapter 2. A company with a market for

FIGURE 4–1

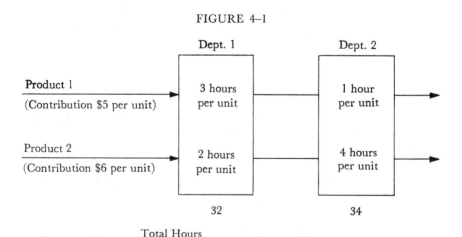

and productive facilities sufficient to manufacture two products, is attempting to determine which of the many possible combinations of these two products will produce the greatest possible total contribution. The problem is illustrated in schematic form in Figure 4–1. Each of the two departments through which each product must pass poses a constraint upon production because of the limited number of hours available. We shall again refer to department 1 as the lathe department, and department 2 as the drill press department. $X_1$ represents the quantity of product 1 to be produced (automobile engine pistons), and $X_2$ represents the quantity of product 2 (connecting rod pins). The constraints (the two inequalities) are the same as they were in the algebraic method:

Constraint for department 1 (lathe)

$$3X_1 + 2X_2 \leq 32$$

Constraint for department 2 (drills)

$$X_1 + 4X_2 \leq 34.$$

Setting up the problem for the simplex method is exactly the same as in the algebraic method. Briefly, the steps are:

1. Express the objective (function) as an equation.
2. Set up the constraint inequalities.
3. Convert the inequalities to equations by adding slack variables.
4. Finally, add zero value variables so that all variables appear in all equations.

The mathematical formulation of the problem for the simplex method, then, follows:

Maximize:

$$Z = \$5X_1 + 6X_2 + \$0S_1 + \$0S_2$$

Subject to:

$$3X_1 + 2X_2 + S_1 + 0S_2 = 32 \qquad \text{(Dept. 1)}$$
$$X_1 + 4X_2 + 0S_1 + S_2 = 34. \qquad \text{(Dept. 2)}$$

**The first solution**

Just as in the algebraic method, it is necessary to get an initial solution to the problem. It need not be a profitable solution by any means, simply one which is feasible (within our capability to manufacture); its sole purpose is to allow us to begin the problem. The first solution we used in the algebraic method was to manufacture no real products (pistons or pins) and to have all of the time in each department left unused. This is also the solution which is used in beginning the simplex method. Its financial value is obviously quite poor, but as we have seen, its computational value as a logical beginning is useful.

## The simplex table

The simplex method employs a format for illustrating relationships between variables, (products, time and cost), which is referred to as the simplex table. Though different books use slightly different formats, all simplex tables are alike in the sense that they provide a definite place for each part of the problem; the format employed in this exposition is a standard one.

A model of the simplex table together with explanations of each of its components is found in Figure 4–2. When referring to specific parts of this table we shall follow the normal convention of using the term rows to represent horizontal direction and columns to represent vertical direction. Thus our simplex table is composed of six rows ↔ and seven columns ↕. We have divided the simplex table into five lettered sections, A, B, C, D, and E, each of which is explained in detail in Figure 4–2.

## Entering the first solution in the table

To enter the first solution (the one in which no products are produced and all time is left unused) into the simplex table, we take the relationship equations:

Equation for Dept. 1 (lathe)

$$3X_1 + 2X_2 + S_1 + 0S_2 = 32$$

Equations for Dept. 2 (drills)

$$X_1 + 4X_2 + 0S_1 + S_2 = 34$$

rewrite them so that the constants (32 and 34) appear on the left side of the equation:

Equation for Dept. 1 (lathe)

$$32 = 3X_1 + 2X_2 + S_1 + 0S_2$$

Equation for Dept. 2 (drills)

$$34 = X_1 + 4X_2 + 0S_1 + S_2$$

FIGURE 4–2
Explanations of Sections of Simplex Table

| Contribution per Unit | | | | "C" | |
|---|---|---|---|---|---|
| | MIX | QTY. | | "B" | |
| | "A" | | | "D" | |
| | | | | | |
| | | | | "E" | |
| | | | | | |

*Section A.* The part of the simplex table which shows the variables in the mix. A column is provided for the letter designation of each variable in the mix (the second column in section A); a column is provided for entering the quantity of each variable in the mix (the third column in section A); a column is provided for illustrating the contribution per unit of each variable in the mix (the first column in section A). This section always contains three columns. The number of rows in section A depends upon the number of variables in the problem.

*Section B.* This part of the simplex table always consists of one row which indicates each of the variables which could be in the mix. In this case, this row would contain $X_1$, $X_2$, $S_1$, and $S_2$, the only variables in this problem. The number of columns in section B will depend upon the number of variables in a given problem.

*Section C.* This part always consists of one row which accommodates the contribution per unit of each of the variables which could be in the mix. The number of columns in section C will depend upon the number of variables in a given problem.

*Section D.* Part of the simplex table which shows the relationships between the variables "in the mix" and the variables which could be in the mix. Each figure in this section represents an exact relationship between two variables. The number of rows and columns in this section will depend upon the number of variables in a given problem.

*Section E.* A section reserved for the "accounting," financial data and calculations which must accompany each solution. Section E will always be the last two rows in the simplex table; each row has a specific meaning which will be explained as we proceed with the problem.

FIGURE 4–3
Relationship Equations Entered in Simplex Table

| Contribution per Unit | | | | "C" | | |
|---|---|---|---|---|---|---|
| | MIX | QTY | | "B" | | |
| | | 32 | 3 | 2 | 1 | 0 |
| | | 34 | 1 | 4 | 0 | 1 |
| | | | "E" | | | |
| | | | | | | |

and enter the coefficients of each term directly into the simplex table in Figure 4–3.

Since this first solution involves a product mix consisting only of

FIGURE 4–4
Sections A and D Completed

| Contribution per Unit | | | | "C" | | |
|---|---|---|---|---|---|---|
| | MIX | QTY. | | "B" | | |
| $0 | $S_1$ | 32 | 3 | 2 | 1 | 0 |
| $0 | $S_2$ | 34 | 1 | 4 | 0 | 1 |
| | | | "E" | | | |
| | | | | | | |

unused time in both departments (slack variables) we can now enter the designations $S_1$ and $S_2$ in the mix column thus indicating that the first product mix consists solely of slack time in each department. Since slack time is worth $0 per hour to us as profit contribution, we will also enter this information to the left of the mix column. These changes have been made in Figure 4–4.

Now that section A is completed, it illustrates that the first solution consists of 32 hours of slack time in department 1 worth $0 per hour and 34 hours of slack time in department 2 worth also $0 per hour. The detailed explanation of the entries in section D will follow shortly.

FIGURE 4–5
Sections A, B, C, and D Completed

| Contribution per Unit | | | $5 | $6 | $0 | $0 |
|---|---|---|---|---|---|---|
| | MIX | QTY. | $X_1$ | $X_2$ | $S_1$ | $S_2$ |
| $0 | $S_1$ | 32 | 3 | 2 | 1 | 0 |
| $0 | $S_2$ | 34 | 1 | 4 | 0 | 1 |
| | | | "E" | | | |
| | | | | | | |

Sections B and C can be filled in by taking each of the possible variables in the problem ($X_1$, $X_2$, $S_1$, and $S_2$) together with their appropriate per unit contributions to profit ($5, $6, $0, and $0) and entering them directly into the simplex table, (Sections B and C.) This has been accomplished in Figure 4–5.

### Explanation of section D (relationships)

Section D was previously described in Figure 4–2 as part of the simplex table which shows the relationships between the variables

FIGURE 4–6
Detailed Explanations of Section D of the Simplex Table

|  |  |  | $X_1$ | $X_2$ | $S_1$ | $S_2$ |
|---|---|---|---|---|---|---|
| $0 | $S_1$ | 32 | 3 | 2 | 1 | 0 |
| $0 | $S_2$ | 34 | 1 | 4 | 0 | 1 |

(a)

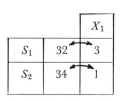

The number values 3 and 1 (under the $X_1$ column) illustrate respectively that *if* we desired to manufacture a unit of $X_1$, we must be prepared to give up *3* hours of the 32 hours available in department 1 and *1* hour of the 34 hours available in department 2. Thus these two numbers express the relationship between variables in the mix and a variable which could be brought into the mix, $X_1$ in this case.

(b)

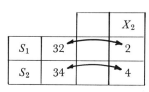

The number values 2 and 4 (under the $X_2$ column) illustrate respectively that *if* we desired to manufacture a unit of $X_2$, we must be prepared to give up *2* hours of the 32 hours available in department 1 and *4* hours of the 34 hours available in department 2.

(c)

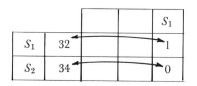

The number values 1 and 0 (under the $S_1$ column) illustrate respectively that if we wanted an hour of $S_1$ (say, to shut down the department for maintenance or to manufacture a special part other than the two we now contemplate producing), we must be prepared to give up *1* of the 32 hours available in department 1 and *0* (none) of the 34 hours available in department 2. Since shutting down department 1 for one hour would have no effect on department 2, we are not surprised that the appropriate numerical value to express this relationship is zero.

FIGURE 4–6 (*Continued*)

(d)

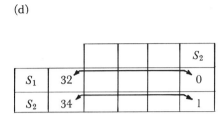

The number values 0 and 1 under the $S_2$ column illustrate respectively that if we wanted an hour of $S_2$ (shutting down department 2 for an hour for maintenance or taking an hour to manufacture a product other than the two we now contemplate), we must be prepared to give up 0 of the 32 hours available in department 1 (shutting down department 2 has no effect on department 1) and we must also be prepared to give up *1* of the 34 hours available in department 2.

"in the mix" and the variables which could be produced. Let us now illustrate that this section is nothing more than the commonsense expression of the relationship between hours of time and units of product as originally stated in the problem. Figure 4–6 illustrates only sections A, B, and D of the simplex table with a detailed explanation of each relationship between variables "in the mix" ($S_1$ and $S_2$) and variables which could be in the mix ($X_1$, $X_2$, $S_1$, and $S_2$).

Before leaving this explanation of the numerical values in section D of the simplex table, we should note that no matter what solution is involved (the first or the last), the numbers found in this section of the table *will always* illustrate the precise relationship between the variables in the mix and the variables it is possible to have in the mix. These relationships will become the basis for our explanation of "why the simplex method works as it does."

### Section E (accounting for transactions)

Since the objective of our procedure is to find that particular combination of variables (products) which will produce the maximum total contribution to fixed costs and profits, it is only logical that each proposed change in the product mix be made on the basis of its effect upon contribution; section E of the simplex table allows us to calculate the financial implications of each proposed change. Figure 4–7 illustrates how part of section E is computed for each proposed change in the product mix.

## FIGURE 4–7
### Calculation of Contribution Lost

(a)

| Contribution per Unit | | | | | | |
|---|---|---|---|---|---|---|
| | MIX | QTY. | $X_1$ | $X_2$ | $S_1$ | $S_2$ |
| $0 | $S_1$ | 32 | 3 | | | |
| $0 | $S_2$ | 34 | 1 | | | |
| Contribution Lost | | | $0 | | | |
| | | | | | | |

If we want to manufacture one unit of $X_1$ we have seen that this will involve giving up three hours in department 1 and one hour in department 2; calculation of contribution we will lose by this exchange is as follows:

3 hours lost at $0 per hour = $0
1 hour lost at $0 per hour = $0
————
Total contribution lost = $0

(b)

| Contribution per Unit | | | | | | |
|---|---|---|---|---|---|---|
| | MIX | QTY. | $X_1$ | $X_2$ | $S_1$ | $S_2$ |
| $0 | $S_1$ | 32 | | 2 | | |
| $0 | $S_2$ | 34 | | 4 | | |
| Contribution Lost | | | | $0 | | |
| | | | | | | |

If we want to manufacture one unit of $X_2$, we have seen that this will involve giving up two hours in department 1 and four hours in department 2; calculation of the effects of this on contribution are as follows:

2 hours lost at $0 per hour = $0
4 hours lost at $0 per hour = $0
————
Total contribution lost = $0

The simplex table with the results of these four calculations regarding contribution lost is illustrated in Figure 4–8. Although all possible exchanges at this point result in no loss of contribution (which is the same as saying that nothing we can do will be any worse than what we are doing), this is not the case with every proposed solution. Only because the first solution involved making no real products ($X_1$ or $X_2$) and involved only slack time in each department ($S_1$ and $S_2$) is the unique situation true. In later solutions it will be seen that proposed changes in the product mix *do* have a pronounced effect upon total contribution for the company.

FIGURE 4–7 (*Continued*)

(c)

| Contri-bution per Unit | | | | | | |
|---|---|---|---|---|---|---|
| | MIX | QTY. | $X_1$ | $X_2$ | $S_1$ | $S_2$ |
| $0 | $S_1$ | 32 | | | 1 | |
| $0 | $S_2$ | 34 | | | 0 | |
| Contri-bution Lost | | | | | $0 | |
| | | | | | | |

If we want to take an hour in department 1 away from productive use for any purpose, we have seen that this simply means giving up 1 of the 32 hours in that department and has no effect upon department 2. Calculations for contribution lost are as follows:

1 hour lost at $0 per hour = $0
0 hours lost at $0 per hour = $0
—
Total contribution lost = $0

(d)

| Contri-bution per Unit | | | | | | |
|---|---|---|---|---|---|---|
| | MIX | QTY. | $X_1$ | $X_2$ | $S_1$ | $S_2$ |
| $0 | $S_1$ | 32 | | | | 0 |
| $0 | $S_2$ | 34 | | | | 1 |
| Contri-bution Lost | | | | | | $0 |
| | | | | | | |

If we want to remove one hour in department 2 from productive work for any reason, we have seen that this will necessitate no loss of productive hours in department 1, but will simply reduce the number of available hours in department 2 by one. Calculations for contribution lost are as follows:

0 hours lost at $0 per hour = $0
1 hour lost at $0 per hour = $0
—
Total contribution lost = $0

FIGURE 4–8
Illustrating Contribution Lost from All Possible
Introduction of Products

| Contribu-tion per Unit | | | | | | |
|---|---|---|---|---|---|---|
| | MIX | QTY. | $X_1$ | $X_2$ | $S_1$ | $S_2$ |
| $0 | $S_1$ | 32 | 3 | 2 | 1 | 0 |
| $0 | $S_2$ | 34 | 1 | 4 | 0 | 1 |
| Contri-bution Lost | | | $0 | $0 | $0 | $0 |
| | | | | | | |

### Completing section E (the simplex criterion)

In the preceding discussion, we have seen how to calculate the loss in contribution occasioned by introducing a unit of any one of the four possible variables into the solution. When we *do* introduce a unit of $X_1$ into the product mix, however, it will bring $5 with it as its contribution to fixed cost and profit. Similarly, introducing a unit of $X_2$ will bring $6 into the profit picture; introduction of a unit of $S_1$ or $S_2$ will not change the total contribution since they have zero value. The illustration in Figure 4–9 is identical to that in Figure 4–8 except that the per unit contribution for each of the possible variables is shown above that variable in section C.

FIGURE 4–9

Illustrating Contribution of Each Variable and Contribution Lost per Unit of That Variable Introduced

| Contri-bution per Unit | | | $5 | $6 | $0 | $0 | ← Contribution per unit of each variable |
|---|---|---|---|---|---|---|---|
| | MIX | QTY. | $X_1$ | $X_2$ | $S_1$ | $S_2$ | |
| $0 | $S_1$ | 32 | 3 | 2 | 1 | 0 | |
| $0 | $S_2$ | 34 | 1 | 4 | 0 | 1 | |
| Contri-bution Lost | | | $0 | $0 | $0 | $0 | ← Contribution lost by intro-ducing a unit of each variable |
| | | | | | | | |

Suppose now, that we remove the two labeled rows from the simplex table in Figure 4–9 and show them as follows:

| $X_1$ | $X_2$ | $S_1$ | $S_2$ | |
|---|---|---|---|---|
| $5 | $6 | $0 | $0 | ← Contribution per unit of each variable |
| $0 | $0 | $0 | $0 | ← Contribution lost by introducing a unit of each variable |

Now if we subtract the second row from the first (subtract contribution lost by introducing a unit of any variable from the contribution that variable brings with it as it enters the product mix), we get the following:

| $X_1$ | $X_2$ | $S_1$ | $S_2$ | |
|---|---|---|---|---|
| $5 | $6 | $0 | $0 ◄— | Contribution per unit of each variable |
| —$0 | —$0 | —$0 | —$0 ◄— | Contribution lost by introducing a unit of each variable |
| $5 | $6 | $0 | $0 | |

↑ Net contribution possible by introducing a unit of each variable

This concept of "net contribution" is often referred to as the *simplex criterion*. It is the basis upon which we decide what the next variable to enter the mix will be. It expresses the possible gain in contribution per unit for each of the possible variables we might bring into the next solution. In the algebraic method, it was necessary to calculate it by hand using simultaneous equations; here in the simplex method, we have calculated it using nothing more involved than simple addition, subtraction, and multiplication.

In future solutions, both to this and other problems, the method

FIGURE 4–10
Completed First Simplex Table

| | Contribution per Unit | | $5 | $6 | $0 | $0 |
|---|---|---|---|---|---|---|
| | MIX | QTY. | $X_1$ | $X_2$ | $S_1$ | $S_2$ |
| $0 | $S_1$ | 32 | 3 | 2 | 1 | 0 |
| $0 | $S_2$ | 34 | 1 | 4 | 0 | 1 |
| Total contribution from this solution | Contribution Lost | ↘ $0 | $0 | $0 | $0 | $0 |
| | Net Contribution | | $5 | $6 | $0 | $0 |

↑— $X_2$ comes into the mix

for calculating the simplex criterion will remain the same; (1) first calculate the contribution which will be lost by bringing a unit of any of the variables into the product mix; (2) then subtract this from the contribution that unit will bring with it when it enters the mix. Obviously, the variable with the largest net contribution per unit is the variable we want to bring into the mix next. In this case $X_2$, with a per unit net contribution of $6 is our choice. Figure 4–10 illustrates the completed first simplex table, showing $X_2$ as the product which will enter the mix in the next solution. The space in the contribution lost row under the quantity column indicates the total contribution this solution generates (zero in this case).

### Determining the quantity of $X_2$ to bring in

Applying the simplex criterion (selecting the product with the largest net gain per unit) has indicated that $X_2$ should be produced; at this point we must determine just how much $X_2$ it is possible to produce without violating one of the constraints. Examining the $X_2$ column in Figure 4–10, we see that for each unit of $X_2$ that comes into the product mix, we must be ready to give up 2 hours of time in department 1 and 4 hours of time in department 2; since department 1 has 32 hours of unused time and department 2 has 34 hours of unused time, the maximum number of units of $X_2$ which can be made without violating the time constraints must be expressed by one of the following divisions:

| Department | Hours Available | Hours Required per Unit of $X_2$ | Maximum Units of $X_2$ Which Can Be Manufactured |
|---|---|---|---|
| $S_1$........ | 32 | 2 | $32/2 = 16$ |
| $S_2$........ | 34 | 4 | $34/4 = 8\frac{1}{2}$ |

Common sense indicates that the smaller number ($8\frac{1}{2}$) is the answer, since to try to produce 16 units of $X_2$ in department 2 will require (16 units of $X_2$) · (4 hours per unit of $X_2$ in department 2) = 64 hours; this is far beyond the time available (34 hours); thus we are limited by the constraints in the problem to production of $8\frac{1}{2}$ units of $X_2$ at this point. The fractional unit is not too unrealistic since we could of course produce 17 units of $X_2$ every two days.

FIGURE 4–11
Illustration of Use of $\theta$ rule

(a)

| MIX | QTY. | $X_1$ | $X_2$ | $S_1$ | $S_2$ | |
|---|---|---|---|---|---|---|
| $0 | $S_1$ | 24 | 2 | 5 | 1 | 0 | $\theta = \dfrac{24}{2} = 12$ |
| $0 | $S_2$ | 16 | 4 | 6 | 0 | 1 | $\theta = \dfrac{16}{4} = 4$ |

↑ IN

(Four units of $X_1$ would be brought into the product mix; to bring in 12 units of $X_1$ would require $12 \times 4 = 48$ hours in department 2 violating a constraint.)

(b)

| | MIX | QTY. | $X_1$ | $X_2$ | $X_3$ | $S_1$ | $S_2$ | $S_3$ |
|---|---|---|---|---|---|---|---|---|
| $\theta = \dfrac{20}{10} = 2$ | $0 | $S_1$ | 20 | 5 | 1 | 10 | 1 | 0 | 0 |
| $\theta = \dfrac{12}{2} = 6$ | $0 | $S_2$ | 12 | 6 | 4 | 2 | 0 | 1 | 0 |
| $\theta = \dfrac{30}{6} = 5$ | $0 | $S_3$ | 30 | 2 | 5 | 6 | 0 | 0 | 1 |

↑ IN

(Two units of $X_3$ would be brought into the product mix; to attempt to bring in 6 units of $X_3$ would require $6 \times 10 = 60$ hours in department 1 thereby violating a constraint; it would also require $6 \times 6 = 36$ hours in department 3 also violating a constraint. To attempt to bring in even 5 units of $X_3$ would require $5 \times 10 = 50$ hours in department 2 thereby exceeding the 20 hours available there; choice of the smallest $\theta$ (two in this case) guarantees that no constraint will be exceeded.

In determining how many units of a product can be accommodated, we will always use the following rule, i.e., *always pick the smallest positive quotient as the maximum quantity of product which can be accommodated by the restraints.* The choice of 16 units of $X_2$ as our answer in this case would have violated the time restraint in department 2, and thus represented an unacceptable answer. This rule is often referred to as the $\theta$ rule (theta rule); it guarantees that the quantity of product we choose to bring into the product mix will be feasible. Two additional examples will help illustrate the use of this rule; in these examples we have arbitrarily shown two partial simplex tables, neither of which is related to the problem illustrated in Figure 4–10. The reader will observe that in Figure 4–11 (b), the problem involves choice among three products produced through three departments.

To this point, we have determined that $X_2$ is the appropriate product to produce; further by applying the $\theta$ rule, we have determined that production of $8\frac{1}{2}$ units of $X_2$ will not violate the time available in both departments. The simplex table of Figure 4–10 with the addition of the product which will enter the mix and the quantity of that product is repeated in Figure 4–12:

FIGURE 4–12
Simplex Table Illustrating Choice of Product to Be Produced and Determination of the Maximum Quantity Which Can Be Produced

First Simplex Table

| Contri-bution per Unit | | | $5 | $6 | $0 | $0 |
|---|---|---|---|---|---|---|
| | MIX | QTY. | $X_1$ | $X_2$ | $S_1$ | $S_2$ |
| $0 | $S_1$ | 32 | 3 | 2 | 1 | 0 |
| $0 | $S_2$ | 34 | 1 | 4 | 0 | 1 |
| Contribution Lost | | $0 | $0 | $0 | $0 | $0 |
| Net Contribution | | | $5 | $6 | $0 | $0 |

$\theta = \dfrac{32}{2} = 16$

$\theta = \dfrac{34}{4} = 8\frac{1}{2}$

$8\frac{1}{2}$ units of $X_2$ can be produced without exceeding the time available in either department

↑ IN

$X_2$ yields the highest net contribution per unit and thus is chosen as the product to be produced

## Beginning the second simplex table

Production of $8\frac{1}{2}$ units of $X_2$ will require a total of $8\frac{1}{2} \times 4 = 34$ hours in department 2 and will use all of the available time in that department. The introduction of $8\frac{1}{2}$ units of $X_2$ into the product mix has replaced $S_2$ in the mix (since there is no more time available in department 2, $S_2$ will take on a value of zero and will not appear in the second solution). We can say that $S_2$ is *replaced* by $8\frac{1}{2}$ units of $X_2$. We must now illustrate this transaction in the second simplex table. Figure 4–13 shows the second simplex table with $8\frac{1}{2}$ units of $X_2$ having replaced 34 hours of $S_2$ in the product mix; note that $S_1$ remains in the product mix since production of $8\frac{1}{2}$ units of $X_2$ will require only $8\frac{1}{2} \times 2 = 17$ hours in department 1, thereby not completely exhausting the 32 hours available in that department.

FIGURE 4–13
Illustrating Entering of New Variable in Second Table

Second Simplex Table

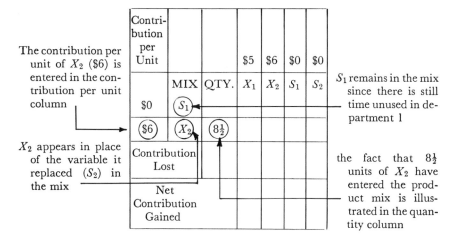

The contribution per unit of $X_2$ ($6) is entered in the contribution per unit column

$X_2$ appears in place of the variable it replaced ($S_2$) in the mix

$S_1$ remains in the mix since there is still time unused in department 1

the fact that $8\frac{1}{2}$ units of $X_2$ have entered the product mix is illustrated in the quantity column

## Completing the new $X_2$ row (the entering row)

The one entry in the new $X_2$ row, $(8\frac{1}{2})$, was calculated by dividing its corresponding entry in the first table (34 hours) by 4 (the rate at which $X_2$ exchanges for $S_2$); this transaction is repeated in Figure 4–14. Now, if dividing 34 by 4 (the appropriate exchange rate) produced the correct entry in the quantity column for new $X_2$ row let us proceed under the assumption that *dividing all of the old entries in the $S_2$ row* by the *same* exchange rate (4) will provide us with the correct

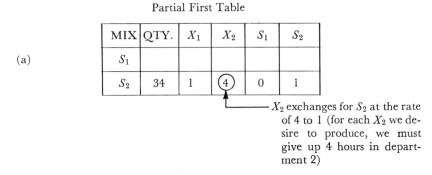

FIGURE 4–14

Showing Calculation of Entry in Quantity Column for New Entering Variable

Partial First Table

(a)

| MIX | QTY. | $X_1$ | $X_2$ | $S_1$ | $S_2$ |
|-----|------|-------|-------|-------|-------|
| $S_1$ |    |       |       |       |       |
| $S_2$ | 34 | 1     | ④     | 0     | 1     |

$X_2$ exchanges for $S_2$ at the rate of 4 to 1 (for each $X_2$ we desire to produce, we must give up 4 hours in department 2)

Partial Second Table

(b)

| MIX | QTY. | $X_1$ | $X_2$ | $S_1$ | $S_2$ |
|-----|------|-------|-------|-------|-------|
| $S_1$ |    |       |       |       |       |
| $X_2$ | 8½ |       |       |       |       |

Producing $8\frac{1}{2}$ $X_2$'s has completely used up the 34 hours in department 2 (the correct numerical value for the quantity was derived by the calculation $\frac{34}{4} = 8\frac{1}{2}$

entries for the new $X_2$ row; when we have accomplished these calculations we would of course only accept this procedure if we could reason logically that the values which result in the new $X_2$ row are indeed the correct ones. Figure 4–15 illustrates calculation of the new $X_2$ row.

Now that we have calculated the values for the new $X_2$ row, let us test the logic of this method by seeing if the newly calculated values *do* represent the correct relationships between the possible variables and the variables in the second solution. Figure 4–16 repeats Figure 4–15(b) with a detailed narrative proof of the validity of each of the values we have just calculated.

The fact that the method we have used to calculate the values for the new $X_2$ row generates the appropriate values is certainly no sur-

FIGURE 4–15
Calculation of New $X_2$ Row

Partial First Table

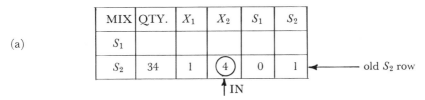

(a)

| MIX | QTY. | $X_1$ | $X_2$ | $S_1$ | $S_2$ |
|-----|------|-------|-------|-------|-------|
| $S_1$ | | | | | |
| $S_2$ | 34 | 1 | ④ | 0 | 1 | ←———— old $S_2$ row |

↑ IN

Partial Second Table

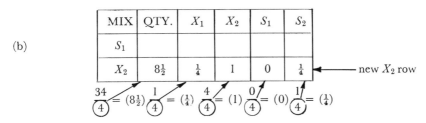

(b)

| MIX | QTY. | $X_1$ | $X_2$ | $S_1$ | $S_2$ |
|-----|------|-------|-------|-------|-------|
| $S_1$ | | | | | |
| $X_2$ | $8\frac{1}{2}$ | $\frac{1}{4}$ | 1 | 0 | $\frac{1}{4}$ | ←———— new $X_2$ row |

$\dfrac{34}{④} = (8\frac{1}{2})$  $\dfrac{1}{④} = (\frac{1}{4})$  $\dfrac{4}{④} = (1)$  $\dfrac{0}{④} = (0)$  $\dfrac{1}{④} = (\frac{1}{4})$

FIGURE 4–16
Explanation of Exchange Rates

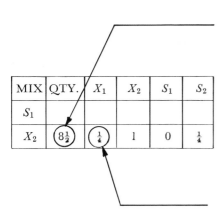

| MIX | QTY. | $X_1$ | $X_2$ | $S_1$ | $S_2$ |
|-----|------|-------|-------|-------|-------|
| $S_1$ | | | | | |
| $X_2$ | $8\frac{1}{2}$ | $\frac{1}{4}$ | 1 | 0 | $\frac{1}{4}$ |

There were originally 34 hours of time in department 2 available; a decision to manufacture $X_2$ was then made. Each unit of $X_2$ produced required 4 hours in department 2. Dividing 34 by 4 yielded $8\frac{1}{2}$ as the answer which represents the production of $8\frac{1}{2}$ units of $X_2$ in exchange for all of the time originally available in department 2.

The value $\frac{1}{4}$ means that if we want to produce one unit of $X_1$, we must be prepared to give up production of $\frac{1}{4}$ unit of $X_2$. Since all the available hours in department 2 are utilized, and since production of a unit of $X_1$ in that department would require 1 hour, the only way to make the 1 hour available is to reduce production of $X_2$ by $\frac{1}{4}$ unit; since $X_2$ requires 4 hours per unit in department 2, producing $\frac{1}{4}$ unit less of $X_2$ would make the necessary hour available.

FIGURE 4–16 (*Continued*)

| MIX | QTY. | $X_1$ | $X_2$ | $S_1$ | $S_2$ |
|-----|------|-------|-------|-------|-------|
| $S_1$ | | | | | |
| $X_2$ | $8\frac{1}{2}$ | $\frac{1}{4}$ | ① | 0 | $\frac{1}{4}$ |

The value 1 means that if we want to produce one more unit of $X_2$, we must be prepared to give up production of 1 of the $8\frac{1}{2}$ units of $X_2$ we are now producing. This is true because the absence of production time in department 2 limits further production of $X_2$ and there is no way to increase production of that product without giving up some of the units of it now produced; simply put, this is like taking a unit of $X_2$ from the "top of the pile" and adding it to the bottom.

The zero value means that if we want to take an hour of production time from department 1, this will have no (zero) effect upon the production of $X_2$. We have already determined that producing $8\frac{1}{2}$ units of $X_2$ *did not* exhaust all of the time available in department 1, so if we want an hour for other purposes than manufacturing in that department, we can "take it" without reducing production of $X_2$.

| MIX | QTY. | $X_1$ | $X_2$ | $S_1$ | $S_2$ |
|-----|------|-------|-------|-------|-------|
| $S_1$ | | | | | |
| $X_2$ | $8\frac{1}{2}$ | $\frac{1}{4}$ | 1 | ⓪ | ①$\frac{1}{4}$ |

The value $\frac{1}{4}$ means that if we want to take an hour of production time away from department 2 for any reason, we must be prepared to give up production of $\frac{1}{4}$ of a unit of $X_2$. Time in department 2 is exhausted; $X_2$ requires four hours per unit of production time in department 2; therefore if we want one hour back in that department, we will have to reduce production of $X_2$ by $\frac{1}{4}$ unit to release that hour.

prise. Having established that $X_2$ substitutes for $S_2$ at the rate of 4 to 1, it was only logical to believe that using this exchange rate of 4 to 1 on all of the elements in the old $S_2$ row would produce the correct values for the new $X_2$ row; this did indeed turn out to be the case, and generated a series of new relationship values in the second table each of which could be logically defended.

## Determining the new $S_1$ row of the second table

Let us begin to develop the new $S_1$ row in the second simplex table by first calculating the value which is appropriate for the quantity column in that row. The quantity column entry in the first simplex table was 32 hours; now that we have decided to produce $8\frac{1}{2}$ units of $X_2$, we must determine what effect this decision has upon the hours available in department 1 ($S_1$). This is determined by performing the following calculation:

$$\left\{\begin{matrix}\text{Hours originally}\\ \text{available in}\\ \text{department 1}\end{matrix}\right\} - \left\{\begin{matrix}\text{Hours required for}\\ \text{each unit of } X_2\\ \text{in department 1}\end{matrix}\right\} \times \left\{\begin{matrix}\text{Quantity of } X_2\\ \text{which is}\\ \text{produced}\end{matrix}\right\}$$

or in numerical form

$$32 - (2) \times (8\tfrac{1}{2}) = 15.$$

Thus 15 hours of time in department 1 would remain after the production of $8\frac{1}{2}$ units of $X_2$. Figure 4–17 illustrates the second simplex table with this figure entered in its proper location.

FIGURE 4–17
Quantity of Time Which Remains in Department 1 Entered

| MIX | QTY. | $X_1$ | $X_2$ | $S_1$ | $S_2$ |
|-----|------|-------|-------|-------|-------|
| $S_1$ | 15 | | | | |
| $X_2$ | $8\frac{1}{2}$ | $\frac{1}{4}$ | 1 | 0 | $\frac{1}{4}$ |

Employing this same procedure to determine all the elements of the new $S_1$ row, we get the following:

| Elements in $S_1$ Row of First Simplex Table | − | Rate at Which $X_2$ Exchanges for $S_1$ | × | Elements in $X_2$ Row of Second Simplex Table | = | New Elements for $S_1$ Row of Second Simplex Table |
|---|---|---|---|---|---|---|
| 32 | − | (2) | × | $(8\frac{1}{2})$ | = | 15 |
| 3 | − | (2) | × | (1/4) | = | 5/2 |
| 2 | − | (2) | × | (1) | = | 0 |
| 1 | − | (2) | × | (0) | = | 1 |
| 0 | − | (2) | × | (1/4) | = | −1/2 |

FIGURE 4–18
$S_1$ Row of Second Simplex Table Completed

| | MIX | QTY. | $X_1$ | $X_2$ | $S_1$ | $S_2$ |
|---|---|---|---|---|---|---|
| 15 unused hours remain in department 1 | $S_1$ | (15) | 5/2 | 0 | 1 | $-\frac{1}{2}$ |
| $8\frac{1}{2}$ units of $X_2$ are being produced | $X_2$ | $(8\frac{1}{2})$ | $\frac{1}{4}$ | 1 | 0 | $\frac{1}{4}$ |

Taking the elements of the new $S_1$ row thus determined and entering them into the second simplex table has been accomplished in Figure 4–18. We must now show that our methodology has provided us with the correct answers. In Figure 4–19, we have taken the values calculated for the new $S_1$ row and given a narrative proof of the validity of each one.

FIGURE 4–19
Explanation of the New $S_1$ Row

There were originally 32 hours of time available in department 1; a decision to manufacture $8\frac{1}{2}$ units of $X_2$ was then made; each unit of $X_2$ requires 2 hours in department 1; $8\frac{1}{2}$ units of $X_2$ will then require $8\frac{1}{2} \times 2$ or 17 hours. Deducting the 17 hours used from the 32 hours originally available leaves 15 hours unused.

| MIX | QTY. | $X_1$ | $X_2$ | $S_1$ | $S_2$ |
|---|---|---|---|---|---|
| $S_1$ | (15) | (5/2) | 0 | 1 | $-\frac{1}{2}$ |
| $X_2$ | $8\frac{1}{2}$ | $\frac{1}{4}$ | 1 | 0 | $\frac{1}{4}$ |

The value 5/2 means that if we want to produce a unit of $X_1$ we must be prepared to give up 5/2 of an hour in department 1. The reasoning here requires two steps: (a) Directly below the 5/2 we find the value $\frac{1}{4}$; we have previously seen that producing a unit of $X_1$ requires that we give up production of $\frac{1}{4}$ of a unit of $X_2$; this would free up $\frac{1}{4} \times 2$ hours or $\frac{1}{2}$ hour in department 1 since the $\frac{1}{4}$ unit of $X_2$ not made would not go through this department. (b) Bringing in one unit of $X_1$ would require three hours in department 1; with $\frac{1}{2}$ hour freed up and three hours required for the entering product, the net required time is $3 - \frac{1}{2}$ or 5/2 hours per unit.

FIGURE 4–19 (*Continued*)

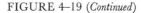

| MIX | QTY. | $X_1$ | $X_2$ | $S_1$ | $S_2$ |
|-----|------|-------|-------|-------|-------|
| $S_1$ | 15 | 5/2 | 0 | 1 | $-\frac{1}{2}$ |
| $X_2$ | $8\frac{1}{2}$ | $\frac{1}{4}$ | 1 | 0 | $\frac{1}{4}$ |

The value zero means that if we want to increase the production of $X_2$ by one unit, this will have no effect upon the time in department 1. We have previously seen that to increase production of $X_2$ by one unit will simply mean giving up one of the units of $X_2$ we now make (taking from the top of the pile and adding to the bottom). If we did this, it is obvious that the effect upon department 1 would be zero, i.e., the entering unit of $X_2$ would use up exactly the same amount of time as the unit of $X_2$ withdrawn.

The value 1 means simply that if we want to withdraw an hour of time in department 1 from active production for maintenance or some other purpose, we will have to give up 1 of the 15 hours which remain unused.

The $-\frac{1}{2}$ value means that if we want to withdraw an hour of time in department 2 from active production, we will get back (you might say "receive a gift") of $\frac{1}{2}$ of an hour in department 1. The negative sign means "get back" instead of "give up." The value $\frac{1}{4}$ directly below the $-\frac{1}{2}$ value means as we have previously shown, that removing one hour from production in department 2 means giving up production of $\frac{1}{4}$ unit of $X_2$; doing this would "free up" or return the time this $\frac{1}{4}$ unit of $X_2$ originally required in department 1 ($\frac{1}{4} \times 2$ hours $= \frac{1}{2}$ hour). The term $-\frac{1}{2}$ represents this $\frac{1}{2}$ hour of free time we receive.

| MIX | QTY. | $X_1$ | $X_2$ | $S_1$ | $S_2$ |
|-----|------|-------|-------|-------|-------|
| $S_1$ | 15 | 5/2 | 0 | 1 | $-\frac{1}{2}$ |
| $X_2$ | $8\frac{1}{2}$ | $\frac{1}{4}$ | 1 | 0 | $\frac{1}{4}$ |

Once again, our method has generated the correct values for the new $S_1$ row; again we should not be surprised since we employed as the exchange rate governing these five transactions the value 2, the rate at which $X_2$ exchanges for $S_1$, i.e., 2 to 1. In generating the new $X_2$ row and the new $S_1$ row in the second simplex table, we have demonstrated the methodology of the simplex procedure and have illustrated that by using common sense, one can easily explain each of the values thus generated. No matter how complicated a linear programming problem may be, the simplex procedures just explained can be used to generate each new table in the solution.

### Completing the second table

Now that the new $S_1$ and $X_2$ rows of the second table have been completed, we must complete the accounting section of that table and then determine if further improvement is possible. With the present solution, we are producing $8\frac{1}{2}$ units of $X_2$ which generate a contribution to fixed cost and profit of $8\frac{1}{2} \times \$6 = \$51$; this may be the maximum contribution which can be earned under the restraints in the problem; to determine whether further improvement is possible, let us proceed to complete the second table.

Figure 4–20 illustrates the second solution, ready for calculation of accounting values relating to contribution. The total contribution generated by this solution ($\$6 \times 8\frac{1}{2} = \$51$) is illustrated in the contribution lost row under the quantity column.

FIGURE 4–20
Second Simplex Table

| Contri-bution per Unit | | | $5 | $6 | $0 | $0 |
|---|---|---|---|---|---|---|
| | MIX | QTY. | $X_1$ | $X_2$ | $S_1$ | $S_2$ |
| $0 | $S_1$ | 15 | 5/2 | 0 | 1 | $-\frac{1}{2}$ |
| $6 | $X_2$ | $8\frac{1}{2}$ | $\frac{1}{4}$ | 1 | 0 | $\frac{1}{4}$ |
| Contribu-tion Lost | $51 | | | | | |
| Net Con-tribution | | | | | | |

Calculating contribution lost for the second table has been accomplished in Figure 4–21.

FIGURE 4–21
Calculating Contribution Lost

(a)

| MIX | QTY. | $X_1$ | $X_2$ | $S_1$ | |
|---|---|---|---|---|---|
| \$0  $S_1$ | 15 | 5/2 | | | |
| \$6  $X_2$ | 8½ | ¼ | | | |
| Contribution Lost | \$51 | \$3/2 | | | |

5/2 hour lost at \$0 per hour = \$0
¼ $X_2$ lost at \$6 per unit    = \$3/2

Total Contribution Lost    \$3/2

(b)

| MIX | QTY. | $X_1$ | $X_2$ | $S_1$ | $S_2$ |
|---|---|---|---|---|---|
| \$0  $S_1$ | | | 0 | | |
| \$6  $X_2$ | | | 1 | | |
| Contribution Lost | \$51 | | \$6 | | |

0 hours lost at \$0 per hour = \$0
1 $X_2$ lost at \$6 per unit    = \$6

Total Contribution Lost    \$6

(c)

| MIX | QTY. | $X_1$ | $X_2$ | $S_1$ | $S_2$ |
|---|---|---|---|---|---|
| \$0  $S_1$ | 15 | | | 1 | |
| \$6  $X_2$ | 8½ | | | 0 | |
| Contribution Lost | \$51 | | | \$0 | |

1 hour lost at \$0 per hour = \$0
0 $X_2$ lost at \$6 per unit = \$0

Total Contribution Lost    \$0

(d)

| MIX | QTY. | $X_1$ | $X_2$ | $S_1$ | $S_2$ |
|---|---|---|---|---|---|
| \$0  $S_1$ | 15 | | | | $-\frac{1}{2}$ |
| \$6  $X_2$ | 8½ | | | | ¼ |
| Contribution Lost | \$51 | | | | \$3/2 |

½ hour gained at \$0 per hour = \$0
¼ $X_2$ lost at \$6 per unit    = \$$\frac{3}{2}$

Total Contribution Lost    \$$\frac{3}{2}$

Each of the contributions lost calculated in Figure 4–21 has been entered in the table contained in Figure 4–22 in the row provided for that purpose.

FIGURE 4–22
Second Table Illustrating Contribution Lost

| Contri-bution per Unit | | | $5 | $6 | $0 | $0 |
|---|---|---|---|---|---|---|
| | MIX | QTY. | $X_1$ | $X_2$ | $S_1$ | $S_2$ |
| $0 | $S_1$ | 15 | 5/2 | 0 | 1 | $-\frac{1}{2}$ |
| $6 | $X_2$ | $8\frac{1}{2}$ | $\frac{1}{4}$ | 1 | 0 | $\frac{1}{4}$ |
| Contribution Lost | | $51 | $3/2 | $6 | $0 | $3/2 |

Calculation of the net contribution it is possible to gain from each of the possible entering variables is now accomplished using the method previously described:

| $X_1$ | $X_2$ | $S_1$ | $S_2$ | |
|---|---|---|---|---|
| $5 | $6 | $0 | $0 | ◄— Contribution per unit of each variable |
| $-$3/2 | $-$6 | $-0 | $3/2 | ◄— Contribution lost by introducing a unit of each variable |
| $7/2 | $0 | $0 | $-$3/2 | ◄— Net contribution possible by introducing a unit of each variable |

The resulting net contribution figures determined above have been entered in the appropriate locations in the table in Figure 4–23.

By observing the net contribution row of Figure 4–23, it is obvious that introducing some $X_1$ into the product mix will add to total contribution at the rate of $7/2 per unit introduced. $X_1$ is the only variable that adds any positive contribution; therefore our choice is limited to $X_1$. It is interesting to note here that bringing an hour of $X_2$ back into the mix (that is, removing one hour of $X_2$ from production) will actually cost us $3/2; we are not surprised at such a penalty since time in that department is exhausted and removing any more

FIGURE 4–23
Second Table Completed

| Contri-bution per Unit | | | $5 | $6 | $0 | $0 | |
|---|---|---|---|---|---|---|---|
| | MIX | QTY. | $X_1$ | $X_2$ | $S_1$ | $S_2$ | |
| $0 | $S_1$ | 15 | 5/2 | 0 | 1 | $-\frac{1}{2}$ | $\theta = \dfrac{15}{5/2} = \boxed{6}$ |
| $6 | $X_2$ | $8\frac{1}{2}$ | $\frac{1}{4}$ | 1 | 0 | $\frac{1}{4}$ | $\theta = \dfrac{8\frac{1}{2}}{1/4} = 34$ |
| Contribution Lost | | $51 | $3/2 | $6 | $0 | $\ 3/2 | |
| Net Contribution | | | $7/2 | $0 | $0 | $-3/2 | |

IN↑

productive hours will further curtail production, and thus contribution. The $\theta$ calculations in Figure 4–23 indicate that six units of $X_1$ is the maximum that can be introduced without violating the time constraints. Thus for the next solution, six units of $X_1$ will replace the remaining hours in department 1.

Calculation of the values for the new $X_1$ row has been accomplished in Figure 4–24 using the method previously developed.

FIGURE 4–24
$X_1$ Row in Third Simplex Table Entered

| MIX | QTY. | $X_1$ | $X_2$ | $S_1$ | $S_2$ |
|---|---|---|---|---|---|
| $X_1$ | 6 | 1 | 0 | 2/5 | −1/5 |
| | | | | | |

$$\frac{15}{5/2} = (6) \quad \frac{5/2}{5/2} = (1) \quad \frac{0}{5/2} = (0) \quad \frac{1}{5/2} = (2/5) \quad \frac{-1/2}{5/2} = (-1/5)$$

The new values for the $X_2$ row of the third table are calculated as follows:

$$
\begin{Bmatrix} \text{Elements of } X_2 \\ \text{row of the} \\ \text{second sim-} \\ \text{plex table} \end{Bmatrix} - \begin{Bmatrix} \text{Rate at} \\ \text{which } X_1 \\ \text{exchanges} \\ \text{for } X_2 \end{Bmatrix} \times \begin{Bmatrix} \text{Element in} \\ X_1 \text{ row of} \\ \text{third table} \end{Bmatrix} = \begin{Bmatrix} \text{New elements} \\ \text{of } X_2 \text{ row} \\ \text{of third} \\ \text{table} \end{Bmatrix}
$$

| | | | | | | | |
|---|---|---|---|---|---|---|---|
| $8\frac{1}{2}$ | $-$ | $(\frac{1}{4})$ | $\times$ | $(6)$ | $=$ | $7$ |
| $\frac{1}{4}$ | $-$ | $(\frac{1}{4})$ | $\times$ | $(1)$ | $=$ | $0$ |
| $1$ | $-$ | $(\frac{1}{4})$ | $\times$ | $(0)$ | $=$ | $1$ |
| $0$ | $-$ | $(\frac{1}{4})$ | $\times$ | $(\frac{2}{5})$ | $=$ | $-\frac{1}{10}$ |
| $\frac{1}{4}$ | $-$ | $(\frac{1}{4})$ | $\times$ | $(-\frac{1}{5})$ | $=$ | $\frac{3}{10}$ |

Figure 4–25 illustrates the new values for both the $X_1$ and $X_2$ rows of the third table.

FIGURE 4–25
$X_1$ and $X_2$ Row in Third Simplex Table

| MIX | QTY. | $X_1$ | $X_2$ | $S_1$ | $S_2$ |
|---|---|---|---|---|---|
| $X_1$ | 6 | 1 | 0 | $2/5$ | $-1/5$ |
| $X_2$ | 7 | 0 | 1 | $-1/10$ | $3/10$ |

Contribution which would be lost by bringing into the product mix each of the possible variables is illustrated in Figure 4–26.

FIGURE 4–26
Third Table Illustrating Contribution Lost

| Contri-bution per Unit | | | $5 | $6 | $0 | $0 |
|---|---|---|---|---|---|---|
| | MIX | QTY. | $X_1$ | $X_2$ | $S_1$ | $S_2$ |
| $5 | $X_1$ | 6 | 1 | 0 | $2/5$ | $-1/5$ |
| $6 | $X_2$ | 7 | 0 | 1 | $-1/10$ | $3/10$ |
| Contribution Lost | | $72 | $5 | $6 | $7/5 | $4/5 |
| | | | | | | |

The net contribution row is illustrated in Figure 4–27, thus completing the third table. The total contribution which this product mix of six units of $X_1$ and seven units of $X_2$ produces is also shown.

FIGURE 4–27
Completed Third Table—Optimum Solution

| Contribution per Unit | | | $5 | $6 | $0 | $0 |
|---|---|---|---|---|---|---|
| | MIX | QTY. | $X_1$ | $X_2$ | $S_1$ | $S_2$ |
| $5 | $X_1$ | 6 | 1 | 0 | $2/5$ | $-1/5$ |
| $6 | $X_2$ | 7 | 0 | 1 | $-1/10$ | $3/10$ |
| Contribution Lost | | $72 | $5 | $6 | $7/5$ | $4/5$ |
| Net Contribution | | | $0 | $0 | $-7/5$ | $-4/5$ |

Examination of the net contribution row of the completed third table assures us that no possible product will yield any positive contribution per unit; thus we have achieved the optimum solution. It is interesting to note in this connection that the two entries in the net contribution row under columns $S_1$ and $S_2$ are both negative. We would interpret this to mean that at this point, if we desired to reduce the time available in either of these departments, we would suffer some loss of contribution, specifically $7/5 per hour of time removed from production in department 1 and $4/5 per hour of time removed from production in department 2.

Let us suppose that management decides that one hour must be made available (removed from production) to manufacture some sample items, and that either department is capable of doing the work; obviously then, we would choose to reduce productive time in department 2 by one hour, since loss of one hour there reduces total contribution by $4/5 ($0.80), whereas reduction of productive time in department 1 by one hour reduces total contribution by $7/5 ($1.40). Analysis of the net contribution row by management can indicate which of many possible alternative actions will have the least undesirable financial effect upon the organization.

Now assume for a moment that management can *increase* the productive time available in either department through the use of overtime, additional investment, or other means. If adding an hour of productive capacity to either department can be accomplished for the *same* amount of money, management would prefer to make the expenditure in department 1. This can be defended logically by noting that if loss of an hour in department 1 is more *expensive* than loss of an hour in department 2, then gaining one hour in department 1 would be more desirable than *gaining* an hour in department 2, $0.60 more desirable in this case; ($7/5 − $4/5 = $3/5 or $0.60). Thus the second interpretation of negative values under slack variables in the $C_j - Z_j$ row is that of opportunity profit.

### Standard conventions

Thus far in the exposition we have used the designations "Contribution Lost" and "Net Contribution" to represent the last two rows of the simplex table. In most of the literature on the subject of linear programming it is common to find these rows referred to as $Z_j$ and $C_j - Z_j$, respectively. In maximizing problems, $C_j$ refers to contribution per unit and $Z_j$ refers to contribution lost per unit, thus $C_j - Z_j$ is net contribution per unit. From this point on in the text we shall also use these two conventions.

### Simplex solution to a second problem

Figure 4–28 illustrates a second product mix type problem; it is similar to the one developed in this chapter with the exception that it involves three possible products, each passing through three production departments. We shall not go into the same degree of detail we did with the original problem, since the solution method used will not change. Each of the tables will be shown along with the supporting calculations.

Statement of the constraints in this problem in algebraic form would take the following form:

$$3X_1 + 4X_2 + 2X_3 \leq 60 \quad \text{Constraint for department 1}$$

$$2X_1 + X_2 + 2X_3 \leq 40 \quad \text{Constraint for department 2}$$

$$X_1 + 3X_2 + 2X_3 \leq 80 \quad \text{Constraint for department 3}$$

FIGURE 4–28
Problem Illustration

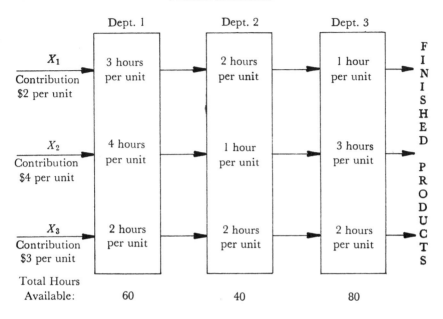

Addition of appropriate slack variables to each of the inequalities produces the following set of equations describing the constraints.

$$3X_1 + 4X_2 + 2X_3 + S_1 = 60$$
$$2X_1 + X_2 + 2X_3 + S_2 = 40$$
$$X_1 + 3X_2 + 2X_3 + S_3 = 80.$$

And addition of balancing variables with zero coefficients to each equation puts the equations in proper form for the first simplex table:

$$3X_1 + 4X_2 + 2X_3 + S_1 + 0S_2 + 0S_3 = 60$$
$$2X_1 + X_2 + 2X_3 + 0S_1 + S_2 + 0S_3 = 40$$
$$X_1 + 3X_2 + 2X_3 + 0S_1 + 0S_2 + S_3 = 80.$$

Figure 4–29 represents the first simplex table completed for the new problem. Analysis of the net contribution row indicates that $X_2$ is the variable which would add the greatest contribution per unit introduced, therefore $X_2$ will enter the mix in the second table replacing $S_1$. Performing the three $\theta$ calculations indicates that 15 units of $X_2$

FIGURE 4–29
First Simplex Table

| Contri-bution per Unit | | | $2 | $4 | $3 | $0 | $0 | $0 | |
|---|---|---|---|---|---|---|---|---|---|
| | MIX | QTY. | $X_1$ | $X_2$ | $X_3$ | $S_1$ | $S_2$ | $S_3$ | |
| $0 | $S_1$ | 60 | 3 | 4 | 2 | 1 | 0 | 0 | $\theta = \dfrac{60}{4} = \boxed{15}$ |
| $0 | $S_2$ | 40 | 2 | 1 | 2 | 0 | 1 | 0 | $\theta = \dfrac{40}{1} = 40$ |
| $0 | $S_3$ | 80 | 1 | 3 | 2 | 0 | 0 | 1 | $\theta = \dfrac{80}{3} = 26\frac{2}{3}$ |
| $Z_j$ | | $0 | $0 | $0 | $0 | $0 | $0 | $0 | |
| $C_j - Z_j$ | | | $2 | $4 | $3 | $0 | $0 | $0 | |

↑ IN

is the maximum quantity that can enter the mix without violating any constraints. The second simplex table with the new $X_2$ row completed appears in Figure 4–30.

FIGURE 4–30
$X_2$ Row Completed in Second Table

| Contri-bution per Unit | | | $2 | $4 | $3 | $0 | $0 | $0 | $\dfrac{60}{4} = 15$ |
|---|---|---|---|---|---|---|---|---|---|
| | MIX | QTY. | $X_1$ | $X_2$ | $X_3$ | $S_1$ | $S_2$ | $S_3$ | $3/4 = 3/4$ |
| $4 | $X_2$ | 15 | 3/4 | 1 | 1/2 | 1/4 | 0 | 0 | $4/4 = 1$ |
| $0 | $S_2$ | | | | | | | | $2/4 = 1/2$ |
| $0 | $S_3$ | | | | | | | | $1/4 = 1/4$ |
| | | | | | | | | | $0/4 = 0$ |
| | | | | | | | | | $0/4 = 0$ |

The second simplex table for this problem together with the supporting calculations for the $S_2$ and $S_3$ rows, appears in Figure 4–31.

FIGURE 4–31
Second Table Simplex Complete

| Contribution per Unit | | | $2 | $4 | $3 | $0 | $0 | $0 | |
|---|---|---|---|---|---|---|---|---|---|
| | MIX | QTY. | $X_1$ | $X_2$ | $X_3$ | $S_1$ | $S_2$ | $S_3$ | |
| $4 | $X_2$ | 15 | 3/4 | 1 | 1/2 | 1/4 | 0 | 0 | $\theta = \dfrac{15}{1/2} = 30$ |
| $0 | $S_2$ | 25 | 5/4 | 0 | 3/2 | −1/4 | 1 | 0 | $\theta = \dfrac{25}{3/2} = \boxed{16\frac{2}{3}}$ |
| $0 | $S_3$ | 35 | −5/4 | 0 | 1/2 | −3/4 | 0 | 1 | $\theta = \dfrac{35}{1/2} = 70$ |
| $Z_j$ | | $60 | $3 | $4 | $2 | $1 | $0 | $0 | |
| $C_j - Z_j$ | | | $−1 | $0 | $1 | $−1 | $0 | $0 | |

IN

New $S_2$ Row

$40 - (1)(15)\ \ = 25$
$2 - (1)(3/4) = 5/4$
$1 - (1)(1)\ \ \ \ = 0$
$2 - (1)(1/2) = 3/2$
$0 - (1)(1/4) = -1/4$
$1 - (1)(0)\ \ \ \ = 1$
$0 - (1)(0)\ \ \ \ = 0$

New $S_3$ Row

$80 - (3)(15)\ \ = 35$
$1 - (3)(3/4) = -5/4$
$3 - (3)(1)\ \ \ \ = 0$
$2 - (3)(1/2) = 1/2$
$0 - (3)(1/4) = -3/4$
$0 - (3)(0)\ \ \ \ = 0$
$1 - (3)(0)\ \ \ \ = 1$

Analysis of the net contribution row of the second table indicates now that $X_3$ is the logical variable to enter the solution with a possible per unit contribution of $1. Performing the $\theta$ calculations suggests that $16\frac{2}{3}$ units of $X_3$ be brought into the mix in the third solution replacing $S_2$. The third solution with supporting calculations appears in Figure 4–32.

Analysis of the net contribution row $(C_j - Z_j)$ of the third simplex table in Figure 4–32 reveals that there is no positive entry, thus no further improvement is possible and we have reached the optimum solution. In this case, the optimum product mix is to produce $6\frac{2}{3}$ units of $X_2$, $16\frac{2}{3}$ units of $X_3$ and no $X_1$. Observe that there is unused time in the third department, specifically $26\frac{2}{3}$ hours. Even though we have not exhausted all of the available hours in this department, we still have reached the optimum solution, a condition which is not

FIGURE 4–32
Third Simplex Table Complete

| Contribution per Unit | | | $2 | $4 | $3 | $0 | $0 | $0 |
|---|---|---|---|---|---|---|---|---|
| | MIX | QTY. | $X_1$ | $X_2$ | $X_3$ | $S_1$ | $S_2$ | $S_3$ |
| $4 | $X_2$ | $6\frac{2}{3}$ | 1/3 | 1 | 0 | 1/3 | −1/3 | 0 |
| $3 | $X_3$ | $16\frac{2}{3}$ | 5/6 | 0 | 1 | −1/6 | 2/3 | 0 |
| $0 | $S_3$ | $26\frac{2}{3}$ | −5/3 | 0 | 0 | −2/3 | −1/3 | 1 |
| $Z_j$ | | $76.67 | $\dfrac{\$23}{6}$ | $4 | $3 | $5/6 | $2/3 | $0 |
| | | | | | | | | |
| $C_j - Z_j$ | | | $\dfrac{-\$11}{6}$ | $0 | $0 | $-5/6 | $-2/3 | $0 |

New $X_3$ Row

$$\frac{25}{3/2} = 16\frac{2}{3}$$

$$\frac{5/4}{3/2} = 5/6$$

$$\frac{0}{3/2} = 0$$

$$\frac{3/2}{3/2} = 1$$

$$\frac{-1/4}{3/2} = -1/6$$

$$\frac{1}{3/2} = 2/3$$

$$\frac{0}{3/2} = 0$$

New $X_2$ Row

$$15 - (1/2)(16\frac{2}{3}) = 6\frac{2}{3}$$

$$3/4 - (1/2)(5/6) = 1/3$$

$$1 - (1/2)(0) = 1$$

$$1/2 - (1/2)(1) = 0$$

$$1/4 - (1/2)(-1/6) = 1/3$$

$$0 - (1/2)(2/3) = -1/3$$

$$0 - (1/2)(0) = 0$$

New $S_3$ Row

$$35 - (1/2)(16\frac{2}{3}) = 26\frac{2}{3}$$

$$-5/4 - (1/2)(5/6) = -5/3$$

$$0 - (1/2)(0) = 0$$

$$\tfrac{1}{2} - (1/2)(1) = 0$$

$$-3/4 - (1/2)(-1/6) = -2/3$$

$$0 - (1/2)(2/3) = -1/3$$

$$1 - (1/2)(0) = 1$$

unusual in operational problem solving with linear programming. The total contribution to fixed costs and profits we can make with this solution is: $6\frac{2}{3} \times \$4$ plus $16\frac{2}{3} \times \$3$ or \$76.66. This figure appears in the contribution lost row under the quantity column.

## Problems

1. Maximize $Z = 5X_1 + 6X_2$
   Subject to: $16X_1 + 2X_2 \leq 225$
   $\quad\quad\quad\quad X_1 + 14X_2 \leq 212.$

2. Maximize $Z = 27X_1 + 32X_2$
   Subject to: $125X_1 + 50X_2 \leq 2550$
   $\quad\quad\quad\quad 75X_1 + 75X_2 \leq 1025.$

3. Maximize $Z = 2X_1 + 4X_2 + 3X_3$
   Subject to: $X_1 + X_2 + 3X_3 \leq 12$
   $\quad\quad\quad\quad 4X_1 + X_2 + 6X_3 \leq 24.$

4. Maximize $Z = 6X_1 + 4X_2 + 5X_3$
   Subject to: $5X_1 + 7X_2 + 8X_3 \leq 925$
   $\quad\quad\quad\quad 6X_1 + X_2 + 15X_3 \leq 975$
   $\quad\quad\quad\quad X_1 + 3X_2 + 7X_3 \leq 545.$

5. The CLR Company produces gadgets and wadgets. Raw materials for gadgets cost \$2 per unit, whereas raw materials for each wadget cost \$2.50. A wadget requires two hours of direct labor in department 1 and three hours in department 2, while a gadget requires four hours in department 1 and two hours in department 2. Assume an hourly wage rate of \$2. If both products sell for \$18, and the number of labor hours available in the two departments each week equals 160 and 180 respectively, determine the product mix maximizing total profits.

6. A coffee processor markets three blends of coffee. They are premium, fine, and regular. He uses three types of coffee beans in his blends. They include a Brazilian bean, a Colombian bean, and a bean from Argentina. The following chart lists the composition of the three blends.

|  | *Brazilian* | *Argentine* | *Colombian* |
|---|---|---|---|
| Premium......... | 25% | 40% | 35% |
| Fine............ | 30% | 30% | 40% |
| Regular......... | 35% | 20% | 45% |

The processor nets a profit of 28 cents per pound of the premium blend, 21 cents per pound of the fine blend, and 19 cents per pound of the regular blend. Assuming that his regular weekly supplies of the three component beans are: Brazilian—20,000 pounds, Argentine—18,000 pounds, and Colombian—24,000 pounds, compute the product mix which maximizes net profits by means of the simplex method.

7. The XYZ Company manufactures three products; A, B, and C. Currently demand is greater for these products than the supply generated by the firm. With limited resources in its three departments, the firm must determine the best allocation of its resources. It has established the maximization of profits to be its objective. The following are the required man-hours for each product in each department.

|  | A | B | C | Available per Day |
|---|---|---|---|---|
| Dept. 1........ | 3.50 | 2.00 | 0.50 | 48 |
| Dept. 2........ | 3.00 | 6.00 | 4.50 | 88 |
| Dept. 3........ | 0.50 | 1.50 | 3.00 | 56 |

The average wage rate in department 1 is $22.50 per day (assuming a $7\frac{1}{2}$ hour work day). Similarly, the average wage per day in department 2 is $26.25, and the workers in department 3 all earn $2.50 per hour. Material costs for the three products are:

$$
\begin{array}{ll}
\text{A........} & \$5 \text{ per unit} \\
\text{B........} & \$12 \text{ per unit} \\
\text{C........} & \$5.50 \text{ per unit}
\end{array}
$$

Assuming that the firm operates six days per week, in what quantities should the firm produce each of the three products on a weekly basis. Product A is sold for $50 per unit, product B for $62, and product C for $55.

8. Maximize $Z = 23X_1 + 18X_2 + 15X_3$
   Subject to: $295X_1 + 33X_2 + 195X_3 \leq 10,950$
   $5X_1 + 13X_2 + 15X_3 \leq 1,255$
   $65X_1 + 137X_2 + 18X_3 \leq 6,025$

# chapter 5

# The simplex method of linear programming—minimization

## Introduction

The problems thus far have dealt with maximization of contribution to fixed costs and profits. Linear programming is also useful as a decision-making aid in problems where minimization is the criterion. For example, a manager might use linear programming to help him find the lowest possible cost of producing a product from among a large number of alternative production methods too numerous to evaluate with ordinary methods. If a company operated several factories supplying many warehouses with identical products, they might want to know which particular shipping schedule would minimize the total cost of transportation. Another example might be a manufacturer of animal feeds who must mix and sell feeds which conform to guaranteed analysis when raw material prices change daily; obviously there is some particular mixture for him which will conform to the analysis and still represent the lowest total cost of ingredients. Linear programming can be of significant help in the solution to these and other similar problems.

### Relationship of minimizing to maximizing

Use of the simplex method of linear programming in the solution of problems involving minimization of some criterion requires only minor changes. The objective must still be quantifiable; the restraints (or constraints) under which minimization will take place must be known and quantifiable, and the variables in the problem must still be linearly related. The solution to the problem involves the same steps studied in Chapter 4; the significant differences between minimizing and maximizing are those concerned with setting up the problem in proper form. After a brief discussion of the concept of linearity in costs, we shall consider just how such problems are stated mathematically and solved using the simplex method.

### Linearity in cost

One of the requirements in linear programming is that the variables be related linearly; we have shown how use of the concept of "contribution" in maximizing problems adheres to this requirement and still generates an answer which in effect acts to maximize the total profit of the firm. Since minimization must deal with certain aspects of cost it is important therefore that the costs chosen involve linear relationships. The concept of linear costs was briefly mentioned in Chapter 1. At the risk of some repetition, we shall explore this idea in some greater detail as a background for the material to come.

Decision making and financial planning in management today assume two broad classifications of cost, *fixed* and *variable*. Fixed costs are those which do not change *appreciably* with changes in volume. Examples of these would be rent, officers' salaries, property taxes, depreciation, and the like. Although we assume that these do not change in total over the accounting period, we know from practical experience that small changes in them do occur; the assumption of constant fixed costs as a computational aid does not detract markedly from decisions made thereon.

Variable costs on the other hand are usually defined as those costs which vary almost directly with volume or output. These are composed mainly of direct labor and direct materials; direct factory overhead is also an example of variable cost. Simply put, if a company manufactures chairs, and one chair requires two board feet of lumber, then two chairs will require four board feet and so on. Thus the cost of lumber at least would rise almost directly in proportion to the volume of output; of course when we purchase large quantities of lumber we are eligible for a quantity discount which might reduce the unit cost per chair. Labor cost also fits this pattern; if it requires a man-hour of labor input to manufacture one chair, then two man-hours would be our requirement for the production of two chairs, and so forth. Here too, however, there are some factors which tend to make the relationship between direct labor cost and output not *perfectly* linear. If we have to operate on overtime during peak periods of demand, then the cost of direct labor rises faster than volume due to the overtime payments involved. Management is always aware of these assumptions which underly the definitions of fixed and variable costs and makes them a part of decisions involving costs. The difference between formal definitions of fixed and variable cost and their actual behavior in business today is usually not large enough to present a serious problem in decision making.

Linear programming requires linearity among the variables in the problems to which it is applied. Thus, if we attempt to minimize cost per unit produced, it must vary linearly with volume. A simulated example will illustrate the proper treatment of cost per unit in linear programming problems. We shall assume that a small company with two classifications of cost as follows:

Yearly Fixed Cost......... $10,000
Variable Cost per Unit..... $10

Figure 5–1 illustrates calculation of the total cost and total cost per unit at various levels of output.

FIGURE 5–1
Behavior of Total Cost per Unit at Various Output Levels

| Volume (Units) | Fixed Cost | Variable Cost | Total Cost | Total Cost per Unit |
|---|---|---|---|---|
| 10..... | $10,000 | $ 100 | $ 10,000 | $1,010 |
| 20..... | 10,000 | 200 | 10,200 | 510 |
| 50..... | 10,000 | 500 | 10,500 | 210 |
| 100..... | 10,000 | 1,000 | 11,000 | 110 |
| 500..... | 10,000 | 5,000 | 15,000 | 30 |
| 1,000..... | 10,000 | 10,000 | 20,000 | 20 |
| 10,000..... | 10,000 | 100,000 | 110,000 | 11 |

It is obvious that total cost is not linearly related with volume since it increases much slower than volume. We can infer from this simple example then that total cost is not an acceptable minimization criterion. However, since total variable cost varies directly with volume it can be used as a criterion in minimization problems. The net effect upon the firm would be the same if we minimized variable cost, since the $10,000 of fixed cost would result (at least in the short run), regardless of the level of output. This argument summed up briefly is the same one used by the advocates of "direct costing" as a cost accounting system. If we take action to minimize the variable cost, this is in the best possible interest of the company, since short-run fixed cost will remain the same regardless of the level of volume and thus need not enter the decision. In the application of the simplex minimization process to actual problems, it is always variable cost which is minimized for this reason.

## Statement of the problem

The problem we have chosen to illustrate the simplex minimization process concerns a manufacturer of commercial chemicals. Currently he has an order for 100 pounds of a mixture consisting of three ingredients; the customer places certain requirements on the mixture in the way of minimum and maximum quantities of each ingredient; the problem is expressed as follows:

Required: 100 pounds of a mixture consisting of three ingredients:

$X_1$ which costs $4 per pound

$X_2$ which costs $5 per pound

$X_3$ which costs $3 per pound.

Restrictions on the mixture:

1. It cannot contain more than 30 pounds of $X_1$.
2. It must contain at least 20 pounds of $X_2$.
3. It cannot contain more than 40 pounds of $X_3$.

Our chemical manufacturer wants to find a mixture of the three ingredients which satisfies his customer's requirements and still yields the minimum total cost of raw materials. Obviously, the solution to this problem can be obtained in a minute using only a little common sense; however, common sense as a solution method begins to break down as the number of ingredients and restraints climbs and with 10 or more ingredients and a similar number of restraints, solution by methods other than linear programming is a difficult undertaking. In this problem, since the cost to be minimized involves only raw materials and the cost of each of these is considered to be constant per pound, we meet the linearity requirement with no further trouble.

## Stating the problem mathematically

There are four restrictions which must be observed; these are simply the customer's requirements stated first in narrative then in mathematical form as follows:

1. The mix cannot contain more than 30 pounds of $X_1$.

$$X_1 \leq 30$$

($X_1$ less than or equal to 30)

2. The mix must contain at least 20 pounds of $X_2$.

$$X_2 \geq 20$$

($X_2$ equal to or greater than 20)

3. The mix cannot contain more than 40 pounds of $X_3$.

$$X_3 \leq 40$$

($X_3$ less than or equal to 40)

4. We must deliver 100 pounds of the mix.

$$X_1 + X_2 + X_3 = 100$$

($X_1$ plus $X_2$ plus $X_3$ must equal to 100)

Restraints (1) and (3) are of the less-than or equal-to type we have used before and are familiar to us; restraint (2) is a new type where the inequality is reversed, and restraint (4) involves an equation; we have not treated either (2) or (4) in the book thus far.

When linear programming was used in maximization the restraints had to be stated as equations; a similar requirement exists in minimization. Beginning with restraint (1), the addition of a slack variable to the left side will generate an equation as follows:

$$X_1 \leq 30 \tag{1}$$

$$X_1 + S_1 = 30.$$

The slack variable we have added represents the amount of $X_1$ in any solution which is less than the 30 pound maximum; thus if $X_1$ were 25 pounds in the final solution, $S_1$ would be 5 pounds; (25 is 5 less than 30). Similarly, if $X_1$ were zero in one of the solutions, $S_1$ would appear in that solution as 30.

Restriction (2) can be reformed into an equation by subtracting a slack variable from the left side as follows:

$$X_2 \geq 20 \qquad (2)$$
$$X_2 - S_2 = 20.$$

Here the function of $S_2$ is to represent the quantity of $X_2$ in any solution which is more than 20 pounds (the minimum required). For example, if $X_2$ turned out to be 34 pounds in one of the solutions, $S_2$ would take on a value of 14. If $X_2$ were exactly 20 pounds in one of the solutions, $S_2$ would take on a zero value.

Restraint (3) is identical in form to restraint (1) and is treated similarly; a slack variable is added to the left side to generate an equation, as follows:

$$X_3 \leq 40 \qquad (3)$$
$$X_3 + S_3 = 40.$$

The function of $S_3$ is to represent the quantity of $X_3$ in any solution which is less than the maximum permissible 40 pounds. If in the final solution $X_3$ were 27 pounds, then of course $S_3$ would have to be 13 pounds.

The fourth restraint appeared originally in the form of an equation, i.e., $X_1 + X_2 + X_3 = 100$ and for now needs no further treatment. Figure 5–2 illustrates the four restraints in equation form.

FIGURE 5–2
Restraints Expressed in Equation Form

$$X_1 + S_1 = 30 \qquad (1)$$
$$X_2 - S_2 = 20 \qquad (2)$$
$$X_3 + S_3 = 40 \qquad (3)$$
$$X_1 + X_2 + X_3 = 100 \qquad (4)$$

## Formulating a first solution

Just as we were required to do in the maximizing examples, we must find a first solution for minimizing problems; it does not have to be one which involves low total costs; its sole function (just as in maximizing) is to "get us started" toward lower cost solutions. For this reason the only requirement made on a first solution is that it be feasible; i.e., within our capacity to mix. There are basically two approaches to finding a first solution; one of course is to find some value for $X_1$, $X_2$, and $X_3$, and $S_1$, $S_2$, and $S_3$ which do not violate any of the restraints. This, at least for the simple illustrative problem, does not appear to be much of a task. We could let $X_1 = 1$ pound, $X_2 = 20$ pounds, and $X_3 = 1$ pound; then $S_1$ would have to equal 29 pounds, $S_2$ 0, and $S_3$ 39 pounds. Then the first three restraints would be satisfied:

$$1 + 29 = 30 \tag{1}$$
$$20 + 0 = 20 \tag{2}$$
$$1 + 39 = 40. \tag{3}$$

But what about restraint (4)? $1 + 20 + 29$, does not equal 100; thus restraint (4) is violated. Now we must go back and find another set of values for the six variables in the problem which satisfies *all four* restraints. With no more than six variables, we can find a first solution which satisfies all the restraints in a few minutes. *But*, what happens when the number of variables in the problem rises to 50; or even 100? It is difficult to estimate just how long it would take one to find a first solution by trial and error. To eliminate the need for trial and error search, an operationally sound procedure for finding a first solution has been developed; it is called an "artificial first solution." A short discussion of this procedure should convince most readers that using it is far preferable to the trial and error method.

### The artificial first solution

The basic concept behind the artificial first solution method is that the best value to assign to each of the ingredient variables ($X_1$, $X_2$, and $X_3$) is *zero;* this is analogous to the first solution in product mix maximizing problems where no real products were manufactured in the first solution, and all time remained unused. Though this was not a profitable solution by any means, it did allow the solution of the problem to begin. The function of the artificial first solution in minimizing problems is simply to generate a beginning point from which lower cost solutions can be derived. Let us now take each of the four restraints and demonstrate how to use this method.

In restraint (1), if we let the ingredient variable ($X_1$) equal zero in the first solution, this simply means that $S_1$ will appear in the first solution with a value of 30 shown as follows:

$$X_1 + S_1 = 30$$
$$0 + S_1 = 3 \tag{1}$$
$$S_1 = 30.$$

Not having $X_1$ in the first solution is quite feasible because the original restraint is still satisfied:

$$X \leq 30 \tag{1}$$
$$0 \leq 30.$$

In restraint (2), if we let the ingredient variable ($X_2$) equal zero, the resulting equation is:

$$X_2 - S_2 = 20$$
$$0 - S_2 = 20 \tag{2}$$
$$S_2 = -20.$$

At this point we are in trouble because we have a negative quantity in the first solution; ($S_2 = -20$). You will recall from Chapter 2, "The Graphical Method," that solutions to linear programming problems occur in the first quadrant where all variables are positive. Our problem can be solved by introducing a new "artificial" variable, called $A_1$ and letting *both* $X_2$ and $S_2$ be zero in the first solution. We can think of the artificial variable $A_1$ as a substitute for $X_2$. But since $A_1$ is only an artificial ingredient, we would not want it included in the final mix of ingredients. To ensure that it will not appear in the final (lowest cost) solution we shall arbitrarily assign it a cost per pound of $100; it will then be removed in some subsequent solution in favor of one of the lower priced ingredients. With this artificial variable added restraint (2) becomes:

$$X_2 - S_2 = 20$$
$$X_2 - S_2 + A_1 = 20 \tag{2}$$
$$0 + 0 + A_1 = 20$$
$$A_1 = 20.$$

Thus to satisfy the second restraint, we can assume that we will purchase 20 pounds of $A_1$ at $100 per pound and use it; the actual purchase would never be made of course. The function of $A_1$ is only to produce a first solution which is feasible.

The third restraint ($X_3 \leq 40$), is of the more familiar type and when $X_3$ takes on a zero value in the first solution, the restraint appears as follows:

$$X_3 + S_3 = 40$$
$$0 + S_3 = 40 \tag{3}$$
$$S_3 = 40.$$

$S_3$ will then appear in the first solution with a value of 40. The restraint is satisfied; $X_3$ was not required to be in the mix at all. The only requirement was that $X_3$ not *exceed* 40 pounds.

Restraint (4), in its original form was:

$$X_1 + X_2 + X_3 = 100. \tag{4}$$

Now with $X_1$, $X_2$, and $X_3$ all equal to zero in the first solution, we have the problem of:

$$0 + 0 + 0 = 100.$$

To deal with this situation, we will define another "artificial" variable ($A_2$). We will consider $A_2$ as a substitute for the entire mixture (analogous to going out and buying 100 pounds of a substitute mixture). To ensure that $A_2$ will not appear in the final mixture, we will assign it a very high cost (again $100 per pound). Thus the final restraint will be satisfied:

$$X_1 + X_2 + X_3 = 100$$
$$X_1 + X_2 + X_3 + A_2 = 100 \tag{4}$$
$$0 + 0 + 0 + 100 = 100$$
$$100 = 100.$$

Collecting the four restraints for placement in the first simplex table we have:

$$X_1 + S_1 = 30 \tag{1}$$
$$X_2 - S_2 + A_1 = 20 \tag{2}$$
$$X_3 + S_3 = 40 \tag{3}$$
$$X_1 + X_2 + X_3 + A_2 = 100 \tag{4}$$

And finally when we have added balancing variables so that each term appears in each equation (even with a zero coefficient), we finish with the set of equations illustrated in Figure 5–3.

FIGURE 5-3
Restraint Equations

$$X_1 + 0X_2 + 0X_3 + S_1 + 0S_2 + 0S_3 + 0A_1 + 0A_2 = 30 \qquad (1)$$
$$0X_1 + X_2 + 0X_3 + 0S_1 - S_2 + 0S_3 + A_1 + 0A_2 = 20 \qquad (2)$$
$$0X_1 + 0X_2 + X_3 + 0S_1 + 0S_2 + S_3 + 0A_1 + 0A_2 = 40 \qquad (3)$$
$$X_1 + X_2 + X_3 + 0S_1 + 0S_2 + 0S_3 + 0A_1 + A_2 = 100 \qquad (4)$$

Analysis of the equations in Figure 5–3 indicates that the first solution does not contain any real ingredients ($X_1$, $X_2$, and $X_3$ are zero in the first solution). We offer to our customer 100 pounds of a substitute mixture ($A_2 = 100$), consisting partly of 20 pounds of $A_1$ (a substitute for the one required ingredient $X_2$). Figure 5–4 shows each of the variables in the problem with the value it takes on in the first solution.

FIGURE 5-4
Variables in the First Solution

$$
\begin{array}{lll}
X_1 = 0 & S_1 = 30 & A_1 = 20 \\
X_2 = 0 & S_2 = 0 & A_2 = 100 \\
X_3 = 0 & S_3 = 40 &
\end{array}
$$

This is obviously a very expensive and very artificial first solution to the problem; its sole purpose, however, is to allow us to begin the simplex solution to the problem. As such it avoids searching for a feasible first solution using trial and error methods. Figure 5–5 represents a brief review of the way in which we treated each type of restraint.

FIGURE 5-5
Methods for Treating Restraints

| Type of Restraint | Example | Treatment |
|---|---|---|
| I | $X \leq 5$ | Add a slack variable. |
| II | $X \geq 10$ | Subtract a slack variable and add an artificial variable. |
| III | $X = 20$ | Add an artificial variable. |

### The simplex table for minimization problems

In most respects, the simplex table used for solutions to minimization problems is like the one first developed in Chapter 4. Differences appear in the $C_j$ row and column, the $Z_j$ row, and the $C_j - Z_j$ row. Figure 5–6 indicates the new designation for each of these areas of the simplex table. The other sections of the simplex table serve the same purpose they did in the maximization table. *Mix* refers to the variables currently in any mix; *quantity* indicates the number of pounds of each variable currently in the mix. The two rows directly to the right of the mix and quantity columns will contain the substitution rates between the possible variables and the variables currently in the mix.

FIGURE 5–6
Simplex Table for Minimization

$C_j$ (the cost per pound of each of the possible variables in the problem)

(the total cost of any solution is entered in this cell)

$Z_j$ (the cost which each of the possible variables would displace as it entered the mix)

$C_j - Z_j$ (the *net* reduction in cost possible by bringing a pound of any of the possible variables into the mix, i.e., the cost per pound of the variable entering the mix less the cost which that pound displaces or removes when it comes into this mix)

$C_j$ (the cost per pound for each of the variables in the mix for any solution)

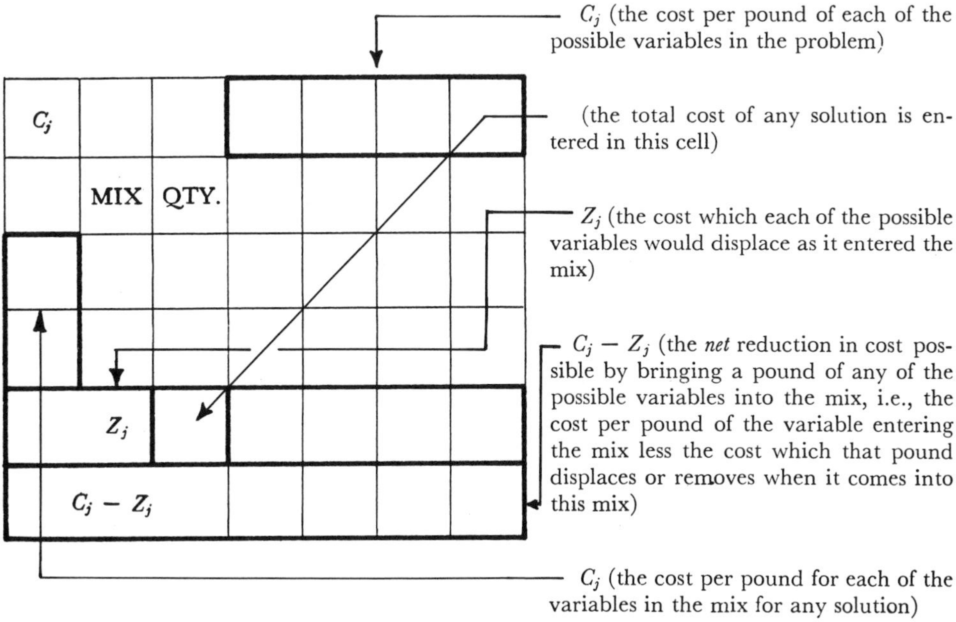

### Entering the first solution in the simplex table

To enter the set of restraint equations contained in Figure 5–3 in the first simplex table, we proceed as we did in maximizing. We know

FIGURE 5-7
First Solution, Variables Entered

| $C_j$ | | | | | | | | | | | |
|---|---|---|---|---|---|---|---|---|---|---|---|
| | MIX | QTY. | | | | | | | | | |
| $0 | $S_1$ | 30 | | | | | | | | | |
| $100 | $A_1$ | 20 | | | | | | | | | |
| $0 | $S_3$ | 40 | | | | | | | | | |
| $100 | $A_2$ | 100 | | | | | | | | | |
| $Z_j$ | | | | | | | | | | | |
| $C_j - Z_j$ | | | | | | | | | | | |

that only one variable from each equation can take on a value other than zero in the first solution, and Figure 5-4 indicates which of the variables will take on nonzero values. These four variables $S_1$, $S_3$, $A_1$, and $A_2$ with their appropriate cost per pound and the quantity of each in the first solution have been entered in the table illustrated in Figure 5-7. Figure 5-8 illustrates the addition of the *possible* variables in the problem together with their appropriate costs per pound. To complete the entry of the first solution in the simplex table, we take the coefficients of the variables in the restraint equations (Figure 5-3)

FIGURE 5-8
Possible Variables Entered

| $C_j$ | | | $4 | $5 | $3 | $0 | $0 | $0 | $100 | $100 |
|---|---|---|---|---|---|---|---|---|---|---|
| | MIX | QTY. | $X_1$ | $X_2$ | $X_3$ | $S_1$ | $S_2$ | $S_3$ | $A_1$ | $A_2$ |
| $0 | $S_1$ | 30 | | | | | | | | |
| $100 | $A_1$ | 20 | | | | | | | | |
| $0 | $S_3$ | 40 | | | | | | | | |
| $100 | $A_2$ | 100 | | | | | | | | |
| $Z_j$ | | | | | | | | | | |
| $C_j - Z_j$ | | | | | | | | | | |

and enter them directly into the table. These then represent the substitution rates between the possible variables in the problem and the variables in the first solution. This has been accomplished in Figure 5–9; finally we calculate the total cost of this solution, $(30 \times \$0) + (20 \times \$100) + (40 \times \$0) + (100 \times \$100)$ and enter the result ($12,000) in the $Z_j$ row under the quantity column. The first solution is now entered.

FIGURE 5–9
First Solution Entered

| $C_j$ | | | $4 | $5 | $3 | $0 | $0 | $0 | $100 | $100 |
|---|---|---|---|---|---|---|---|---|---|---|
| | MIX | QTY. | $X_1$ | $X_2$ | $X_3$ | $S_1$ | $S_2$ | $S_3$ | $A_1$ | $A_2$ |
| $0 | $S_1$ | 30 | 1 | 0 | 0 | 1 | 0 | 0 | 0 | 0 |
| $100 | $A_1$ | 20 | 0 | 1 | 0 | 0 | $-1$ | 0 | 1 | 0 |
| $0 | $S_3$ | 40 | 0 | 0 | 1 | 0 | 0 | 1 | 0 | 0 |
| $100 | $A_2$ | 100 | 1 | 1 | 1 | 0 | 0 | 0 | 0 | 1 |
| $Z_j$ | | $12,000 | | | | | | | | |
| $C_j - Z_j$ | | | | | | | | | | |

## Developing an improved solution

To learn how best to reduce the total cost of the first solution, let us consider bringing a pound of $X_1$ into the present mix. Using the substitution rates directly under the $X_1$ column heading we see that bringing a pound of this variable into the mix will replace:

$$
\begin{aligned}
1 \text{ pound of } S_1 \text{ at } \$0 \text{ per pound} &= \$0 \\
0 \text{ pounds of } A_1 \text{ at } \$0 \text{ per pound} &= \$0 \\
0 \text{ pounds of } S_3 \text{ at } \$100 \text{ per pound} &= \$0 \\
1 \text{ pound of } A_2 \text{ at } \$100 \text{ per pound} &= \underline{\$100} \\
&\phantom{=} \$100
\end{aligned}
$$

Thus the proper entry for the $Z_j$ row under the $X_1$ column is $100. This same reasoning has been applied to the other seven variables and the resulting dollar amounts have been entered in the $Z_j$ row of the simplex table of Figure 5–10.

FIGURE 5–10
$Z_j$ Row Completed

| $C_j$ | | | $4 | $5 | $3 | $0 | $0. | $0 | $100 | $100 |
|---|---|---|---|---|---|---|---|---|---|---|
| | MIX | QTY. | $X_1$ | $X_2$ | $X_3$ | $S_1$ | $S_2$ | $S_3$ | $A_1$ | $A_2$ |
| $0 | $S_1$ | 30 | 1 | 0 | 0 | 1 | 0 | 0 | 0 | 0 |
| $100 | $A_1$ | 20 | 0 | 1 | 0 | 0 | −1 | 0 | 1 | 0 |
| $0 | $S_3$ | 40 | 0 | 0 | 1 | 0 | 0 | 1 | 0 | 0 |
| $100 | $A_2$ | 100 | 1 | 1 | 1 | 0 | 0 | 0 | 0 | 1 |
| | $Z_j$ | | $12,000 | $100 | $200 | $100 | $0 | $−100 | $0 | $100 | $100 |
| | $C_j - Z_j$ | | | | | | | | | |

To complete the first table, we must now calculate the *net* reduction in cost possible from bringing a pound of any of the variables into the mix $(C_j - Z_j)$. This can be done by taking the cost per pound of any variable $(C_j)$ and subtracting from this the reduction in cost occasioned by bringing a pound of that variable into the mix $(Z_j)$. These $C_j - Z_j$ calculations have been done and are illustrated in the

FIGURE 5–11
$C_j - Z_j$ Row Completed

| $C_j$ | | | $4 | $5 | $3 | $0 | $0 | $0 | $100 | $100 |
|---|---|---|---|---|---|---|---|---|---|---|
| | MIX | QTY. | $X_1$ | $X_2$ | $X_3$ | $S_1$ | $S_2$ | $S_3$ | $A_1$ | $A_2$ |
| $0 | $S_1$ | 30 | | | | | | | | |
| $100 | $A_1$ | 20 | | | | | | | | |
| $0 | $S_3$ | 40 | | | | | | | | |
| $100 | $A_2$ | 100 | | | | | | | | |
| | $Z_j$ | | $12,000 | $100 | $200 | $100 | $0 | $−100 | $0 | $100 | $100 |
| | $C_j - Z_j$ | | | $−96 | $−195 | $−97 | $0 | $100 | $0 | $0 | $0 |

| Calculations | | | | | | | | | |
|---|---|---|---|---|---|---|---|---|---|
| | $4 | $5 | $3 | $0 | | $0 | $0 | $100 | $100 |
| | −100 | −200 | −100 | −0 | | −(−100) | −0 | −100 | −100 |
| | $−96 | $−195 | $−97 | $0 | | $100 | $0 | $0 | $0 |

simplex table of Figure 5–11. Since our objective is to *minimize* total cost we naturally want to bring into the second mix that variable which offers the greatest possible cost reduction. Cost reduction in minimization is denoted by a minus sign, hence we would choose to bring in some of $X_2$ (for a reduction of $195 per pound that enters). Other variables also reduce cost (for example, $X_1$ and $X_3$) but none of them reduces cost as much as $X_2$. Thus the *simplex criterion* for minimization problems becomes one of choosing *that variable which reduces cost the most.* Put another way, we choose that variable whose $C_j - Z_j$ value is the most negative. We can also see at this point that when all of the values in the $C_j - Z_j$ row are zero or positive, we will have reached the optimum solution to the problem since only a negative sign indicates further improvement (more cost reduction) to be possible.

### Developing the second solution

A decision to bring some quantity of $X_2$ into the mix has been made; now we must determine how much $X_2$ can enter the mix

FIGURE 5–12
Calculation of $\theta$

| | $C_j$ | | | $4 | $5 | $3 | $0 | $0 | $0 | $100 | $100 | |
|---|---|---|---|---|---|---|---|---|---|---|---|---|
| | | MIX | QTY | $X_1$ | $X_2$ | $X_3$ | $S_1$ | $S_2$ | $S_3$ | $A_1$ | $A_2$ | |
| | $0 | $S_1$ | 30 | 1 | 0 | 0 | 1 | 0 | 0 | 0 | 0 | $\theta = \dfrac{30}{0}$ = Not defined |
| OUT → | $100 | $A_1$ | 20 | 0 | 1 | 0 | 0 | −1 | 0 | 1 | 0 | $\theta = \dfrac{20}{1} = 20$ |
| | $0 | $S_3$ | 40 | 0 | 0 | 1 | 0 | 0 | 1 | 0 | 0 | $\theta = \dfrac{40}{0}$ = Not defined |
| | $100 | $A_2$ | 100 | 1 | 1 | 1 | 0 | 0 | 0 | 0 | 1 | $\theta = \dfrac{100}{1} = 100$ |
| | $Z_j$ | | $12,000 | $100 | $200 | $100 | $0 | $-100 | $0 | $100 | $100 | |
| | $C_j - Z_j$ | | | $-96 | $-195 | $97 | $0 | $100 | $0 | $0 | $0 | |

IN

without violating any of the restraints in the problem. The method of determining this quantity is the same as that used in the simplex maximizing problems; this method was first referred to in Chapter 4 as the $\theta$ (theta) rule. Figure 5–12 illustrates the first table of our minimizing problem with each of the four possible thetas calculated.

Two of the $\theta$'s (30/0 and 40/0) are not mathematically defined quantities and are therefore eliminated from consideration. Of the remaining two (20/1 and 100/1), 20/1 is the smaller quotient and would be chosen using the same reasoning we did in Chapter 4; thus 20 pounds of $X_2$ is brought into the mix in the second solution, replacing the $A_1$ row. The value (1) which appears at the intersection of the entering column ($X_2$) and the replaced row ($A_1$) is the rate of exchange between $X_2$ and $A_1$; the new $X_2$ row in the second table is obtained exactly as in maximization, i.e., by dividing each of the elements in the old $A_1$ row by the exchange rate (1). The second table with the $X_2$ row completed appears in Figure 5–13.

FIGURE 5-13
$X_2$ Row in Second Simplex Table

| $C_j$ | | | $4 | $5 | $3 | $0 | $0 | $0 | $100 | $100 | |
|---|---|---|---|---|---|---|---|---|---|---|---|
| | MIX | QTY. | $X_1$ | $X_2$ | $X_3$ | $S_1$ | $S_2$ | $S_3$ | $A_1$ | $A_2$ | $20/1 = 20$ |
| $0 | $S_1$ | | | | | | | | | | $0/1 = 0$ |
| | | | | | | | | | | | $1/1 = 1$ |
| $5 | $X_2$ | 20 | 0 | 1 | 0 | 0 | $-1$ | 0 | 1 | 0 | $0/1 = 0$ |
| | | | | | | | | | | | $0/1 = 0$ |
| $0 | $S_3$ | | | | | | | | | | $-1/1 = -1$ |
| | | | | | | | | | | | $0/1 = 0$ |
| $100 | $A_2$ | | | | | | | | | | $1/1 = 1$ |
| $Z_j$ | | | | | | | | | | | $0/1 = 0$ |
| $C_j - Z_j$ | | | | | | | | | | | |

In this particular case, the new $X_2$ row is identical to the old $A_1$ row simply because the intersection element was 1.

The remaining three rows of the second table are derived exactly as they were in the maximizing examples. The $S_1$, $S_3$, and $A_2$ rows of the second table together with the supporting calculations appear in Figure 5–14.

FIGURE 5-14
$S_1$, $S_3$, and $A_2$ Row of Second Table Completed

| $C_j$ | | | $4 | $5 | $3 | $0 | $0 | $0 | $100 | $100 |
|---|---|---|---|---|---|---|---|---|---|---|
| | MIX | QTY. | $X_1$ | $X_2$ | $X_3$ | $S_1$ | $S_2$ | $S_3$ | $A_1$ | $A_2$ |
| $0 | $S_1$ | 30 | 1 | 0 | 0 | 1 | 0 | 0 | 0 | 0 |
| $5 | $X_2$ | 20 | 0 | 1 | 0 | 0 | −1 | 0 | 1 | 0 |
| $0 | $S_3$ | 40 | 0 | 0 | 1 | 0 | 0 | 1 | 0 | 0 |
| $100 | $A_2$ | 80 | 1 | 0 | 1 | 0 | 1 | 0 | −1 | 1 |
| $Z_j$ | | $8100 | | | | | | | | |
| $C_j - Z_j$ | | | | | | | | | | |

| *New $S_1$ Row* | *New $S_3$ Row* | *New $A_2$ Row* |
|---|---|---|
| 30 − (0)(20) = 30 | 40 − (0)(20) = 40 | 100 − (1)(20) = 80 |
| 1 − (0)(0) = 1 | 0 − (0((0) = 0 | 1 − (1)(0) = I |
| 0 − (0)(1) = 0 | 0 − (0)(1) = 0 | 1 − (1)(1) = 0 |
| 0 − (0)(0) = 0 | 1 − (0)(0) = 1 | 1 − (1)(0) = 1 |
| 1 − (0)(0) = 1 | 0 − (0)(0) = 0 | 0 − (1)(0) = 0 |
| 0 − (0)(−1) = 0 | 0 − (0)(−1) = 0 | 0 − (1)(−1) = 1 |
| 0 − (0)(0) = 0 | 1 − (0)(0) = 1 | 0 − (1)(0) = 0 |
| 0 − (0)(1) = 0 | 0 − (0)(1) = 0 | 0 − (1)(1) = −1 |
| 0 − (0)(0) = 0 | 0 − (0)(0) = 0 | 1 − (1)(0) = 1 |

Again we see that in this instance, two of the new rows ($S_1$ and $S_3$) remained unchanged; this was because their intersection element with the entering row ($X_2$) was in both cases zero. Whenever this is the case, it eliminates mathematical calculations since no change occurs. The total cost of this solution is:

30 pounds of $S_1$ at $0 = $0
20 pounds of $X_2$ at $5 = $100
40 pounds of $S_3$ at $0 = $0
80 pounds of $A_2$ at $100 = $8,000
$8,100

this figure is entered in the $Z_j$ row under the quantity column.

FIGURE 5–15
Second Simplex Table Completed

| $C_j$ | | | $4 | $5 | $3 | $0 | $0 | $0 | $100 | $100 |
|---|---|---|---|---|---|---|---|---|---|---|
| | MIX | QTY. | $X_1$ | $X_2$ | $X_3$ | $S_1$ | $S_2$ | $S_3$ | $A_1$ | $A_2$ |
| $0 | $S_1$ | 30 | 1 | 0 | 0 | 1 | 0 | 0 | 0 | 0 |
| $5 | $X_2$ | 20 | 0 | 1 | 0 | 0 | −1 | 0 | 1 | 0 |
| $0 | $S_3$ | 40 | 0 | 0 | 1 | 0 | 0 | 1 | 0 | 0 |
| $100 | $A_2$ | 80 | 1 | 0 | 1 | 0 | 1 | 0 | −1 | 1 |
| | $Z_j$ | $8,100 | $100 | $5 | $100 | $0 | $95 | $0 | $−95 | $100 |
| | $C_j − Z_j$ | | $−96 | $0 | $−97 | $0 | $−95 | $0 | $195 | $0 |

↑ IN

## Developing the third solution

To determine whether a third solution offers any greater chance for cost reduction, we must complete the $Z_j$ and the $C_j − Z_j$ rows of the second table. This has been accomplished in Figure 5–15. We observe that $X_3$ has the most negative $C_j − Z_j$ value and thus offers us the opportunity to reduce cost $97 per pound introduced. $X_3$ will then appear in the next solution. The $\theta$ calculations are as follows:

$$30/0 = \text{Not Defined}$$
$$20/0 = \text{Not Defined}$$
$$40/1 = 40 \quad \longleftarrow \quad \text{Smallest Value}$$
$$80/1 = 80$$

From this we see that the next solution will contain 40 pounds of $X_3$ in place of $S_3$. Following the procedure, used to develop the second solution we develop the third solution in Figure 5–16; the supporting calculations are illustrated. Total cost of the mix has now fallen to $4220.

## Developing the remaining solutions

Examination of the $C_j − Z_j$ row of the third simplex table (Figure 5–16), indicates that bringing some $X_1$ into the mix will reduce total

FIGURE 5-16
Third Simplex Table Completed

| $C_j$ | | | $4 | $5 | $3 | $0 | $0 | $0 | $100 | $100 | New |
|---|---|---|---|---|---|---|---|---|---|---|---|
| | MIX | QTY. | $X_1$ | $X_2$ | $X_3$ | $S_1$ | $S_2$ | $S_3$ | $A_1$ | $A_2$ | $X_3$ Row |
| $0 | $S_1$ | 30 | 1 | 0 | 0 | 1 | 0 | 0 | 0 | 0 | $40/1 = 40$ |
| $5 | $X_2$ | 20 | 0 | 1 | 0 | 0 | $-1$ | 0 | 1 | 0 | $0/1 = 0$ |
| | | | | | | | | | | | $0/1 = 0$ |
| $3 | $X_3$ | 40 | 0 | 0 | 1 | 0 | 0 | 1 | 0 | 0 | $1/1 = 1$ |
| | | | | | | | | | | | $0/1 = 0$ |
| $100 | $A_2$ | 40 | 1 | 0 | 0 | 0 | 1 | $-1$ | $-1$ | 1 | $0/1 = 0$ |
| | | | | | | | | | | | $1/1 = 1$ |
| | $Z_j$ | $4220 | $100 | $5 | $3 | $0 | $95 | $-97 | $-95 | $100 | $0/1 = 0$ |
| | | | | | | | | | | | $0/1 = 0$ |
| | $C_j - Z_j$ | | $-96 | $0 | $0 | $0 | $-95 | $97 | $195 | $0 | |

↑ IN

New $S_1$ Row

$30 - (0)(40) = 30$
$1 - (0)(0) = 1$
$0 - (0)(0) = 0$
$0 - (0)(1) = 0$
$1 - (0)(0) = 1$
$0 - (0)(0) = 0$
$0 - (0)(1) = 0$
$0 - (0)(0) = 0$
$0 - (0)(0) = 0$

New $X_2$ Row

$20 - (0)(40) = 20$
$0 - (0)(0) = 0$
$1 - (0)(0) = 1$
$0 - (0)(1) = 0$
$0 - (0)(0) = 0$
$-1 - (0)(0) = -1$
$0 - (0)(1) = 0$
$1 - (0)(0) = 1$
$0 - (0)(0) = 0$

New $A_2$ Row

$80 - (1)(40) = 40$
$1 - (1)(0) = 1$
$0 - (1)(0) = 0$
$1 - (1)(1) = 0$
$0 - (1)(0) = 0$
$1 - (1)(0) = 1$
$0 - (1)(1) = -1$
$-1 - (1)(0) = -1$
$1 - (1)(0) = 1$

cost by $96 for each pound which enters. The $\theta$ calculations to determine the maximum number of pounds of $X_1$ which can enter without violating a restraint are as follows:

$30/1 = 30$ ◄——— Smallest Value
$20/0 =$ Not Defined
$40/0 =$ Not Defined
$40/1 = 40$

Thus 30 pounds of $X_1$ will appear in the next solution, completely replacing the $S_1$ row. The fourth solution appears in Figure 5-17; we observe that the total cost of the mix is now $1,340. On figures 5-17 and 5-18 supporting calculations are omitted.

FIGURE 5-17
Fourth Simplex Table Completed

| $C_j$ | | | $4 | $5 | $3 | $0 | $0 | $0 | $100 | $100 |
|---|---|---|---|---|---|---|---|---|---|---|
| | MIX | QTY. | $X_1$ | $X_2$ | $X_3$ | $S_1$ | $S_2$ | $S_3$ | $A_1$ | $A_2$ |
| $4 | $X_1$ | 30 | 1 | 0 | 0 | 1 | 0 | 0 | 0 | 0 |
| $5 | $X_2$ | 20 | 0 | 1 | 0 | 0 | −1 | 0 | 1 | 0 |
| $3 | $X_3$ | 40 | 0 | 0 | 1 | 0 | 0 | 1 | 0 | 0 |
| $100 | $A_2$ | 10 | 0 | 0 | 0 | −1 | 1 | −1 | −1 | 1 |
| $Z_j$ | | $1,340 | $4 | $5 | $3 | $−96 | $95 | $−97 | $−95 | $100 |
| $C_j − Z_j$ | | | $0 | $0 | $0 | $96 | $−95 | $97 | $195 | $0 |

↑ IN

Examination of the $C_j − Z_j$ row of the table in Figure 5–17 indicates that only one opportunity for cost reduction is now open, i.e., bringing some $S_2$ into the mix. Appropriate $\theta$ calculations for the amount to enter are:

$$30/0 = \text{Not Defined}$$
$$20/−1 = −20$$
$$40/0 = \text{Not Defined}$$
$$10/1 = 10 \quad \longleftarrow \quad \text{Smallest Value}$$

We choose 10 pounds of $S_2$ to enter the mix as the smallest $\theta$ value; it is worthwhile noting here that one of the $\theta$'s is negative ($−20$). A negative $\theta$ value would have the connotation of pounds *leaving* the mix, not entering, and therefore would be disregarded, even if it were the smallest value. Figure 5–18 illustrates the fifth simplex table with $S_2$ completely replacing the $A_2$ row. The total cost of this solution is $390.

The $C_j − Z_j$ row of the fifth simplex table in Figure 5–18 contains only zeros and positive values, indicating that no further cost reduction is possible and that we have reached the optimum (least cost) solution to the problem. The final solution is to have the mix contain these real ingredients: 30 pounds of $X_1$, 30 pounds of $X_2$, and 40 pounds of $X_3$. The total cost of the 100 pounds is $390. Each of the restraints

FIGURE 5–18
Fifth Simplex Table Completed

| $C_j$ | | | $4 | $5 | $3 | $0 | $0 | $0 | $100 | $100 |
|---|---|---|---|---|---|---|---|---|---|---|
| | MIX | QTY. | $X_1$ | $X_2$ | $X_3$ | $S_1$ | $S_2$ | $S_3$ | $A_1$ | $A_2$ |
| $4 | $X_1$ | 30 | 1 | 0 | 0 | 1 | 0 | 0 | 0 | 0 |
| $5 | $X_2$ | 30 | 0 | 1 | 0 | $-1$ | 0 | $-1$ | 0 | 1 |
| $3 | $X_3$ | 40 | 0 | 0 | 1 | 0 | 0 | 1 | 0 | 0 |
| $0 | $S_2$ | 10 | 0 | 0 | 0 | $-1$ | 1 | $-1$ | $-1$ | 1 |
| $Z_j$ | | $390 | $4 | $5 | $3 | $-1 | $0 | $-2 | $0 | $5 |
| $C_j - Z_j$ | | | $0 | $0 | $0 | $1 | $0 | $2 | $100 | $95 |

in the original problem has been satisfied; this can be demonstrated by noting that:

1. $X_1$ in the final solution is 30 pounds. The first restraint limited the amount of $X_1$ to not more than 30; our solution satisfies this restraint.
2. $X_2$ in the final solution is 30 pounds. The second restraint required at least 20 pounds of $X_2$; having 30 pounds of $X_2$ in the mix satisfies this constraint. $S_3$ represents the amount of $X_2$ above the minimum requirement (10 pounds in this instance).
3. $X_3$ in the final solution is 40 pounds. The third restraint limited the amount of $X_3$ to not more than 40 pounds; our solution satisfies this restraint.
4. The sum of $X_1$, $X_2$, and $X_3$ is 100 pounds, the required total poundage of the mixture; this restraint is thus satisfied.

## General procedures for handling restraints

The restraints we have encountered thus far in both maximizing and minimizing problems have been of three types:

$$\text{I. } X \leq C$$
$$\text{II. } X \geq C$$
$$\text{III. } X = C$$

In generating first solutions to linear programming problems, we have treated each of these restraints in a specific manner. Because this treatment can be successfully applied wherever these types of restraints are encountered, we present in Figure 5–19 a brief summary of the methods we have used.

FIGURE 5–19
Method for Treating Restraints

|  | Original Restraint | Action Required | Resulting Equality |
|---|---|---|---|
| I | $X \leq C$ | Add a slack variable | $X + S = C$ |
| II | $X \geq C$ | Add slack variable and subtract an artificial variable | $X + S - A = C$ |
| III | $X = C$ | Add an artificial variable | $X + A = C$ |

Often it is impossible or economically unwise to state the restraints in exact terms. For example, it may be technically impossible to state exactly how much of a certain ingredient must be in the mixture because of certain chemical reactions which may occur during mixing. Also, with respect to certain high-priced ingredients, the manufacturer is often given some tolerances as to the amount of these ingredients. This is quite common in the mixing of commercial fertilizers. Although the manufacturer may state on the fertilizer bag that it contains 5 percent nitrogen, the government authorities who inspect the product are usually willing to accept any mixture which contains between 4.8 percent and 5.2 percent as meeting the legal requirements. Therefore, when using linear programming to determine optimum mixtures, a firm may wish to state restraints in an approximate fashion. This gives them flexibility in certain manufacturing processes, and allows the linear program to reduce or increase slightly the quantities of each ingredient when it is economically advantageous to do so.

Another example of the use of approximate restraints is found in handling maximum or minimum hours worked by employees in product mix problems. A manufacturer may be unwilling to state that the total hours worked *must* be equal to or greater than 40 per week (if working fewer hours in a certain department will increase the total contribution of the firm). On the other hand, he knows that to work any department less than a minimum number of hours per week (regardless of contribution) would probably result in labor problems. He therefore prefers to state his restraints in the form "total hours worked per week must be *between* two limits." Let us assume, for example, that a chemical blending firm wishes to produce a certain mixture where the quantity of one of its ingredients $(X_1)$ must be between 100 and 120 pounds. This can be stated in terms of inequalities by first restraining $X_1$ to be equal to or greater than 100 pounds:

$$X_1 \geq 100$$

and then restraining $X_1$ to be less than or equal to 120 pounds:

$$X_1 \leq 120.$$

Thus by using two restraints, we achieve the desired effect of ensuring that $X_1$ will fall between these two limits in the final solution. The conversion of these two inequalities to equations follows the usual form; appropriate slack and artificial variables are added as follows.

Original Inequality:

$$X_1 \geq 100 \tag{1}$$
$$X_1 \leq 200 \tag{2}$$

Resulting Equation:

$$X_1 - S_1 \qquad = 100 \tag{1}$$
$$X_1 - S_1 + A_1 = 100$$
$$X_1 + S_2 \qquad = 200 \tag{2}$$

In the case of restraints on minimum and maximum hours worked per week, we would use the same procedure, i.e., simply state what our acceptable limits are, and then convert them into the form required by the simplex method. Suppose we felt that 1,200 was the minimum number of man-hours we could operate a department and 1,500 was the maximum number of man-hours we could operate. These two restraints would appear then in the following form:

(Each product manufactured)(hours required per unt) $\leq$ 1,500 hours

(Each product manufactured)(hours required per unit) $\geq$ 1,200 hours.

The determination of just how few hours one can operate a department and still maintain the work force depends, of course, on company policy. In the case of textile operations, the working of fewer than 40 hours is known as "short time" and the extent to which this can successfully be practiced is known with reasonable accuracy.

## Standard convention for artificial variables

In our treatment of artificial variables, we assigned them a unit cost of $100 so that they would always be removed from the mixture in favor of some lower cost ingredient. If the real (nonartificial) ingredients cost in excess of $100, then we would have to assign our artificial variables costs significantly higher than $100 to ensure that they remained as undesirable alternatives. To avoid the inconvenience of assigning explicit monetary values to artificial variables, it is common practice to assign them a $C_j$ cost of $M$, where $M$ is assumed to be an infinitely high cost. Thus regardless of the cost of the real ingredients, $M$ will still represent a less desirable alternative.

In Figure 5–20, we have illustrated the simplex table from Figure 5–12. In place of the $100 costs we have substituted $M$. The reader will see that the use of the $M$ convention produces the same result, while greatly simplifying the calculations.

FIGURE 5–20
Using the $M$ Convention

| $C_j$ | | | 4 | 5 | 3 | 0 | 0 | 0 | $M$ | $M$ |
|---|---|---|---|---|---|---|---|---|---|---|
| | MIX | QTY. | $X_1$ | $X_2$ | $X_3$ | $S_1$ | $S_2$ | $S_3$ | $A_1$ | $A_2$ |
| 0 | $S_1$ | 30 | 1 | 0 | 0 | 1 | 0 | 0 | 0 | 0 |
| $M$ | $A_1$ | 20 | 0 | 1 | 0 | 0 | $-1$ | 0 | 1 | 0 |
| 0 | $S_3$ | 40 | 0 | 0 | 1 | 0 | 0 | 1 | 0 | 0 |
| $M$ | $A_2$ | 100 | 1 | 1 | 1 | 0 | 0 | 0 | 0 | 1 |
| $Z_j$ | | $120M$ | $M$ | $2M$ | $M$ | 0 | $-M$ | 0 | $M$ | $M$ |
| $C_j - Z_j$ | | | $4 - M$ | $5 - 2M$ | $3 - M$ | 0 | $M$ | 0 | 0 | 0 |

⬆
└──── Lowest Value

It is helpful to remember that once an artificial variable has been removed from the product mix, it will not reappear because of its very high cost. It is therefore not necessary to perform the calculations for any column headed by an artificial variable once that variable has been removed from the mix: this further simplifies the minimizing simplex procedure.

## Problems

1. Minimize $Z = 3X_1 + 5X_2$
   Subject to: $13X_1 + 7X_2 \geq 182$
   $9X_1 + 10X_2 \geq 147.$

2. Minimize $Z = 25X_1 + 28X_2$
   Subject to: $X_1 + 3X_2 \geq 76$
   $6X_1 + 7X_2 \leq 198.$

3. Minimize $Z = 18X_1 + 22X_2 + 14X_3$
   Subject to: $8X_1 + 7X_2 + 11X_3 \geq 130$
   $2X_1 + X_2 + X_3 \geq 50$
   $15X_1 + 10X_2 + 18X_3 \geq 195.$

4. Minimize $Z = 5X_1 + 4X_2 + 3X_3 + 6X_4$
   Subject to: $X_1 + X_2 + X_3 + X_4 \geq 15$
   $6X_1 + 3X_3 + 2X_4 \leq 150$
   $2X_1 + 3X_2 + X_3 + 7X_4 \leq 125$
   $2X_1 + X_2 + X_3 + 3X_4 \geq 35.$

5. A small manufacturing company markets two products which are sold at the same price. Each product must be processed in the company's two production departments. Product A requires 3.5 hours in department 1, 2.5 hours in department 2, and product B requires 3 hours in department 1 and 4 hours in department 2. The labor rate in department 1 is $2.50 per hour and the rate for labor in department 2 is $2 per hour. Similarly, direct materials for product A cost $3.65 per unit and $3.50 per unit for product B. Given that the total hours available in department 1 each week are equal to 120 and those available in department 2 equal 130 per week, determine the product mix minimizing total costs of production. (Due to a commitment to a regular customer, weekly production of product A must at least equal 10 units.)

6. A coffee processor markets three blends of coffee. They are premium, fine, and regular. Three types of coffee beans are used in the blends. They include a Brazilian bean, a Colombian bean, and a bean from Argentina. The following table lists the composition of the three blends.

|  | Brazilian | Argentine | Colombian |
|---|---|---|---|
| Premium........ | 25% | 40% | 35% |
| Fine........... | 30% | 30% | 40% |
| Regular........ | 35% | 20% | 45% |

Each pound of Brazilian beans costs 25 cents, while a pound of the Argentine and Colombian beans costs 30 cents and 24 cents, respectively. The coffee processor wishes to produce to his weekly capacity of 65,000 pounds of blended coffee per week. Commitments to his regular customers are such that he must produce at least 15,000 pounds of *premium*, 20,000 pounds of *fine*, and 25,000 pounds of *regular* coffee each week.

Suppose the coffee processor wishes to minimize the total costs of ingredients used in making the coffee. Determine this optimal mix, assuming unlimited supply of each of the three components.

7. The dietician at the Playday Boy's Camp is planning breakfast for the first day of camp. The camp has 1,000 boys attending this year. Thus, expenditures for food during the summer are anticipated to be considerable. The dietician has the responsibility of providing the menu which satisfies the minimum nutrient requirements at the lowest cost. Three types of foods are being considered for the breakfast. For simplicity, these will be referred to as type I, type II, and type III. Each of these foods contains a certain amount of vitamins a, b, and c. Each unit of food type I contains 0.35 milligrams of vitamin a, 1.1 milligrams of vitamin b, and 0.75 milligrams of vitamin c. Each unit of food type II contains 0.0015 grams of vitamin a, 0.0005 grams of vitamin b, and 0.0004 grams of vitamin c. Similarly, each unit of type III foods contains 0.25 milligrams of vitamin a, 0.35 milligrams of vitamin b, and 1.35 milligrams of vitamin c. The minimum daily requirements of these vitamins are estimated to be:

| Vitamin | Centigrams |
|---------|-----------|
| a | 0.25 |
| b | 0.35 |
| c | 0.45 |

The unit costs of the food types are:

| Food Type | Cost per Unit |
|-----------|---------------|
| I | $.20 |
| II | .15 |
| III | .18 |

Assuming that the dietician wishes to have breakfast satisfy the minimum daily requirements of these three vitamins, determine by the simplex method the quantities of each type of food which should be ordered to minimize food costs for breakfast.

8. The Petro Petroleum Corporation produces three grades of gasoline. These are regular, super, and premium. In the manufacture of these

gasolines certain specifications must be met. They are shown in the following chart.

| Specifications | Regular | Super | Premium |
|---|---|---|---|
| Vapor pressure index........ | $\leq 30$ | $\leq 29$ | $\leq 29.5$ |
| Octane number............ | $\geq 80$ | $\geq 85$ | $\geq 90$ |
| Viscosity index............. | $\leq 5$ | $\leq 4.5$ | $\leq 4.4$ |

The three grades of gasoline are blended from five component blends $(A_1, A_2, A_3, A_4, A_5)$. The cost per barrel of each component is shown below along with the maximum quantities available each week for blending.

| | | |
|---|---|---|
| $A_1$ | \$2.60 | 32,000 barrels |
| $A_2$ | 2.45 | 28,000      ,, |
| $A_3$ | 2.53 | 35,000      ,, |
| $A_4$ | 2.80 | 40,000      ,, |
| $A_5$ | 2.65 | 37,500      ,, |

The following chart gives the characteristics of the different components.

| | $A_1$ | $A_2$ | $A_3$ | $A_4$ | $A_5$ |
|---|---|---|---|---|---|
| Vapor pressure index. . . | 25 | 23 | 27.5 | 25.5 | 32 |
| Fraction distilling off at 225° F............. | 32% | 40% | 30% | 28% | 33% |
| Viscosity index........ | 4.1 | 5.0 | 3.5 | 4.5 | 4.0 |
| Octane number....... | 75.0 | 84.5 | 90.5 | 95.5 | 87.5 |

Assuming that the company sells its regular blend at \$0.10 per gallon, its super blend at \$0.125 per gallon, and its premium blend at \$0.145 per gallon, determine the blending scheme maximizing weekly profits or contribution to overhead while satisfying the requirements of each grade of gasoline. Assume that one barrel equals 30 gallons and that the characteristics of the components blend in a linear manner (i.e., blending a unit having an octane number of 80 with a unit having an octane number of 90 will yield two units having an octane number of 85, etc.)

# chapter 6

# *Special purpose algorithms*

Some types of linear programming problems may be solved by using more efficient and less-tedious computational procedures than the simplex technique. One of the most useful of these special purpose algorithms is the transportation method. This procedure will be examined in the present chapter. In addition, the assignment method, which is a special case of the more general transportation problem will be treated.

## The transportation method—definition

As its name implies, the transportation method was first formulated as a special procedure for finding the minimum cost program for distributing a product from several points of supply (sources) to a number of points of demand (destinations). For example, a manufacturer may have five plants (sources) and 20 warehouses (destinations) all located at various geographical points. For a specified time period, each source has a given capacity, and each destination has a given requirement. Knowing the costs of shipping the product from each source to each destination, the objective is to schedule shipments from sources to destinations in such a way as to minimize the total transportation cost. The earliest formulation of this basic transportation problem was stated by F. L. Hitchcock in 1941 and later expanded by T. C. Koopmans. The linear programming formulation was first given by G. B. Dantzig. In 1953, W. W. Cooper and A. Charnes developed the stepping-stone method, a special purpose algorithm for solving the transportation problem. Subsequent improvements led to the computationally easier modified-distribution (MODI) method in 1955.

As will be shown in Chapter 9, problems which can be solved by the transportation method can be solved by the more general simplex procedure. In this sense the two methods are very similar. Like the simplex technique, the transportation method is an iterative procedure. After an initial solution has been formulated, the transportation method provides a logical step-by-step procedure for developing improved solutions until the optimal solution is found. In this case, the best solution is that combination of routes which will minimize total transportation costs. The logic underlying the transportation method will be demonstrated in the following problem.

## Practical applications of the transportation method

### The balanced case

The Wrenn Concrete Company has received a contract to supply concrete for three new construction projects. These projects are located in the towns of Marysville, Franklin, and Belair. Construction engineers have estimated the required amounts of concrete which will be needed at the three construction projects. They are:

| Project | Location | Requirements per Week |
|---|---|---|
| A.......... | Marysville | 70 truckloads |
| B.......... | Franklin | 100 truckloads |
| C.......... | Belair | 40 truckloads |
| | Total requirements......,.... | 210 truckloads |

The Wrenn Company has three plants—sand and gravel pits—located in the towns of Sandyhill, Rayston, and Wellsburg. The concrete required for the construction projects can be supplied by these three plants. Wrenn's chief dispatcher has calculated the amounts of concrete which can be supplied by each plant. They are:

| Project | Location | Amount Available per Week |
|---------|----------|---------------------------|
| W.......... | Sandyhill | 55 truckloads |
| X.......... | Rayston | 80 truckloads |
| Y.......... | Wellsburg | 75 truckloads |
| | Total amount available.... | 210 truckloads |

At this point we see that the total amount available is exactly equal to the total amount required. When total supply is equal to total demand, a balanced condition is said to exist. Although the balanced case is very unlikely in actual practice, it will enable us to focus on the basic ideas underlying the transportation method. The unbalanced case where supply and demand are unequal will be discussed later in the chapter.

The company has computed the delivery costs from each plant to each project site. As in the linear programming problems discussed in previous chapters, we assume that the variables in the problem must be linearly related. Thus, in this case, delivery costs per truckload between each plant and project site vary directly with the quantity distributed. These costs are shown in Figure 6–1.

FIGURE 6–1

| From | To | Project A Cost per Truckload | Project B Cost per Truckload | Project C Cost per Truckload |
|------|-----|---------|---------|---------|
| Plant W..... | | $5 | $10 | $10 |
| Plant X...... | | $20 | $30 | $20 |
| Plant Y...... | | $10 | $20 | $30 |

Given the amounts required at each project and the amounts available at each plant, the company's problem is to schedule shipments from each plant to each project in such a manner as to minimize the total transportation cost within the constraints imposed by plant capacities and project requirements. In this statement of the transportation problem, one should recognize its similarity to the general linear programming problem. First there is an objective—to minimize total transportation costs. Second, there are alternative ways of achieving the objective. For example, concrete can be supplied for any of the three projects by any of the three plants. Finally, we have constraints on the attainment of the objective. In this case there are plant capacity constraints and project requirement constraints. Stating the objective and constraints as equations will be shown in Chapter 9.

At this point we have all the information necessary to solve Wrenn's problem.

*Step 1. Set up the transportation table.* The transportation table serves the same basic purpose as the simplex table; it provides a framework for presenting all of the relevant data in a concise manner and facilitates the search for progressively better solutions. In Figure 6–2, the standard format for the transportation table has been divided into five lettered sections A, B, C, D, and E, each of which will be explained in detail.

FIGURE 6–2

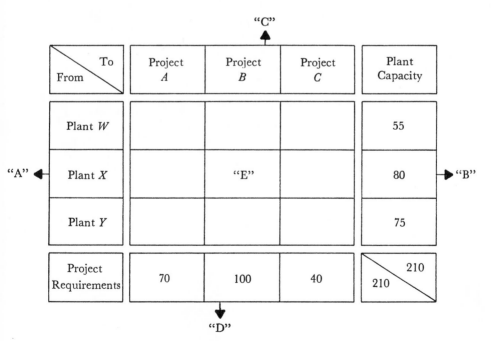

*Section A.*  In this part we list the sources of supply, i.e., plants *W*, *X*, and *Y*. Each plant represents a row in the table.

*Section B.*  The capacity for each plant is shown in section B. Thus we can think of the rows of the table as representing the capacity constraints. These are also referred to as the "rim" requirements for the rows. In our problem we have three, one for each plant. For example, the rim requirement in the first row means that plant *W* can supply no more than 55 truckloads per week.

*Section C.*  The destination points are listed in this section, i.e., projects *A*, *B*, and *C*. Each project represents a column in the table.

*Section D.*  The requirements for each project are placed in this part. The columns, then, represent the project constraints or rim requirements for the columns. In this problem we have three, one for each project. For example, the rim requirement for column one signifies that project *A* requires exactly 70 truckloads per week. The total number of rim requirements in our problem is six, three for the rows and three for the columns.

*Section E.*  In this section, there are nine squares or cells, representing the alternative source-to-destination assignments that could be made. For example, the 55 truckloads per week available at plant *W* may be used, in whole or in part, to fulfill the requirements of any of the three projects. Any combination of shipments from plant *W* would be acceptable as long as the total equaled exactly 55 truckloads. Similarly, the 70 truckloads required at project *A* may be met by any combination of shipments from the various plants as long as the total equals 70.

To complete the table, it will be helpful to add to each square of section E an identification symbol and a delivery cost figure. This has been done in Figure 6–3.

Let us examine square *WA* as enlarged in Figure 6–4:

A. The "*WA*" in the upper left-hand corner of the square is the identification symbol. This square represents the plant *W* to project *A* combination and, therefore, is identified as square *WA*.
B. The "5" in the upper right-hand corner is the transportation cost per truckload between plant *W* and project *A*. The costs in each subsquare were obtained from Figure 6–1.
C. "*X*" represents the number of truckloads shipped from plant *W* to project *A*. In other words, all *X*'s in Figure 6–3 denote the number of shipments between each plant and each project. The value of all *X*'s will be a positive whole number or zero. If in a particular solution the *X* value is missing for a square, this means that no quantity is shipped between the plant and project in question.

FIGURE 6-3

| To<br>From | Project<br>A | Project<br>B | Project·<br>C | Plant<br>Capacity |
|---|---|---|---|---|
| Plant $W$ | $WA$    5 <br> $(X_1)$ | $WB$    10 <br> $(X_2)$ | $WC$    10 <br> $(X_3)$ | 55 |
| Plant $X$ | $XA$    20 <br> $(X_4)$ | $XB$    30 <br> $(X_5)$ | $XC$    20 <br> $(X_6)$ | 80 |
| Plant $Y$ | $YA$    10 <br> $(X_7)$ | $YB$    20 <br> $(X_8)$ | $YC$    30 <br> $(X_9)$ | 75 |
| Project<br>Requirements | 70 | 100 | 40 | 210<br>210 |

Before going on to the next step in the solution to our problem, several points should be made. As previously mentioned, the requirements necessary to apply the simplex technique are similar to those necessary to apply the transportation method. If, however, the transportation method is to be applicable, another condition must exist: the product being considered must be homogeneous. In other words, the quality and mixture of the concrete in our problem are assumed to be identical regardless of the plant supplying the concrete. This means that truckloads of concrete may be transferred within the schedule on a one-for-one basis. If for example, we give up shipping 50 truckloads from plant $W$ to project $A$, we must be able to substitute

FIGURE 6-4

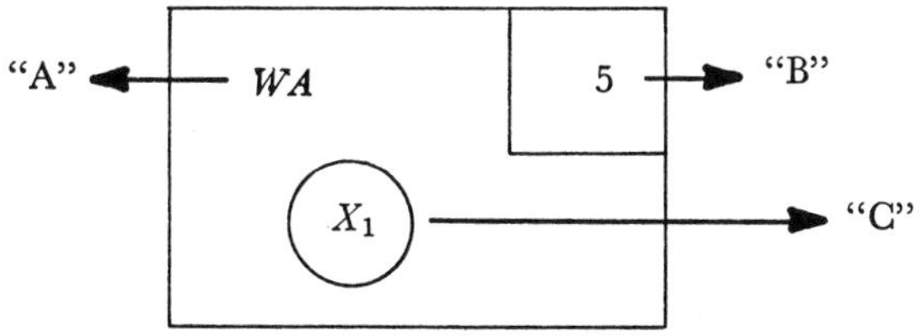

for that shipment, a shipment of exactly 50 truckloads from either plant $X$ or plant $Y$ to project $A$. The reader should recall that the condition of homogeneity was not a requirement for the application of the simplex method, i.e., the exchange rates were not all on a one-for-one basis.

*Step 2. Develop an initial solution.* Now that the data have been arranged in table form, the next step is to find a solution to the problem in order to provide a starting point which leads into the procedure for developing improved solutions. Thus the initial solution in the transportation method serves the same purpose as the initial solution in the simplex method. Unlike the simplex technique, however, the initial solution in the transportation method need not be the worst possible solution. The only requisite is that the initial solution be feasible; that is, it must satisfy all rim requirements.

A systematic and logical procedure known as the Northwest Corner Rule has been developed for setting up the initial solution. Although it is not absolutely necessary to use this rule, it does have the advantage of being systematic rather than trial and error. Having a logical procedure is important when using a computer; and, for small problems, it permits the computations to be delegated to clerical personnel.

The Northwest Corner Rule may be stated as follows:

FIGURE 6–5a
The Initial Solution

| To \ From | Project A | | Project B | | Project C | | Plant Capacity |
|---|---|---|---|---|---|---|---|
| Plant W | WA | 5 | WB | 10 | WC | 10 | 55 |
| | (55) | | | | | | |
| Plant X | XA | 20 | XB | 30 | XC | 20 | 80 |
| | (15) ---- (65) | | | | | | |
| Plant Y | YA | 10 | YB | 20 | YC | 30 | 75 |
| | | | (35) ---- (40) | | | | |
| Project Requirements | 70 | | 100 | | 40 | | 210 / 210 |

1. Starting at the upper left-hand corner (the northwest corner) of the table, the supply available at each row must be exhausted before moving down to the next row; and the rim requirement of any column must be exhausted before moving to the right to the next column.

2. Check to see that *all* rim requirements have been satisfied.

The results of this procedure are shown in Figure 6–5a.

An explanation of each assignment made in the initial solution shown in Figure 6–5a is made below:

*Square WA.* Beginning in the upper left-hand corner, we compared the quantity available at plant $W$ (55) with the quantity required at project $A$ (70). Exhausting the supply at plant $W$, 55 truckloads are shipped to project $A$. This leaves project $A$ short 15 truckloads. Move down to the second row in the same column to square $XA$.

*Square XA.* Plant $X$ has 80 truckloads available. Since project $A$ is 15 short, plant $X$ will ship 15 of its 80 available truckloads to project $A$. The requirements for project $A$ have now been met. Since plant $X$ has 65 truckloads remaining, we move right to the next column to square $XB$.

*Square XB.* Project $B$ needs 100 truckloads. The remaining 65 truckloads from plant $X$ will then be shipped to project $B$, leaving project $B$ short 35 truckloads. Since the amount available at plant $X$ has been exhausted, we move vertically downward to the next row to square $YB$.

*Square YB.* Plant $Y$ has 75 truckloads available. Project $B$ needs 35 more truckloads to fully satisfy its requirements. Hence plant $Y$ will ship 35 of its 75 available truckloads to project $B$. We now move right to the next column to square $YC$.

*Square YC.* Plant $Y$ has 40 truckloads remaining which are shipped to project $C$ requiring 40 truckloads. The schedule of shipments is now complete.

The initial solution, then, includes the following five source-destination combinations:

FIGURE 6–5b

| From Plant | To Project | Quantity (Truckloads per Week) |
|:---:|:---:|:---:|
| W | A | 55 |
| X | A | 15 |
| X | B | 65 |
| Y | B | 35 |
| Y | C | 40 |
| | Total | 210 |

The squares within which no circled values appear are referred to as unused squares; that is, no quantity is shipped between the two points represented by each unused square. These squares therefore are not in the initial solution.

We must now determine the cost of this first solution. To do this, we multiply the quantities shipped between each source-destination combination in the solution times the respective unit cost. The results are shown in Figure 6–6.

FIGURE 6–6
Total Cost of Initial Solution

| Source-Destination Combination | Quantity Shipped | Unit Cost | Total Cost |
|---|---|---|---|
| WA............ | 55 | $ 5 | $  275 |
| XA............ | 15 | 20 | 300 |
| XB............ | 65 | 30 | 1,950 |
| YB............ | 35 | 20 | 700 |
| YC............ | 40 | 30 | 1,200 |
| | | Total | $4,425 |

Before proceeding to the next step in the solution to our problem, several points should be made. The initial solution is a feasible one, since all rim requirements have been met; that is, the sum of each row or column is equal to its rim requirement. Initial solutions obtained by using the Northwest Corner Rule can always be recognized by their stair-step appearance, as shown by the path described in Figure 6–5. Finally, for any solution the number of used squares must be equal to the total number of rim requirements minus one. In our first solution, there are five used squares or source-destination combinations. The total rim requirements are six, one for each plant (row) and project (column). Thus:

$$\text{Used squares} = \text{Total rim requirements} - 1$$
$$5 = 6 - 1.$$

When *any* solution does not conform to the above rule, a condition referred to as degeneracy is said to exist. The procedure for handling a degenerate solution will be discussed in a later section. The important point here is that each solution should be tested for degeneracy; that is, the number of used squares must be equal to the total rim requirements minus one.

*Step 3. Test the solution for improvement.*   Having obtained a first solution to our problem, the next step is to determine whether this solution is the best, or least cost, solution. The evaluation procedure involves the examination of each unused square in the table to see whether it is more desirable to move a shipment into one of them. The purpose of this evaluation is to determine whether a better schedule of shipments from plants to projects can be developed. Two alternative procedures for evaluating the unused squares will be presented—the stepping-stone and MODI methods. Although the stepping-stone method has been replaced, for the most part, by the modified-distribution (MODI) method, it is the basis for and provides a good introduction to the MODI method.

### The stepping-stone method

The used squares, those containing circled values, are said to be "in solution," and will be referred to as stone squares. In applying the stepping-stone method, we ask this question: What would happen if *one* truckload of concrete were tentatively shipped or assigned to an unused square? If this tentative assignment results in a favorable effect (reduces cost), the unused square evaluated then becomes a possible candidate for entering the next solution. This is analogous to the examination of the $C_j - Z_j$ row of the simplex method to determine which variable should be brought into the mix.

Let us now apply this reasoning to our present problem. In Figure 6–5, we note that the square *WB* is unused. Suppose that we assigned *one* truckload to square *WB*, i.e., ship one truckload from plant *W* to project *B*. In order to make this assignment and still satisfy the capacity restriction (rim requirement) for plant *W* we must subtract from square *WA* one truckload so that the total shipments from plant *W* do not exceed 55.   However, if we subtract one truckload from square *WA*, we must then add one truckload to square *XA* in order to meet the rim requirement for project *A*. Adding one truckload to square *XA* means that we must subtract one truckload from square *XB* in order to satisfy the rim requirement for that row (plant *X*). Finally, the truckload subtracted from square *XB* enables project *B* requirements to still total 100, since one truckload had been tentatively added to square *WB* at the start of the evaluation. The evaluation is now back where it started. These changes in the shipping program can be much more readily seen in Figure 6–7.

FIGURE 6–7
Adjustments Required in Evaluating Square *WB*

| To \ From | Project A | Project B | Project C | Plant Capacity |
|---|---|---|---|---|
| Plant W | WA    5  ⑤⑤ – | WB    10  + | WC    10 | 55 |
| Plant X | XA    20  ⑮ + | XB    30  ⑥⑤ – | XC    20 | 80 |
| Plant Y | YA    10 | YB    20  ㉟ | YC    30  ㊵ | 75 |
| Project Requirements | 70 | 100 | 40 | 210 / 210 |

Note that the net change for any row or column is zero; i.e., wherever one truckload was added to a square, another square was decreased by the same amount.

The question we now ask is: What effect will the assignment of one truckload to the unused square *WB* have on total cost? Looking at the path described in evaluating square *WB*, Figure 6–7, we see that shipping one truckload from plant *X* to project *B* results in an increase of $10 in distribution costs. The $10 cost per truckload between the two points is given in the upper right-hand corner of square *WB*. A similar increase from plant *X* to project *A* results in an additional cost of $20 (square *XA*). Likewise, the decrease of one truckload between plant *W* and project *A* reduces total costs by $5 (square *WA*). In addition, the decrease of one truckload between plant *X* and project *B* results in a reduction of $30 (square *XB*). The *net* change in costs, referred to as the improvement index, is computed as follows:

*Addition to cost*
From plant $W$ to project $B$........ $10
From plant $X$ to project $A$........  20      $30

*Reduction in cost*
From plant $W$ to project $A$.......  $ 5
From plant $X$ to project $B$........  30       35
Improvement index..........                    −5

The same answer can be obtained by following the path used directly
and resorting to a sort of shorthand as follows:

Improvement index for square $WB = WB - WA + XA - XB$.

Now substituting the cost per truckload for each source-destination
combination in the above equation we have:

Improvement index for square $WB = \$10 - \$5 + \$20 - \$30$
$$= -\$5.$$

The "−$5" means that for every truckload shipped from plant $W$
to project $B$, total transportation costs would be reduced by $5. Since
this is true, it would be advantageous to use this route, if this were
the only choice available. However, the evaluation of other unused
squares in our table might bring about an even greater reduction.
The task remaining then is to evaluate all remaining unused squares.

In evaluating any unused square, the following procedure is used:

1. Choose the unused square to be evaluated.

2. Beginning with the selected unused square, trace a closed path (moving
horizontally and vertically only) from this unused square via stone squares
back to the original unused square. Only one closed path exists for each
unused square in a given solution. Although the path may skip over stone
or unused squares, corners of the closed path may occur only at the stone
squares and the unused square being evaluated. Only the most direct route
is used.

3. Assign plus (+) and minus (−) signs alternately at each corner square
of the closed path, beginning with a plus sign at the unused square. The
direction of assigning these signs may start either in a clockwise or counter-
clockwise direction. The positive and negative signs represent the addition
or subtraction of one unit (truckload in this case) to a square.

4. Determine the net change in costs as a result of the changes made in
tracing the path. Summing the unit cost in each square with a plus sign will
give the addition to cost. The decrease in cost is obtained by summing the
unit cost in each square with a negative sign. Comparing the additions to
cost with the decreases will give the improvement index.

5. Repeat the above steps until an improvement index has been determined for each unused square.

If all the indexes are greater than, or equal to, zero, an optimal solution has been found. Conversely, if any of the indexes are negative, an improved solution is possible.

The above rules were used in tracing the path and determining the improvement index for square $WB$, Figure 6-7. Let us now evaluate the unused square $WC$. The traced path used in evaluating this square is shown in Figure 6-8.

FIGURE 6-8

| To<br>From | Project<br>A | Project<br>B | Project<br>C | Plant<br>Capacity |
|---|---|---|---|---|
| Plant W | WA    5<br>(55) — | WB    10 | WC    10<br>+ | 55 |
| Plant X | XA    20<br>(15) + | XB    30<br>(65) — | XC    20 | 80 |
| Plant Y | YA    10 | YB    20<br>(35) + | YC    30<br>(40) — | 75 |
| Project<br>Requirements | 70 | 100 | 40 | 210   210 |

The improvement index for unused square $WC$ traced in Figure 6-8 is computed as follows:

$$\text{Improvement index } (WC) = WC - WA + XA - XB + YB - YC$$
$$= \$10 - \$5 + \$20 - \$30 + \$20 - \$30$$
$$= -\$15.$$

The closed paths and improvement indexes for the remaining two unused squares are given below:

Path for square $XC$:

$$(+)XC \rightarrow (-)XB \rightarrow (+)YB \rightarrow (-)YC$$

$$\text{Improvement index } (XC) = XC - XB + YB - YC$$
$$= 20 - 30 + 20 - 30$$
$$= -20.$$

Path for square $YA$:

$$(+)YA \rightarrow (-)XA \rightarrow (+)XB \rightarrow (-)YB$$

$$\text{Improvement index } (YA) = YA - XA + XB - YB$$
$$= 10 - 20 + 30 - 20$$
$$= 0.$$

We have now completed the evaluation of all unused squares, each of which represents an alternative route that might be taken. The improvement index for each unused square is shown in Figure 6–9.

A brief summary might be helpful at this point. Step 3 called for testing the solution for improvement. In order to do this, the stepping-stone procedure was used to evaluate each unused square. The objective was to determine whether it would be profitable to use some other route, represented by each unused square. If any improvement index is negative, the best solution has not been obtained. Since our

FIGURE 6–9
All Unused Squares Evaluated

| To / From | Project A | | Project B | | Project C | | Plant Capacity |
|---|---|---|---|---|---|---|---|
| Plant $W$ | $WA$ (55) | 5 | $WB$ $-5$ | 10 | $WC$ $-15$ | 10 | 55 |
| Plant $X$ | $XA$ (15) | 20 | $XB$ (65) | 30 | $XC$ $-20$ | 20 | 80 |
| Plant $Y$ | $YA$ 0 | 10 | $YB$ (35) | 20 | $YC$ (40) | 30 | 75 |
| Project Requirements | 70 | | 100 | | 40 | | 210 / 210 |

evaluation resulted in three unused squares with negative improvement indexes, we know that a better solution is possible. The next step, then, is to develop the new solution.

*Step 4. Develop the improved solution.* Each negative improvement index represents the amount by which total transportation costs could be reduced if *one* truckload were shipped to that source-destination combination. In this sense the improvement indexes are analogous to the values in the $C_j - Z_j$ row of the simplex method. For example, the improvement index for square *XC* means that for every truckload shipped from plant *X* to project *C*, total transportation costs will be reduced by $20. The question now is: given three alternative routes with negative improvement indexes (squares *WB*, *WC*, and *XC*), which one shall we choose in developing the improved solution? Similar to the minimization of cost problems of Chapter 5, we will select that route (unused square) with the largest negative improvement index. In our problem, this is square *XC* with a negative index of $20.

FIGURE 6-10

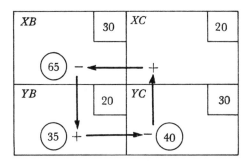

Since using this route will reduce costs more than any other alternative route, we must now decide how many truckloads to ship via this route, i.e., from plant *X* to project *C*. To do this, we must reconstruct the closed path traced in evaluating unused square *XC*. This has been done in Figure 6–10, using only the relevant part of the table.

Now the maximum quantity which we may ship from plant *X* to project *C* is found by determining the smaller stone in a negative position on the closed path. The closed path for square *XC* has negative corners at squares *XB* and *YC*, and the smaller of these two stones is 40 truckloads per week. To obtain our new solution, we add

40 truckloads to all squares on the closed path with plus signs, and we subtract this quantity from all squares on the path assigned minus signs, as shown in Figure 6–11.

FIGURE 6–11

| XB | XC |
|----|----|
| −<br><br>$65 - 40 = $ (25) | +<br><br>$0 + 40 = $ (40) |
| YB | YC |
| +<br><br>$35 + 40 = $ (75) | −<br><br>$40 - 40 = 0$ |

Why did we choose the smallest stone in a negative position on the closed path as the maximum number of truckloads that could be shipped from plant $X$ to project $C$? Suppose that we add 65 truckloads to square $XC$ instead of 40. In order to satisfy our rim requirements, we would have to do the following: add 65 to $XC$; subtract 65 from $XB$; add 65 to $YB$; and subtract 65 from $YC$. The results are:

$$XC: \quad 0 + 65 = 65$$
$$XB: \quad 65 - 65 = 0$$
$$YB: \quad 35 + 65 = 100$$
$$YC: \quad 40 - 65 = -25.$$

The computation for square $YC$ shows that plant $Y$ would ship $(-25)$ truckloads to project $C$. This negative shipment is both meaningless in an actual problem and a violation of the requirement prohibiting the assignment of negative stone squares. Like the simplex method, all values in the solution must be greater than or equal to zero. Hence the maximum quantity which may be brought into a solution is found by determining the smallest stone in a negative position on the closed path of the square with the highest negative improvement index. This quantity is added to all squares on the closed path with plus signs and subtracted from all squares on the path with minus signs. The new improved solution is shown in Figure 6–12.

Note that square $YC$, which was a stone square in the initial solution, is now an unused square. Square $XC$ has entered the improved

FIGURE 6–12
The Second Solution

| To<br>From | Project<br>A | Project<br>B | Project<br>C | Plant<br>Capacity |
|---|---|---|---|---|
| Plant W | WA ⑤⑤    5 | WB    10 | WC    10 | 55 |
| Plant X | XA ⑮    20 | XB ㉕    30 | XC ㊵    20 | 80 |
| Plant Y | YA    10 | YB ㊌    20 | YC    30 | 75 |
| Project Requirements | 70 | 100 | 40 | 210<br>210 |

solution in place of square *YC*. As can be seen in Figure 6–13 below, the total transportation cost for the new shipping assignments of our second solution is an improvement upon the cost of the first solution ($4,425).

FIGURE 6–13
Total Cost of Second Solution

| Shipping<br>Assignments | Quantity<br>Shipped | | Unit Cost | | Total Cost |
|---|---|---|---|---|---|
| WA | 55 | × | $ 5 | = | $275 |
| XA | 15 | × | 20 | = | 300 |
| XB | 25 | × | 30 | = | 750 |
| XC | 40 | × | 20 | = | 800 |
| YB | 75 | × | 20 | = | 1,500 |
| Total transportation cost.............. | | | | | $3,625 |

We now go back to *step 3* to determine if further improvement is possible. Using the stepping-stone method described in that section, we will calculate an improvement index for each unused square in the second solution. The closed path and improvement index for each unused square in Figure 6–12 are shown in Figure 6–14.

FIGURE 6–14

Closed Paths and Improvement Indexes for Unused Squares of Figure 6–12

| Unused Square | Closed Path | Computation of Improvement Index |
|---|---|---|
| WB | $+WB - WA + XA - XB$ | $+10 - 5 + 20 - 30 = -5$ |
| WC | $+WC - WA + XA - XC$ | $+10 - 5 + 20 - 20 = +5$ |
| YA | $+YA - XA + XB - YB$ | $+10 - 20 + 30 - 20 = 0$ |
| YC | $+YC - XC + XB - YB$ | $+30 - 20 + 30 - 20 = +20$ |

As previously mentioned, in tracing a closed path the most direct route may require skipping over stone squares as well as unused squares. This occurs in tracing the path for square $WC$ and is shown in Figure 6–15.

FIGURE 6–15

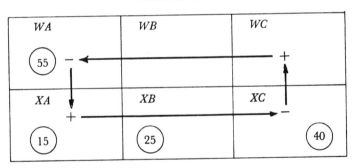

Looking at the improvement indexes computed in Figure 6–14, we find one negative index for unused square $WB$, indicating that further improvement is possible. For each truckload assigned to square $WB$, total costs will be reduced \$5. To determine the number of truckloads to be shipped, we select the smallest stone in a negative position on the closed path traced in evaluating square $WB$ (step 4).

$$+WB - WA + XA - XB$$
$$+ \to -\!\widehat{55} \to +\!\widehat{15} \to -\!\widehat{25}$$

As seen above, the smallest stone in a negative position is 25. This quantity is added to all squares on the path with plus signs and subtracted from all squares on the path with minus signs, as shown in Figure 6–16.

FIGURE 6–16

| WA | WB |
|---|---|
| 55 − 25 = (30) | 0 + 25 = (25) |
| XA | XB |
| 15 + 25 = (40) | 25 − 25 = 0 |

The third solution is given in Figure 6–17.

FIGURE 6–17
The Third Solution

| To \ From | Project A | | Project B | | Project C | | Plant Capacity |
|---|---|---|---|---|---|---|---|
| Plant W | WA (30) | 5 | WB (25) | 10 | WC | 10 | 55 |
| Plant X | XA (40) | 20 | XB | 30 | XC (40) | 20 | 80 |
| Plant Y | YA | 10 | YB (75) | 20 | YC | 30 | 75 |
| Project Requirements | 70 | | 100 | | 40 | | 210 / 210 |

The total cost of the third solution is shown in Figure 6–18.

FIGURE 6–18
Total Cost of Third Solution

| Shipping Assignments | Quantity Shipped | | Unit Cost | | Total Cost |
|---|---|---|---|---|---|
| WA | 30 | × | $ 5 | = | $150 |
| WB | 25 | × | 10 | = | 250 |
| XA | 40 | × | 20 | = | 800 |
| XC | 40 | × | 20 | = | 800 |
| YB | 75 | × | 20 | = | 1,500 |

Total transportation cost . . . . . . . . . . . . . . . $3,500

Again we go back to step 3 to determine if further improvement is possible. The closed paths and improvement indexes for the unused squares in Figure 6–17 are given in Figure 6–19.

FIGURE 6–19
Closed Paths and Improvement Indexes for Figure 6–17

| Unused Square | Closed Path | Computation of Improvement Index | |
|---|---|---|---|
| WC | +WC − WA + XA − XC | +10 − 5 + 20 − 20 | = +5 |
| XB | +XB − WB + WA − XA | +30 − 10 + 5 − 20 | = +5 |
| YA | +YA − WA + WB − YB | +10 − 5 + 10 − 20 | = −5 |
| YC | +YC − YB + WB − WA + XA − XC | +30 − 20 + 10 − 5 + 20 | = +15 |

The negative improvement index for square *YA* indicates that the best solution has not been obtained. Now following the same procedure discussed in step 4, we find that the maximum quantity to assign to square *YA* is 30 truckloads; and the new solution is given in Figure 6–20. This is indeed the optimum solution, since the improvement indexes for Figure 6–20 are all greater than or equal to zero (see Figure 6–21).

FIGURE 6–20
The Optimum Solution

| From \ To | Project *A* | Project *B* | Project *C* | Plant Capacity |
|---|---|---|---|---|
| Plant *W* | *WA* 5 | *WB* 10 (55) | *WC* 10 | 55 |
| Plant *X* | *XA* 20 (40) | *XB* 30 | *XC* 20 (40) | 80 |
| Plant *Y* | *YA* 10 (30) | *YB* 20 (45) | *YC* 30 | 75 |
| Project Requirements | 70 | 100 | 40 | 210 \ 210 |

FIGURE 6–21
Closed Paths and Improvement Indexes for Figure 6–20

| *Unused Squares* | *Closed Path* | *Computation of Improvement Index* | |
|---|---|---|---|
| *WA* | $+WA - YA + YB - WB$ | $+5 - 10 + 20 - 10$ | $= 5$ |
| *WC* | $+WC - XC + YA - YB + WB$ | $+10 - 20 + 20 - 10 + 20 - 10$ | $= 10$ |
| *XB* | $+XB - YB + YA - XZ$ | $+30 - 20 + 10 - 20$ | $= 0$ |
| *YC* | $+YC - XC + XA - YA$ | $+30 - 20 + 20 - 10$ | $= 20$ |

The total cost for the optimum solution is shown in Figure 6–22.

The reader may question the use of a somewhat tedious method for solving such a simple problem. Why not use a trial and error method? It appears plausible that one would begin by simply choosing the lowest cost route and using it to the fullest extent. Then we might select the next highest rate and use it to the fullest extent, and so on until we have satisfied all the requirements for the project. The assumption underlying this thought process is that making the best possible choice in each part of the scheduling program will

FIGURE 6–22
Total Cost of Optimum Solution

| Shipping Assignments | Quantity Shipped | | Unit Cost | | Total Cost |
|---|---|---|---|---|---|
| WB | 55 | × | $10 | = | $550 |
| XA | 40 | × | 20 | = | 800 |
| XC | 40 | × | 20 | = | 800 |
| YA | 30 | × | 10 | = | 300 |
| YB | 45 | × | 20 | = | 900 |
| Total transportation cost. . . . . . . . . . . . . | | | | | $3,350 |

automatically result in the best overall program. An examination of the final solution to our simple problem indicates that the assumption is not a valid one. Figure 6–20 shows that two of the least cost routes, squares *WA* and *WC*, are *not* included in the optimal solution. Here we recognize the importance of a characteristic of operations research discussed in Chapter 1: it is essential to study a problem in terms of the total system, not merely the separate parts. The optimal source-destination combinations are often far from being apparent, even in the smallest problem.

### Alternative optimal solutions

Let us examine further the optimal solution to our problem, and in particular the improvement index of square *XB* computed in Figure 6–21. The improvement index for square *XB* is zero. What does this signify? A zero improvement index for an unused square means that if this route were brought into the solution, the shipping assignments would change, but the total transportation cost would be the same. Thus if we were to assign one truckload to unused square *XB*, the total cost program would neither increase nor decrease. We can conclude then that in addition to our present optimal shipping schedule, another equally profitable schedule exists. To determine what this alternate optimal solution is, we follow the same procedure used for bringing any route into the solution (step 4). In this case the maximum number of truckloads that can be assigned to square *XB* is 40. The alternate solution and its total cost are given in Figure 6–23. The improvement indexes are also included in the table.

FIGURE 6–23
Alternate Optimal Solution

| To<br>From | Project<br>A | Project<br>B | Project<br>C | Plant<br>Capacity |
|---|---|---|---|---|
| Plant W | WA    5<br>+5 | WB    10<br>(55) | WC    10<br>+10 | 55 |
| Plant X | XA    20<br>0 | XB    30<br>(40) | XC    20<br>(40) | 80 |
| Plant Y | YA    10<br>(70) | YB    20<br>(5) | YC    30<br>+20 | 75 |
| Project<br>Requirements | 70 | 100 | 40 | 210 / 210 |

*Total Cost*

$$
\begin{array}{rcl}
55 \times \$10 &=& \$\ \ 550 \\
40 \times \$30 &=& 1{,}200 \\
40 \times \$20 &=& 800 \\
70 \times \$10 &=& 700 \\
5 \times \$20 &=& \underline{\ \ \ 100} \\
& & \$3{,}350
\end{array}
$$

We see that the total cost is exactly the same as the total cost of the original optimal solution. Also, the improvement indexes are positive except for square *XA*, which equals zero. This is to be expected, since square *XA* was the one replaced in the original optimal solution. From a practical viewpoint, the existence of alternate optimal solutions gives valuable flexibility to the decision maker.

### The unbalanced case

One prerequisite to the application of the transportation method is that supply and demand be equal; i.e., the rim requirements for the rows must equal the rim requirements for the columns. As mentioned earlier, this is a very unlikely situation. Most real problems will be of the so-called unbalanced type, supply and demand are unequal. In such cases, there is a method for handling the inequality.

*Demand less than supply.* Considering our original problem, suppose that plant $W$ has a capacity of 75 truckloads per week rather than 55. The company would be able to supply 230 truckloads per week. However the project requirements remain the same. Using the Northwest Corner Rule to establish an initial solution, we would have the program shown in Figure 6–24.

FIGURE 6–24
Unbalanced Form when Demand Is Less Than Supply

| To / From | Project A | Project B | Project C | Plant Capacity |
|---|---|---|---|---|
| Plant W | WA  5  (70) | WB  10  (5) | WC  10 | 75 |
| Plant X | XA  20 | XB  30  (80) | XC  20 | 80 |
| Plant Y | YA  10 | YB  20  (15) | YC  30  (40) | 75 |
| Project Requirements | 70 | 100 | 40 | 210 / 230 |

Obviously the rim requirements for the rows and columns are not balanced. Plant $Y$ still has 20 truckloads available for supply. The method employed to balance this type of problem is to create a fictitious destination or project requiring 20 truckloads per week. This fictitious project serves the same purpose as the slack variable in the simplex method. Since these truckloads will never be shipped the transportation costs to this "dummy" project are equal to zero. An additional column is required to handle the dummy project in the transportation table. Again the Northwest Corner Rule is used to determine the initial solution, as shown in Figure 6–25.

The problem can now be solved using the steps discussed earlier. Let us look, however, at the final table or optimal solution to this problem, Figure 6–26. The optimal solution shows a shipment of 20

FIGURE 6–25
Balanced Form when Demand Is Less Than Supply

| To<br>From | Project<br>A | Project<br>B | Project<br>C | Dummy<br>D | Plant<br>Capacity |
|---|---|---|---|---|---|
| Plant W | 5<br>(70) | 10<br>(5) | 10 | 0 | 75 |
| Plant X | 20 | 30<br>(80) | 20 | 0 | 80 |
| Plant Y | 10 | 20<br>(15) | 30<br>(40) | 0<br>(20) | 75 |
| Project<br>Requirements | 70 | 100 | 40 | 20 | 230<br>230 |

*Total Cost*

$$
\begin{aligned}
70 \times \$\ 5 &= \$\ \ 350 \\
5 \times\ \ 10 &= \ \ \ \ \ 50 \\
80 \times\ \ 30 &= 2{,}400 \\
15 \times\ \ 20 &= \ \ \ 300 \\
40 \times\ \ 30 &= 1{,}200 \\
20 \times\ \ \ 0 &= \ \ \ \ \ \ 0 \\
\hline
&\ \ \$4{,}300
\end{aligned}
$$

truckloads to the dummy project. This means that plant $X$ will have an excess of 20 truckloads. With this information the decision maker knows not only the optimal shipping program but also which plant should not be utilized at full capacity.

*Demand greater than supply.* Another type of unbalanced condition occurs when total demand is greater than total supply; that is, the customers, projects in our case, require more units than the plants can supply. Again, referring to our sample problem, assume that project $A$ will require 10 additional truckloads per week and that project $C$ estimates additional requirements of 20 truckloads. The total project requirements now would be equal to 240 truckloads as opposed to the 210 available from the plants. Similar to the previous type of unbalance, the key to solving the problem is to set it up with balanced conditions. To accomplish this, we create a dummy plant having a capacity exactly equal to the additional demand (30 truckloads). The distribution costs from this plant are equal to zero, since no actual deliveries will be made from this dummy plant.

FIGURE 6–26

| To<br>From | Project<br>A | Project<br>B | Project<br>C | Dummy<br>D | Plant<br>Capacity |
|---|---|---|---|---|---|
| Plant W | 5 | 10 ⓻⑤ | 10 | 0 | 75 |
| Plant X | 20 | 30 ⑳ | 20 ㊵ | 0 ⑳ | 80 |
| Plant Y | 10 ⑦⓪ | 20 ⑤ | 30 | 0 | 75 |
| Project<br>Requirements | 70 | 100 | 40 | 20 | 230 / 230 |

*Total Cost*

$$
\begin{array}{rcl}
75 \times \$10 & = & \$\ 750 \\
20 \times 30 & = & 600 \\
40 \times 20 & = & 800 \\
20 \times 0 & = & 0 \\
70 \times 10 & = & 700 \\
5 \times 20 & = & \underline{\phantom{0}100} \\
& & \$2{,}950
\end{array}
$$

As can be seen in the initial solution table, Figure 6–27, the inclusion of a dummy plant results in an additional row.

Having established the balanced condition, we solve the problem using exactly the same procedure as outlined in the previous sections. The optimal solution to this problem is given in Figure 6–28.

FIGURE 6–27
Balanced Form when Demand Is Greater Than Supply

| To / From | Project A | Project B | Project C | Plant Capacity |
|---|---|---|---|---|
| Plant W | 5 (55) | 10 | 10 | 55 |
| Plant X | 20 (25) | 30 (55) | 20 | 80 |
| Plant Y | 10 | 20 (45) | 30 (30) | 75 |
| Dummy | 0 | 0 | 0 (30) | 30 |
| Project Requirements | 80 | 100 | 60 | 240 / 240 |

*Total Cost*

$$55 \times \$\ 5 = \$\ \ \ 275$$
$$25 \times \ \ 20 = \ \ \ \ \ 500$$
$$55 \times \ \ 30 = \ \ 1{,}650$$
$$45 \times \ \ 20 = \ \ \ \ \ 900$$
$$30 \times \ \ 30 = \ \ \ \ \ 900$$
$$30 \times \ \ \ \ 0 = \ \ \ \ \ \ \ \ 0$$
$$\overline{\ \ \ \ \ \ \ \ \ \$4{,}225}$$

This particular type of unbalanced problem implies that one or more of the projects will not have its requirements satisfied. In this case, the optimal solution indicates that project *B* will be short 30 truckloads per week, since it receives 30 from the dummy plant.

### The MODI method

The modified-distribution method referred to as the MODI method is very similar to the stepping-stone method except that it provides a more efficient means of computing the improvement

FIGURE 6-28

| To \ From | Project A | Project B | Project C | Plant Capacity |
|---|---|---|---|---|
| Plant W | 5 | 10 55 | 10 | 55 |
| Plant X | 20 20 | 30 | 20 60 | 80 |
| Plant Y | 10 60 | 20 15 | 30 | 75 |
| Dummy | 0 | 0 30 | 0 | 30 |
| Project Requirements | 80 | 100 | 60 | 240 / 240 |

Total Cost

$$
\begin{array}{rl}
55 \times \$10 = & \$\ \ 550 \\
20 \times \ 20 = & 400 \\
60 \times \ 20 = & 1{,}200 \\
60 \times \ 10 = & 600 \\
15 \times \ 20 = & 300 \\
30 \times \ \ 0 = & \underline{\ \ \ \ \ 0} \\
& \$3{,}050
\end{array}
$$

indexes for the unused squares. The major difference between these two methods concerns that step in the problem solution at which the closed paths are traced. In order to calculate the improvement indexes for a particular solution, it was necessary in the stepping-stone method to trace a closed path for each unused square. The unused square with the most improvement potential (the largest negative value) was then selected to enter the next solution.

In the MODI method, however, the improvement indexes can be calculated without drawing the closed paths. The MODI method in fact requires tracing only one closed path. This path is drawn after the unused square with the highest improvement index has been identified. As in the stepping-stone method, the purpose of this path is to determine the maximum quantity that can be assigned to the unused square entering the next solution.

Using the same problem, we will illustrate the procedures used in applying the MODI method. Beginning with the same initial solution obtained by using the Northwest Corner Rule, the first step is to compute a value for each row and each column in the transportation table. These values depend on the particular solution and are used to compute the improvement indexes for the unused squares. Assigning a number to each row and column requires a slight modification in the transportation table. This modification together with the initial solution is shown in Figure 6–29.

FIGURE 6–29
Transportation Table Using MODI Method

| $K_j$ / $R_i$ | | $K_1 =$ | $K_2 =$ | $K_3 =$ | |
|---|---|---|---|---|---|
| | To / From | Project A | Project B | Project C | Plant Capacity |
| $R_1 =$ | Plant $W$ | WA ⟨55⟩ 5 | WB 10 | WC 10 | 55 |
| $R_2 =$ | Plant $X$ | XA ⟨15⟩ 20 | XB ⟨65⟩ 30 | XC 20 | 80 |
| $R_3 =$ | Plant $Y$ | YA 10 | YB ⟨35⟩ 20 | YC ⟨40⟩ 30 | 75 |
| | Project Requirements | 70 | 100 | 40 | 210 / 210 |

In this table we let $R$ and $K$ represent the row and column values. We have attached a subscript to denote the specific row and column value. In our case, we have $R_1$, $R_2$, and $R_3$ to represent the rows and $K_1$, $K_2$, and $K_3$ to represent the columns. In general, then, we can say:

$$R_i = \text{The value assigned to row } i$$

and

$K_j$ = The value assigned to column $j$.

The transportation cost, as in previous tables, is shown in the upper right-hand corner or subsquare of each large square.

For identification purposes, we can let

$$C_{ij} = \text{The cost in square } ij \text{ (the square at}$$
$$\text{the intersection of row } i \text{ and column } j).$$

For example, $C_{12}$ represents the cost in the square located at the intersection of row one and column two. Now to compute the values for each row and column, we will use the following formula:

$$R_i + K_j = C_{ij} \text{ (the cost at } stone\ square\ ij).$$

It must be emphasized that this formula is applied *only* to the stone squares in a particular solution. Since there are five stone squares in our problem, we must have five equations. For the stone square located at the intersection of row one and column one we would write:

$$R_1 + K_1 = C_{11} \tag{1}$$

and, since there is a stone square at the intersection of row two and column one,

$$R_2 + K_1 = C_{21} \tag{2}$$

and, similarly,

$$R_2 + K_2 = C_{22} \tag{3}$$
$$R_3 + K_2 = C_{32} \tag{4}$$
$$R_3 + C_3 = C_{33}. \tag{5}$$

Since we are given the cost figure for each square in the table, we can substitute for each $C_{ij}$ in our equations the appropriate value. The results are given below:

$$R_1 + K_1 = 5 \tag{1}$$
$$R_2 + K_1 = 20 \tag{2}$$
$$R_2 + K_2 = 30 \tag{3}$$
$$R_3 + K_2 = 20 \tag{4}$$
$$R_3 + K_3 = 30. \tag{5}$$

Notice that we have six unknowns and only five equations. Thus this system of equations cannot be solved as it now exists. In order to find a solution (a value for each $R$ and $K$), we will let $R_1 = 0$. We could have chosen any value for any row or column, but the usual procedure is to let row one ($R_1$) equal zero. This is legitimate since the entire process is a comparative one. In other words, the significance of the row and column values is not their absolute numerical value. We are interested only in comparing the figures, not the figures themselves.

To solve the five equations, then, we proceed as follows:

if $R_1 = 0$, then

$$R_1 + K_1 = 5$$
$$0 \ + K_1 = 5 \qquad (1)$$
$$K_1 = 5$$

since $K_1 = 5$, then

$$R_2 + K_1 = 20$$
$$R_2 + 5 \ \ = 20 \qquad (2)$$
$$R_2 = 15$$

since $R_2 = 15$, then

$$R_2 + K_2 = 30$$
$$15 + K_2 = 30 \qquad (3)$$
$$K_2 = 15$$

since $K_2 = 15$, then

$$R_3 + K_2 = 20$$
$$R_3 + 15 = 20 \qquad (4)$$
$$R_3 = 5$$

since $R_3 = 5$, then

$$R_3 + K_3 = 30$$
$$5 \ + K_3 = 30 \qquad (5)$$
$$K_3 = 25$$

The $R$ and $K$ values need not always be positive. Depending on the problem, they may be positive, negative, or zero. After some practice, computing the $R$ and $K$ values can usually be done mentally instead of writing out each equation as above. The transportation table with the $R$ and $K$ values included is shown in Figure 6–30.

With the row and column valeus computed, the next step in the MODI method is to evaluate each unused square in the present solution, i.e., compute the improvement indexes. Computing the improvement index for any unused square is accomplished in the fol-

FIGURE 6–30
Initial Solution with $R$ and $K$ Values

| $R_i$ \ $K_j$ | | $K_1 = 5$ | $K_2 = 15$ | $K_3 = 25$ | |
|---|---|---|---|---|---|
| | To \ From | Project A | Project B | Project C | Plant Capacity |
| $R_1 = 0$ | Plant $W$ | $WA$   5   (55) | $WB$   10 | $WC$   10 | 55 |
| $R_2 = 15$ | Plant $X$ | $XA$   20   (15) | $XB$   30   (65) | $XC$   20 | 80 |
| $R_3 = 5$ | Plant $Y$ | $YA$   10 | $YB$   20   (35) | $YC$   30   (40) | 75 |
| | Project Requirements | 70 | 100 | 40 | 210 / 210 |

lowing manner: from the cost of an unused square subtract the corresponding row value and column value. Stating this rule as a general formula, we have:

$$C_{ij} - R_i - K_j = \text{Improvement index.}$$

If the result is negative, then further improvement is possible. When all indexes are equal to or greater than zero, the optimal solution has been obtained.

Each unused square in the initial solution (Figure 6–30) can now be evaluated. For example, the route from plant $W$ to project $B$ at the intersection of row one and column two is one of the unused routes (unused square) in our initial solution. Using our formula we have:

$$(\text{Unused square 12}) \; C_{12} - R_1 - K_2 = \text{Improvement index}$$

$$10 - 0 - 15 = -5.$$

Similarly, for the other unused squares we have:

| (Unused Square) | Improvement Index |
|:---:|:---:|
| 13 | $C_{13} - R_1 - K_3$ |
| | $10 - 0 - 25 = -15$ |
| 23 | $C_{23} - R_2 - K_3$ |
| | $20 - 15 - 25 = -20$ |
| 31 | $C_{31} - R_3 - K_1$ |
| | $10 - 5 - 5 = 0$ |

Comparing the above improvement indexes with those obtained using the stepping-stone method (see Figure 6–9), we find them to be identical. From this point on then, the procedure for developing a new improved solution is identical to the one discussed in the previous sections. For convenience, the procedure is briefly outlined here.

1. Trace a closed path for the cell having the largest negative improvement index.

2. Plus and minus signs are placed at each corner of the path, beginning with a plus sign at the unused square.

3. The smallest stone on the closed path indicates the maximum quantity that can be assigned to the unused square being entered into the solution. This quantity is added to all squares on the closed path with plus signs and subtracted from those squares with minus signs.

4. Finally, the transportation costs for the new solution are calculated.

Using this procedure the second solution is obtained, Figure 6–31.

FIGURE 6–31
Second Solution

| $R_i$ \ $C_j$ | | | $K_1 = 5$ | $K_2 = 15$ | $K_3 = 5$ | |
|:---:|:---:|:---:|:---:|:---:|:---:|:---:|
| | | To \ From | Project A | Project B | Project C | Plant Capacity |
| $R_1 = 0$ | | Plant W | WA ⑤⑤    5 | WB    10 | WC    10 | 55 |
| $R_2 = 15$ | | Plant X | XA ⑮    20 | XB ㉕    30 | XC ㊵    20 | 80 |
| $R_3 = 5$ | | Plant Y | YA    10 | YB ㉟    20 | YC    30 | 75 |
| | | Project Requirements | 70 | 100 | 40 | 210 / 210 |

Notice that it is identical to the second solution found using the stepping-stone procedure. This holds true for all solutions, as we shall see in a moment.

To evaluate the unused squares of the second solution using the MODI method, we must calculate new $R$ and $K$ values. This must be done with every new solution. Again we begin by letting $R_1$ equal zero; and using the general formula $R_i + K_j = C_{ij}$ (the cost at stone square $ij$), the $R$ and $K$ values are computed as follows:

$$\text{(Stone square 11) } R_1 + K_1 = 5$$
$$0 + K_1 = 5 \tag{1}$$
$$K_1 = 5.$$

$$\text{(Stone square 21) } R_2 + K_1 = 20$$
$$R_2 + 5 = 20 \tag{2}$$
$$R_2 = 15.$$

$$\text{(Stone square 22) } R_2 + K_2 = 30$$
$$15 + K_2 = 30 \tag{3}$$
$$K_2 = 15.$$

$$\text{(Stone square 23) } R_2 + K_3 = 20$$
$$15 + K_3 = 20 \tag{4}$$
$$K_3 = 5.$$

$$\text{(Stone square 32) } R_3 + K_2 = 20$$
$$R_3 + 15 = 20 \tag{5}$$
$$R_3 = 5.$$

These $R$ and $K$ values were included in Figure 6–31. In comparing our new $R$ and $K$ values with those obtained in the initial solution,

FIGURE 6-32

| Unused Square | $C_{ij} - R_i - K_j = $ Improvement Index |
|:---:|:---|
| 12 | $C_{12} - R_1 - K_2$ <br> $10 - 0 - 15 = -5$ |
| 13 | $C_{13} - R_1 - K_3$ <br> $10 - 0 - 5 = +5$ |
| 31 | $C_{31} - R_3 - K_1$ <br> $10 - 5 - 5 = 0$ |
| 33 | $C_{33} - R_3 - K_3$ <br> $30 - 5 - 5 = +20$ |

FIGURE 6–33
Third Solution

| $R_i$ \ $C_j$ | | $K_1 = 5$ | $K_2 = 10$ | $K_3 = 5$ | |
|---|---|---|---|---|---|
| | From \ To | Project *A* | Project *B* | Project *C* | Plant Capacity |
| $R_1 = 0$ | Plant *W* | *WA* [5] (30) | *WB* [10] (25) | *WC* [10] +5 | 55 |
| $R_2 = 15$ | Plant *X* | *XA* [20] (40) | *XB* [30] +5 | *XC* [20] (40) | 80 |
| $R_3 = 10$ | Plant *Y* | *YA* [10] −5 | *YB* [20] (75) | *YC* [30] +15 | 75 |
| | Project Requirements | 70 | 100 | 40 | 210 \ 210 |

FIGURE 6–34
Optimal Solution

| $R_i$ \ $C_j$ | | $K_1 = 0$ | $K_2 = 10$ | $K_3 = 0$ | |
|---|---|---|---|---|---|
| | From \ To | Project *A* | Project *B* | Project *C* | Plant Capacity |
| $R_1 = 0$ | Plant *W* | *WA* [5] +5 | *WB* [10] (55) | *WC* [10] +10 | 55 |
| $R_2 = 20$ | Plant *X* | *XA* [20] (40) | *XB* [30] 0 | *XC* [20] (40) | 80 |
| $R_3 = 10$ | Plant *Y* | *YA* [10] (30) | *YB* [20] (45) | *YC* [30] +20 | 75 |
| | Project Requirements | 70 | 100 | 40 | 210 \ 210 |

Figure 6–30, we find that all $R$ and $K$ values are the same except for $K_3$ which is equal to 5 in the second table. The point to be made here is that changing the solution makes some if not all of the $R$ and $K$ values incorrect. Hence, with every new solution, new values for $R$ and $K$ must be established in order to determine if further im-provement is possible, i.e., calculate the improvement indexes.

The evaluation of each unused square of the second solution is shown in Figure 6–32.

The remaining improved solutions with their respective $R$ and $K$ values are given in Figures 6–33 and 6–34. The improvement indexes are also included. The reader is encouraged to verify the $R$ and $K$ values as well as the improvement indexes given in these tables.

### Summary of MODI method

1. For each solution compute the $R$ and $K$ values for the table using the formula: $R_i + K_j = C_{ij}$ (the cost at *stone* square $ij$). Row one ($R_1$) is always set equal to zero.

2. Calculate the improvement indexes for all unused squares using the formula:

$$C_{ij} \text{ (cost of } unused \text{ square)} - R_i - K_j = \text{Improvement index.}$$

3. Select the unused square with the largest negative index. If all indexes are equal to or greater than zero, the optimal solution has been obtained.

4. Trace the closed path for the unused square having the largest negative index.

5. Develop improved solution using the same procedure as out-lined in the stepping-stone method.

6. Repeat steps 1–5 until an optimal solution has been found.

### Degeneracy

We previously pointed out that the total number of stone squares in *any* solution must be equal to the number of rim requirements minus one. An alternative way of stating this rule is that the number of stone squares in *any* solution must be equal to the number of rows plus the number of columns minus one. When this rule is not met, the solution is said to be degenerate. The term degenerate is unfor-tunate since it has an alarming connotation. A degenerate solution is simply a small stumbling block on the road to a successful solution. Degeneracy is also encountered using the simplex method. This will be discussed in Chapter 7.

Failure to meet the test for degeneracy in the transportation problem is indicated in two ways. First, there may be an excessive number of stone squares in a solution, i.e., the number of stone squares is greater than the number of rim requirements minus one. This type of degeneracy arises only in developing the initial solution and is caused by an improper assignment or an error in formulating the problem. In such cases, it is necessary to modify the initial solution so as to satisfy the rim requirements minus one rule. Second, there may be an insufficient number of stone squares in a solution. Degeneracy of this type may occur either in the initial solution or in subsequent solutions. It is this type of degeneracy which requires special procedures in order to resolve the degeneracy. With an insufficient number of stone squares in a solution, it would be impossible to trace a closed path for each unused square; and, in using the MODI method, it would be impossible to compute the $R$ and $K$ values.

The procedures for handling degeneracy resulting from an insufficient number of stones will now be presented.

*Degeneracy in establishing an initial solution.* Let us assume that the

FIGURE 6–35
Degenerate Problem—Initial Solution

| To<br>From | A | | B | | C | | Plant<br>Capacity |
|---|---|---|---|---|---|---|---|
| W | WA<br>(30) | 5 | WB<br>(20) | 10 | WC | 10 | 50 |
| X | XA | 20 | XB<br>(20) | 30 | XC | 20 | 20 |
| Y | YA | 10 | YB | 20 | YC<br>(30) | 30 | 30 |
| Project<br>Requirements | 30 | | 40 | | 30 | | 100 / 100 |

plant capacities and project requirements in our sample problem have been changed. Using the Northwest Corner Rule, we obtain the initial solution given in Figure 6–35.

In this solution we have four stone squares. According to our rim requirements minus one rule, we should have five stone squares. Hence the solution is degenerate. This particular case of degeneracy arises when, in using the Northwest Corner Rule, both a column requirement and row requirement are satisfied simultaneously, thus breaking the stair-step pattern. In our case this occurs in square *XB*. Of course, the assignment of a value to the final stone square always satisfies the remaining row and column requirements simultaneously, but this will not result in a degenerate solution.

To resolve this degeneracy we assign a zero stone to one of the unused squares. Although there is a great deal of flexibility in choosing the unused square for the zero stone, the general procedure, when using the Northwest Corner Rule, is to assign it to a square so as to maintain an unbroken chain of stone squares. Figure 6–36 shows the zero stone added to square *XC*, although it could have been assigned to square *YB*.

We now have five stone squares which satisfy the degeneracy test. The problem can now be solved using the same solution procedure with the zero stone square treated just as any other stone

FIGURE 6–36
Degeneracy Resolved

| To / From | A | B | C | Plant Capacity |
|---|---|---|---|---|
| W | 5 (30) | 10 (20) | 10 | 50 |
| X | 20 | 30 (20) | 20 (0) | 20 |
| Y | 10 | 20 | 30 (30) | 30 |
| Project Requirements | 30 | 40 | 30 | 100 / 100 |

square in the solution. This zero stone square has no meaning in a problem; it is merely a computational device which permits the regular solution method to be applied in solving the problem.

*Degeneracy during subsequent solution stages.* The initial solution to another problem is given in Figure 6–37. We observe that the initial solution is not degenerate.

FIGURE 6–37

| To / From | A | B | C | Plant Capacity |
|---|---|---|---|---|
| W | WA　5 〈30〉 | WB　10 〈30〉 | WC　30 +15 | 60 |
| X | XA　10 +10 | XB　5 〈20〉 | XC　10 〈20〉 | 40 |
| Y | YA　20 +10 | YB　5 −10 | YC　20 〈20〉 | 20 |
| Project Requirements | 30 | 40 | 50 | 120 / 120 |

The improvement indexes are shown in the unused squares, and indicate that an improved solution may be obtained by introducing unused square *YB* into the next program. Let us go through the procedure for developing the next solution to this problem and ob-

FIGURE 6–38

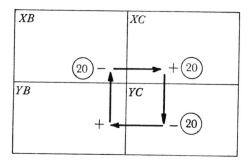

serve what happens. We first trace the closed path for unused square $YB$ and then choose the smallest stone as the quantity to be assigned to unused square $YB$. This is shown in Figure 6–38. Next, we choose the smallest stone as the quantity to be assigned to unused square $YB$. In this case all stones have a value of 20. The results of the assignment of 20 units to square $YB$ are shown in Figure 6–39.

FIGURE 6–39

| | |
|---|---|
| $XB$<br><br>$20 - 20 = 0$ | $XC$<br><br>$20 + 20 = \boxed{40}$ |
| $YB$<br><br>$0 + 20 = \boxed{20}$ | $YC$<br><br>$20 - 20 = 0$ |

When we added 20 units to square $YB$, the quantities shipped through squares $XB$ and $YC$ were *both* reduced to zero. This will always occur when a tie exists between two or more stone squares and these stones represent the smallest stones on the path. Hence, in our problem, adding an unused square resulted in the elimination of two stone squares from the previous solution. In the usual case, remember, adding an unused square resulted in the elimination of only one stone square. Thus, as in the case of degeneracy in an initial solution, we must add a zero stone to one of the squares along the closed path which was assigned a minus sign. We have placed the zero stone to square $XB$ as shown in Figure 6–40.

In some cases more than two stone squares may be eliminated. In such cases zero stones should be added until the number of stone squares in the solution satisfies the rim requirements minus one rule. The above problem can now be solved using the standard procedure discussed in a previous section.

For hand computation, the use of the zero stone square is convenient. However, since an electronic computer cannot distinguish between a zero where there is no assignment and an assignment of zero with a circle around it (zero stone square), the Greek letter $\epsilon$

FIGURE 6-40

Degeneracy Resolved: Subsequent Solution Stage

| To / From | A | B | C | Plant Capacity |
|---|---|---|---|---|
| W | WA  5  ⃝30 | WB  10  ⃝30 | WC  30 | 60 |
| X | XA  10 | XB  5  (0) | XC  10  ⃝40 | 40 |
| Y | YA  20 | YB  5  ⃝20 | YC  20 | 20 |
| Project Requirements | 30 | 50 | 40 | 120 / 120 |

(epsilon) is usually used in place of the zero. The end result is of course the same.

In this presentation of the transportation method, only the basic problem was explored. Essentially we concerned ourselves with the problem of finding the best combination of transportation routes. Many other kinds of problems may be solved using the basic transportation framework. Some of these more complex problems will be discussed in Chapter 9.

## The assignment method

Another special purpose algorithm used in linear programming is the assignment method. Like the transportation method, the assignment method is computationally more efficient than the simplex method for a special class of problems. We will also show that the assignment method is a special case of the transportation problem. In other words we can solve an assignment problem using the transportation method.

### A sample problem

To illustrate the assignment problem, let us consider the assignment of three jobs $A$, $B$, and $C$, to three machines $X$, $Y$, and $Z$. Any one of the jobs can be processed completely on any one of the machines. Furthermore, the cost of processing any job on any machine is known. The assignment of jobs to machines must be on a one-to-one basis; that is, each job will be assigned exclusively to one and only one machine. The objective is to assign the jobs to the machines at a minimum total cost. The cost data are given in Figure 6–41.

FIGURE 6–41
Cost for Each Job-Machine Assignment

| Jobs | Machines | | |
|---|---|---|---|
| | $X$ | $Y$ | $Z$ |
| $A$ | $20 | $26 | $30 |
| $B$ | $10 | $15 | $19 |
| $C$ | $17 | $14 | $12 |

The number of rows (jobs) equals the number of columns (machines). This is one characteristic of all assignment problems. Another characteristic is that in the optimal solution there will be one and only one assignment in a given row or column of the given assignment table. These characteristics are peculiar to the assignment problem. In the general transportation problem, for example, it is not necessary to have an equal number of sources and destinations. Neither does the transportation method require that there be one assignment only in a given row or column of the optimal solution.

### Using the transportation method to solve the assignment problem

Since each job must be assigned to one and only one machine, we can say that the job requirement for each job is one and that the machine capacity for each machine is also one. This might be the case, for example, when the additional setup expenses are such as to prohibit the partial assignment of machines to more than one job. Given the cost data of Figure 6–41, the job requirements and ma-

FIGURE 6–42
The Assignment Problem Set up in the Transportation Table

| From \ To | Machine X | Machine Y | Machine Z | Job Requirement |
|---|---|---|---|---|
| Job A | 20 ① | 26 | 30 | 1 |
| Job B | 10 | 15 ① | 19 | 1 |
| Job C | 17 | 14 | 12 ① | 1 |
| Machine Capacity | 1 | 1 | 1 | 3 / 3 |

FIGURE 6–43

| From \ To | X | Y | Z | Job Requirements |
|---|---|---|---|---|
| A | 20 ① | 26 (0) | 30 | 1 |
| B | 10 | 15 ① | 19 (0) | 1 |
| C | 17 | 14 | 12 ① | 1 |
| Machine Capacity | 1 | 1 | 1 | 3 / 3 |

chine capacities, we can set up the transportation table given in Figure 6–42, showing the initial solution using the Northwest Corner Rule.

There are three stone squares in this initial solution. However, according to the rim requirements minus one rule, we should have five stone squares. Hence we must add two zero stone squares to resolve the degeneracy. This has been done in Figure 6–43.

The problem can now be solved in the usual manner. Because all of the stone squares have a value of one or zero, a degenerate solution will result with each subsequent solution. The reason for this can be attributed to the two special characteristics of the assignment problem mentioned in the previous section. Having to cope with the problem of degeneracy at each solution makes the transportation method computationally inefficient for solving an assignment problem.

### Using the assignment method to solve the assignment problem

The assignment method, known as *Flood's technique* or the *Hungarian method of assignment*, provides a much more efficient method of solving assignment problems. There are basically three steps in the assignment method. We will present the reasoning underlying the procedure, although some of the rationale for the method lies in mathematical theorems which are not discussed in this book.

*Step 1. Determine the opportunity-cost table.* Much of the rationale underlying the assignment method is embedded in the concept of opportunity costs. Hence a brief explanation of this concept may be helpful. The cost of any kind of action or decision consists of the opportunities that are sacrificed in taking that action. Many of us go through an opportunity cost analysis without realizing it. For example, a friend was recently thinking of buying a new home, and one day he drove by in a new Cadillac. He promptly started explaining how nice it was living in an apartment. This is indeed an example of opportunity-cost analysis. If we do one thing, we cannot do another.

Let us now see how this concept plays an important part in the computational mechanics of the assignment method. For convenience, the cost data are given again in Figure 6–44.

Suppose that we decide to assign job $A$ to machine $X$. The table shows that the cost of this assignment is \$20. Since machine $X$ could

FIGURE 6–44
Cost for Each Job-Machine Assignment

| Jobs | Machines | | |
|:---:|:---:|:---:|:---:|
| | X | Y | Z |
| A | $20 | $26 | $30 |
| B | $10 | 15 | 19 |
| C | $17 | 14 | 12 |

just as well process job *B* for $10, it is clear that our assignment of job *A* to machine *X* was not the best decision. Therefore, when we arbitrarily assign job *A* to machine *X*, we are in effect sacrificing the opportunity to save $10 ($20 − $10). This sacrifice is more generally referred to as an opportunity cost. In other words, the decision to assign job *A* to machine *X* precludes the assignment of job *B* to machine *X*, given the restriction that one and only one job can be assigned to a machine. Thus we say that the opportunity cost of the assignment of job *A* to machine *X* is $10, with respect to the lowest cost assignment for machine *X* (or column *X*). Similarly the decision to assign job *C* to machine *X* would involve an opportunity cost of $7 ($17 − $10). Finally, since the assignment of job *B* to machine *X* is the best assignment, we can say that the opportunity cost of this assignment is zero ($10 − $10). More specifically these costs can be called the job-opportunity costs with regard to machine *X*. If we were to subtract the lowest cost of column *Y* (machine *Y*) from all the costs in this column, we would have the job-opportunity costs with regard to machine *Y*. The same procedure in column *Z* would give the job-opportunity costs for machine *Z*.

In addition to these job-opportunity costs, there are machine-opportunity costs. We could, for example, assign job *A* to machine *X*, *Y*, or *Z*. If we assigned job *A* to machine *Y*, there is an opportunity cost attached to this decision. The assignment of job *A* to machine *Y* costs $26, while the assignment of job *A* to machine *X* costs only $20. Therefore the opportunity cost of assigning job *A* to machine *Y* is $6 ($26 − $20). Similarly the assignment of job *A* to machine *Z* involves an opportunity cost of $10 ($30 − $20). A zero opportunity cost is involved in the assignment of job $A$ to machine $X$, since this is the best assignment for job $A$ (row $A$). Hence, we could compute the machine opportunity costs for each row (each job) by subtracting the lowest cost entry in each row from all cost entries in its row.

This discussion on opportunity costs should provide an understanding of the mechanics of the first step in the assignment method which is to develop the total opportunity-cost table. There are two parts to this first step. Part A is as follows: Subtract the lowest entry in each column of the original cost table from all entries in that column. The resulting new table with computations is given in Figure 6–45.

FIGURE 6–45
Part A, Step 1

| Jobs | Machines | | |
|:---:|:---:|:---:|:---:|
| | $X$ | $Y$ | $Z$ |
| $A$ | 10 | 12 | 18 |
| $B$ | 0 | 1 | 7 |
| $C$ | 7 | 0 | 0 |

*Computations:*

| Column X | Column Y | Column Z |
|:---|:---|:---|
| $20 - 10 = 10$ | $26 - 14 = 12$ | $30 - 12 = 18$ |
| $10 - 10 = 0$ | $15 - 14 = 1$ | $19 - 12 = 7$ |
| $17 - 10 = 7$ | $14 - 14 = 0$ | $12 - 12 = 0$ |

The table in Figure 6–45 should be recognized as the job-opportunity table. Now the objective of this first step is to develop a total opportunity-cost table. In other words we want to consider the machine opportunity costs also. Part B of step 1 accomplishes this but not in exactly the same way as our intuitive analysis. The effect however is the same. Part B then is as follows: Subtract the lowest entry in each row of the *table obtained in part A* from all numbers in that row. The new table and computations are shown in Figure 6–46.

*Step 2. Determine whether an optimal assignment can be made.* The objective is to assign the jobs to the machines so as to minimize total costs. With the total opportunity-cost table, this objective will be

FIGURE 6–46
Part B, Step 1
The Total Opportunity-Cost Table

| Jobs | Machines | | |
|---|---|---|---|
| | X | Y | Z |
| A | 0 | 2 | 8 |
| B | 0 | 1 | 7 |
| C | 7 | 0 | 0 |

*Computations*

Row A:  10 − 10 = 0      12 − 10 = 2      18 − 10 = 8
Row B:   0 −  0 = 0       1 −  0 = 1       7 −  0 = 7
Row C:   7 −  0 = 7       0 −  0 = 0       0 −  0 = 0

achieved if we can assign the jobs to the machines in such a way as to obtain a total opportunity cost of zero. In other words we want to make the three best possible assignments. The best possible assignment of a job to a machine would involve an opportunity cost of zero.

Looking at the total opportunity-cost table in Figure 6–46, we find four squares with zeros, each indicating a zero opportunity cost for that square (Assignment). Hence, we could assign job $A$ to machine $X$ and job $C$ to machine $Y$ or $Z$, all assignments having an opportunity cost of zero. If this were done, however, we could not assign job $B$ to any machine with a zero opportunity cost. The reason here is that assigning job $A$ to machine $X$ precludes the assignment of job $B$ to machine $X$. If we had a zero in square $BY$, then we could make an optimal assignment. In other words, to make an optimal assignment of the three jobs to the three machines we must locate three zero squares in the table such that a complete assignment to these squares can be made with a total opportunity cost of zero. This is possible only when no two such zero squares appear in the same row or column.

There is a convenient method for determining whether an optimal assignment can be made. This method consists of drawing straight lines (vertically and horizontally) through the total opportunity-cost table in such a manner as to minimize the numbers of lines necessary to cover all zero squares. If the number of lines equals either the number of rows or columns in the table, an optimal assignment can be made, and the problem is solved. On the other hand, an optimal assignment cannot be made if the number of lines is less than the number of rows or columns. In this case we must develop a new total opportunity-cost table.

The test for optimal assignment has been applied to our present table and is shown in Figure 6–47.

FIGURE 6–47
Test for Optimal Assignment

| Jobs | Machines | | |
|---|---|---|---|
| | X | Y | Z |
| A | 0 | 2 | 8 |
| B | 0 | 1 | 7 |
| C | 7 | 0 | 0 | → line 1 |

line 2

It requires only two lines (row $C$ and column $X$) to cover all the zero squares. Since there are three rows, an optimal assignment is not possible.

*Step 3. Revise the total opportunity-cost table.* If an optimal assignment is not feasible, we must modify the total opportunity-cost table by including some assignment not in the rows and columns covered by the lines. Of course that assignment with the least opportunity cost is chosen; in our problem this would be the assignment of job $B$ to machine $Y$ with an opportunity cost of one. In other words we would like to change the opportunity cost for this assignment from one to zero.

The procedure for accomplishing this task is as follows: (A) select the smallest number in the table not covered by a straight line and subtract this number from all numbers not covered by a straight line; and (B) add this same lowest number to the numbers lying at the intersection of any two lines. The revised total opportunity-cost table and computations of parts A and B of step 3 is shown in Figure 6–48.

The test for optimal assignment described in step 2 is applied again to the revised table. This is shown in Figure 6–49.

Since the minimum number of lines necessary to cover all zeros is three and since this number is equal to the number of rows or columns,

FIGURE 6–48
Revised Opportunity-Cost Table

| Jobs | Machines | | |
|---|---|---|---|
| | X | Y | Z |
| A | 0 | 1 | 7 |
| B | 0 | 0 | 6 |
| C | 8 | 0 | 0 |

*Computations:*

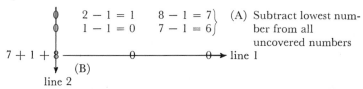

$$2 - 1 = 1 \qquad 8 - 1 = 7$$
$$1 - 1 = 0 \qquad 7 - 1 = 6$$
(A) Subtract lowest number from all uncovered numbers

$7 + 1 + 8$ ——————— line 1
(B)
line 2

(B) Add same smallest number to number lying at the intersection of two lines

an optimal assignment can be made. In this case the optimal assignments are: *A* to *X*, *B* to *Y*, and *C* to *Z*. In larger problems, however, the assignments may not be readily apparent and we must resort to a more systematic procedure. The first step is to select a row or column in which there is only one zero square. The first assignment is made to that zero square. Lines are then drawn through the column and row in which the zero square is located. From the re-

FIGURE 6–49
Test for Optimal Assignment Applied to Revised
Opportunity-Cost Table

| Jobs | Machines | | |
|---|---|---|---|
| | X | Y | Z |
| A | 0 | 1 | 7 |
| B | 0 | 0 | 6 | line 2 |
| C | 8 | 0 | 0 | line 3 |

maining rows and columns we again select that row or column in which there is only one zero cell. Another assignment is made and lines drawn through the respective row and column. The procedure is repeated until a complete assignment has been made. The assignment sequence using this procedure in our problem is shown in Figure 6–50.

FIGURE 6–50
Assignment Sequence

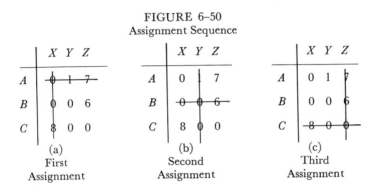

|   | X | Y | Z |
|---|---|---|---|
| A | 0 | 1 | 7 |
| B | 0 | 0 | 6 |
| C | 8 | 0 | 0 |

(a)
First
Assignment

|   | X | Y | Z |
|---|---|---|---|
| A | 0 |   | 7 |
| B | 0 | 0 | 6 |
| C | 8 | 0 | 0 |

(b)
Second
Assignment

|   | X | Y | Z |
|---|---|---|---|
| A | 0 | 1 |   |
| B | 0 | 0 | 6 |
| C | 8 | 0 | 0 |

(c)
Third
Assignment

To calculate the total cost of these assignments, we must go back to the original cost table. The computation of total cost is given below:

| *Assignment* | *Cost* |
|---|---|
| A to X | $20 |
| B to Y | 15 |
| C to Z | 12 |
| Total cost | $47 |

## Summary of the assignment method

1. Determine the opportunity-cost table.
   a) Subtract the lowest entry in each column of the given cost table from all entries in that column.
   b) Subtract the lowest entry in each row of the table obtained in part A from all numbers in that row.
2. Determine whether an optimal assignment can be made. The procedure is to draw straight lines (vertically and horizontally) through the total opportunity-cost table in such a manner as to minimize the number of lines necessary to cover all zero squares. An optimal assignment can be made when the number of lines equals the number of rows or columns. If the number of lines drawn is less than the number of rows or columns, an optimal assignment cannot be made, and the problem is not solved.

3. Revise the total opportunity-cost table.
  *a*) Select the smallest number in the table not covered by a straight line and subtract this number from all numbers not covered by a straight line.
  *b*) Add this same number to the numbers lying at the intersection of any two lines. Go back to step 2.

Finally it should be pointed out that the assignment method has been applied to areas other than the one presented in this chapter. For example, it has been used to assign personnel to jobs and salesmen to sales territories. The reader is encouraged to examine the variety of problems that have been solved using the assignment method, some of which are included in the references at the end of the book.

## Problems

1. Given the following matrix of *unit costs* and supply-demand conditions, solve by the stepping-stone method.

| To⟍From | A | B | C | D | Units Available |
|---|---|---|---|---|---|
| 1 | $3 | $2 | $5 | $1 | 85 |
| 2 | $2 | $1 | $2 | $3 | 120 |
| 3 | $2 | $3 | $4 | $2 | 105 |
| Units Required | 75 | 60 | 80 | 95 | 310 |

2. The ABC Gas and Oil Company has four supply stations. It is concerned as to the best means of supplying oil to its six largest customers. Utilizing the following transportation costs per tank truck, the demand per year (in tank trucks) of the consumers, and the available supply at each supply station, find the best means of furnishing customer annual demands by the stepping-stone method.

| To<br>From | 1 | 2 | 3 | 4 | 5 | 6 | Trucks<br>Available |
|---|---|---|---|---|---|---|---|
| *A* | $30 | $33 | $42 | $26 | $38 | $49 | 25 |
| *B* | $41 | $29 | $34 | $47 | $25 | $43 | 50 |
| *C* | $28 | $40 | $30 | $35 | $25 | $60 | 65 |
| *D* | $43 | $36 | $38 | $27 | $30 | $35 | 55 |
| Trucks<br>Delivered | 20 | 35 | 28 | 47 | 35 | 30 | 195 |

3. The Bubble Soda Company distributes soft drinks on the Eastern coast. Having three plants from which to distribute its products, use the MODI method to solve for the best distribution schedule. Relevant information concerning the six major cities of distribution is as follows: (Assume 250 cases per truckload.)

| To<br>From | Transportation Costs per Truckload | | | | | | Weekly<br>Capacity<br>(Cases) |
|---|---|---|---|---|---|---|---|
| | City *A* | City *B* | City *C* | City *D* | City *E* | City *F* | |
| Plant 1 | $25 | $30 | $35 | $20 | $45 | $25 | 20,000 |
| Plant 2 | $40 | $35 | $20 | $40 | $30 | $30 | 30,000 |
| Plant 3 | $30 | $20 | $40 | $25 | $25 | $30 | 28,000 |
| Weekly<br>Demand<br>(Cases) | 12,000 | 12,500 | 14,500 | 10,000 | 15,000 | 14,000 | 78,000 |

4. Utilizing the following supply-demand conditions and unit costs, solve by the MODI method for the minimum cost solution of the given transportation problem.

| From \ To | A | B | C | D | E | F | G | H | Units Available |
|---|---|---|---|---|---|---|---|---|---|
| 1 | 5 | 8 | 10 | 4 | 6 | 4 | 5 | 9 | 250 |
| 2 | 9 | 4 | 8 | 5 | 10 | 7 | 4 | 7 | 375 |
| 3 | 7 | 6 | 6 | 10 | 7 | 5 | 6 | 9 | 220 |
| 4 | 6 | 5 | 7 | 9 | 8 | 11 | 8 | 10 | 330 |
| Units Required | 120 | 180 | 100 | 195 | 114 | 120 | 135 | 140 | 1,175 1,105 |

5. The XYZ Coal Company has four mines located in Pennsylvania and Ohio. XYZ mining operations supply coal for eight major industries in the two-state area. Weekly coal requirements of the eight firms are as shown below:

| Firm............... | A | B | C | D | E | F | G | H |
|---|---|---|---|---|---|---|---|---|
| Tons Required........ | 90 | 100 | 80 | 90 | 110 | 100 | 90 | 120 |

Mine capacities per week are

| Mine......... | 1 | 2 | 3 | 4 |
|---|---|---|---|---|
| Tons......... | 220 | 180 | 190 | 210 |

The following matrix presents the relevant transportation costs between the different mines and plants (on a cost per railroad car).

| From \ To | A | B | C | D | E | F | G | H |
|---|---|---|---|---|---|---|---|---|
| 1 | $50 | $55 | $60 | $50 | $65 | $55 | $45 | $55 |
| 2 | $60 | $40 | $55 | $35 | $70 | $45 | $50 | $45 |
| 3 | $70 | $50 | $45 | $40 | $50 | $55 | $60 | $45 |
| 4 | $55 | $65 | $40 | $60 | $40 | $50 | $40 | $60 |

Determine the transportation schedule which will minimize weekly total transportation costs using the MODI method. (Assume a railroad car = 10 tons.)

6. A major supplier of concrete has six sand and gravel pits. Recent decreases in interest rates have stimulated construction activity within the area. This firm has benefited from the increased activity, having won contracts for 10 major construction projects. Assuming that all projects to be of similar duration, timewise, the weekly demands for concrete are listed below.

| Project............. | A | B | C | D | E | E | F | G | I | J |
|---|---|---|---|---|---|---|---|---|---|---|
| Weekly Demand (cubic yards)...... | 180 | 207 | 225 | 243 | 198 | 270 | 252 | 216 | 270 | 225 |

Assume that any of the sand gravel pits may supply any of the projects. The following figures represent the capacities of the six pits available for the new projects. (Assume 9 cubic yards = 1 truckload.)

| Supply Sources........... | 1 | 2 | 3 | 4 | 5 | 6 |
|---|---|---|---|---|---|---|
| Weekly Capacity (cubic yards)........... | 418 | 450 | 360 | 540 | 360 | 360 |

The following table is a distance matrix for all relevant points.

| To<br>From | A | B | C | D | E | F | G | H | I | J |
|---|---|---|---|---|---|---|---|---|---|---|
| 1 | 25 | 40 | 55 | 20 | 70 | 120 | 80 | 30 | 40 | 15 |
| 2 | 60 | 100 | 10 | 45 | 100 | 20 | 40 | 5 | 100 | 40 |
| 3 | 115 | 45 | 15 | 50 | 65 | 10 | 50 | 40 | 45 | 90 |
| 4 | 80 | 75 | 25 | 90 | 20 | 50 | 70 | 100 | 10 | 60 |
| 5 | 10 | 90 | 80 | 35 | 5 | 75 | 10 | 75 | 15 | 20 |
| 6 | 50 | 5 | 70 | 120 | 40 | 50 | 15 | 80 | 20 | 50 |

The company uses a fixed rate of $0.50 per mile to account for variable transportation costs when preparing estimates. You are to set up the first table and use the Northwest Corner Rule to establish an initial solution.

7. Given the following information, solve by the transportation method for the minimum cost solution. Do any other solutions exist for this problem?

| From \ To | Unit Cost | | | Units Available |
|---|---|---|---|---|
| | A | B | C | |
| X | 75 | 50 | 50 | 1,040 |
| Y | 50 | 25 | 75 | 975 |
| Z | 25 | 125 | 25 | 715 |
| Units Required | 1,300 | 910 | 520 | 2,730 |

8. Below is an intermediate solution to a transportation problem. Resolve the problem of degeneracy and solve for the minimum cost solution.

| From \ To | A | B | C | D | E | Capacity |
|---|---|---|---|---|---|---|
| X | 3 | 5 (475) | 7 (1,525) | 5 | 2 | 2,000 |
| Y | 4 | 8 (750) | 10 | 5 (1,750) | 2 | 2,500 |
| Z | 2 (1,950) | 1 | 3 | 8 | 6 (1,550) | 3,500 |
| Requirements | 1,950 | 1,225 | 1,525 | 1,750 | 1,550 | 8,000 |

9. Given the following information, establish an initial solution by the Northwest Corner Method and then solve by the MODI method for the minimum cost solution.

| To<br>From | A | B | C | D | E | F | Units<br>Available |
|---|---|---|---|---|---|---|---|
| W | $ 5 | $10 | $15 | $10 | $20 | $ 5 | 500 |
| X | $20 | $10 | $ 5 | $ 5 | $10 | $20 | 600 |
| Y | $15 | $ 5 | $20 | $20 | $ 5 | $15 | 750 |
| Z | $10 | $20 | $10 | $15 | $ 5 | $25 | 650 |
| Units Required | 300 | 450 | 350 | 425 | 500 | 475 | 2,500 |

10. A manufacturing firm, being job shop in nature, has recently received three jobs. Having three different machines upon which the jobs may be performed, the production manager must determine the assignment which will minimize total production costs for the three jobs. (It is assumed that each job is assigned to just one machine.) Determine the optimal assignment, given the following table of costs, by means of the transportation method.

| Job | Machine | | |
|---|---|---|---|
| | A | B | C |
| 1 | $220 | $230 | $232 |
| 2 | $195 | $185 | $190 |
| 3 | $150 | $160 | $165 |

11. A central dispatcher for the New York City police department has just received four calls for police investigation. Glancing at the locational map above his desk, he notes the locations of the only four squad cars available for assignment to the calls. Assuming that the two patrolmen

in each car are equally adequate for investigating any of the calls, *and* that the time necessary to proceed to the four locations is directly related to the distances between the squad cars and the trouble spots, solve for the optimal assignment of the cars by the assignment method. The following table lists the distances relevant to the problem (in blocks). The objective is to minimize total travel time (distance) for the cars to respond to the four calls.

| Trouble Spot | Squad Car | | | |
|:---:|:---:|:---:|:---:|:---:|
| | #1 | #2 | #3 | #4 |
| A | 20 | 15 | 22 | 18 |
| B | 10 | 12 | 14 | 13 |
| C | 11 | 12 | 10 | 9 |
| D | 8 | 7 | 8 | 10 |

12. A local township has just been caught by surprise by a sudden snowstorm. The city's emergency snow removal plan has been placed in effect and the city manager must determine the best method of assigning his snowplows. The city has six plows presently in operating condition and they are not all alike with respect to speed or scrape-width. The manager must assign these snowplows to the six districts within the city in such a manner as to minimize the total time for complete removal of the snow. This time includes the time necessary for the plow to reach the district plus the time necessary to clear the prescribed streets. Below are time estimates calculated for snow removal by each of the plows for each district (in hours).

| Snowplow | District | | | | | |
|:---:|:---:|:---:|:---:|:---:|:---:|:---:|
| | A | B | C | D | E | F |
| 1 | 5 | 4 | 6 | 5 | 7 | 4 |
| 2 | 6 | 8 | 7 | 5 | 6 | 5 |
| 3 | 7 | 6 | 8 | 5 | 7 | 6 |
| 4 | 5 | 8 | 4 | 7 | 6 | 6 |
| 5 | 6 | 5 | 6 | 6 | 7 | 5 |
| 6 | 5 | 5 | 6 | 7 | 6 | 6 |

Assuming that circumstances particular to this case prevent assignment of a single plow to more than one district, determine by the assignment method the assignment minimizing total removal time.

13. Using the assignment method, determine the optimal assignment for the following problem.

| Job | Machine | | | | |
|-----|---------|---|---|---|---|
| | A | B | C | D | E |
| 1 | $20 | $22 | $21 | $19 | $24 |
| 2 | $32 | $30 | $34 | $33 | $30 |
| 3 | $43 | $45 | $44 | $42 | $41 |
| 4 | $28 | $29 | $24 | $26 | $25 |
| 5 | $25 | $28 | $29 | $27 | $26 |

# chapter 7

# Operational problems

## Introduction

In applying the methods discussed thus far in the book to operational situations, certain practical problems are encountered. Fortunately, workable methods by which many of these problems can be treated exist. The recognition and treatment or these situations is the subject of this chapter.

There are four general areas which often present problems in applying linear programming to operational situations. Each of these will be discussed in detail and solution methods will be presented using illustrative problems. First we shall examine the problem of supplying the necessary data inputs for linear programming problems. Obviously no solution methods can overcome basic deficiencies present in the input data for that algorithm; thus the generation of acceptable solutions using linear programming methods sets certain data requirements which must be met by management.

A second area is the concept of "alternate optima." This term refers to the situation where the linear programming problem has not one but multiple solutions, each of which is optimum. There are cases where management may be indifferent as between several of these alternate optimum solutions; there are also cases where one of these solutions may have certain benefits which make it preferred to the other solutions when one considers the original linear programming problem in a broader sense.

A third problem which arises in some linear programming solutions is called "degeneracy." This condition appears in the solution procedure when we are attempting to determine which particular variable in the current solution is replaced by the entering variable. In the method discussed in Chapters 4 and 5, we illustrated a simple calculation to be performed on each row in the simplex table and indicated the appropriate criterion for choice among all the rows. Degeneracy refers to the situation where the results of two or more of these calculations are identical. A procedure for resolving degeneracy will be illustrated later in this chapter.

The final problem to be treated in this chapter is one referred to as "redundancy." Often in preparing the restraints for a linear programming problem we encounter the case where the system of equations or inequalities is overdefined; i.e., we include more restraints than are really necessary for the solution of the problem. A simple illustration of this situation would be the case where we have two restraints like the following: $X_1 \geq 6$, $X_1 \geq 7$. Obviously the first restraint is redundant and need not be included in the problem. But when the restraints are much more numerous and complex the problem of recognizing redundancy is not nearly this simple, and in these cases, a more formalized approach to the solution of this situation is required.

## Data requirements

In Chapter 1, we reviewed briefly the concept of linearity as applied to linear programming problems. We illustrated why "contribution" instead of profit was an appropriate criterion for use in maximizing problems. Contribution was defined as revenue per unit minus variable cost per unit. Because linear programming problems place a very definite input data requirement on the user of this technique, some additional comment in this area may be productive.

To meet the requirement of linear input data, an organization considering the use of linear programming for a contribution maximization situation must have an operating cost system which isolates variable and fixed cost components (a contribution or direct costing system) rather than one which mixes the two (often called a full or absorption costing system). Direct costing as a cost accounting technique is about 30 years old and is in use by many firms as a basis for management decisions. These systems, if properly designed and used, generate quite acceptable data for linear programming applications.

There is one specific data requirement, however, which must be met by any cost accounting system before linear programming solutions can have operational meaning. When a contribution coefficient is assigned to each variable in a product mix problem for example, we assume that this value will be reliable over a wide range of volume variations in the production of that product. Suppose for example that $X_1$ represents a certain product and that its contribution coefficient is $1.50 per unit. Linear programming assumes that this $1.50 value will be a true representation of the per unit contribution of this product whether we manufacture 10 units, 10,000 units or 100,000 units, i.e., we assume a perfectly linear relationship between total production of this product and total accumulation of contribution. This is a severe requirement to place on any cost accounting system for several reasons. In the first place, production of very large quantities of this product will result in substantial reduction in raw material costs through quantity buying discounts. Then too, longer runs in the factory also reduce per unit labor costs because of the learning experience of employees. The possibility of applying better tooling methods may also produce per unit cost savings and thus increase per unit contribution. Finally, certain *combinations* of input variables have a distinct effect upon the cost and therefore contribution of each other.

Quite obviously, there is no cost accounting system which can take account of these and related factors and produce a single per unit contribution value which will retain its validity through wide ranges of volume. The operational significance of this fact is simply that the linear programming user must realize that solutions involving quantities of products markedly different from those anticipated when cost accounting data were generated have built-in deficiencies and thus operational limitations.

There are several practical solutions to this problem. It is possible to employ certain advanced techniques in mathematical programming which allow cost and contribution functions to be expressed in nonlinear terms; these techniques, however, are beyond the scope of a book such as this.[1] A second approach is to limit the solution variables in the problem to a certain range within which we know cost and contribution data will be nearly constant. This can be accomplished by the use of appropriate restraint inequalities. In this way the final solution obtained will be operational, though not necessarily optimal.

A third workable solution to this problem of nonlinearity in input data is to express each possible solution variable in multiple terms. For example, if we have good reason to expect that the contribution of a certain product is affected by the volume in which it is produced (even after the fixed components of cost have been removed) we might express that variable as shown in Figure 7–1.

FIGURE 7–1

Multiple Notation for Possible Solution Variables

(Variable Defined: Cotton Print Cloth; Style 115–S)

|  | *Contribution per yard on this quantity* |
|---|---|
| $X_1$: production below 1,000 yards.............. | \$0.060 |
| $X_2$: production between 1,001–8,000 yards........ | 0.065 |
| $X_3$: production between 8,001–20,000 yards....... | 0.070 |

Having set up our table of per yard contributions, we would write restraints as follows:

$$X_1 \leq 1,000$$
$$X_2 \geq 1,001$$
$$X_2 \leq 8,000$$
$$X_3 \geq 8,001$$
$$X_3 \leq 20,000$$

(each of the three variables $X_1$, $X_2$, and $X_3$ carries a different $C_j$ value)

Suppose now that the solution to this program because of certain marketing restraints was 1,500 yards of style 115–S; then $X_2$ would appear in the final solution and $X_1$ and $X_3$ would not appear; the con-

---

[1] Readers interested in nonlinear programming are referred to the following references: R. Bellman, "The Theory of Dynamic Programming," *Modern Mathematics for the Engineer* (New York: McGraw-Hill Book Co., 1956), chap. 11. A. Charnes and C. E. Lemke, "Minimization of Non-Linear Separable Functions," (Graduate School of Industrial Administration, Carnegie Institute of Technology, Pittsburgh, Pa., 1954), H. W. Kunn and A. W. Tucker, "Non-linear Programming," *Proceedings of the Second Berkeley Symposium on Mathematical Statistics and Probability* (Berkeley, Calif.: University of California Press, 1951).

tribution would be $0.065 per yard. Another example: suppose that because of production restraints, the production of style 115–S were limited to 900 yards; in this case, $X_1$ would appear in the final solution and $X_2$ and $X_3$ would not; the contribution per yard of cloth produced in this case would be $0.060. In any event, only one of the $X$ variables above could appear in the final solution; by using this multiple notation however, we assure ourselves that the variable which does appear carries the proper contribution per yard produced. In Chapter 8, "Some Economic Considerations in Linear Programming," we shall present some additional material concerning the use of multiple variables.

By no means is the cost accounting problem of providing applicable input data the only one which faces the firm desiring to employ this solution technique. Physical requirements of products, viz a viz, production time required per unit, raw material requirements per unit, production machines required, and the like are also the concern of management. The industrial engineering department or methods and standards department of a company generally supplies this type data from which cost accounting standard costs are later produced. Estimated standard times for production operations when compared with analytically determined standard times are a poor substitute. It is impossible to derive meaningful linear programming solutions when facility capacities, per unit operating times, and associated costs are not available. And finally, in this regard, marketing requirements of linear programming problems play an equally important role in the success of the technique. The solutions to production problems have no meaning without being related to the marketing needs of the organization. Being unable or unwilling to state marketing restraints in quantitative terms means simply that the problem will be solved as a production problem instead of a company problem.

Another problem encountered in applying linear programming concerns the concept of "setup" cost, a fixed charge associated with production of one "batch" or "lot" of product. This charge may include administrative costs required to instigate production, engineering costs, and the cost of setting up the machinery for production. In many cases, this fixed cost is incurred regardless of the number of units produced, and thus if it is included in cost data, the requirement of linearity of costs is violated. Though setup costs cannot be treated using standard linear programming methods, it can be handled by a method developed by Alan S. Manne,[2] or by an integer method using integer constraints developed by R. E. Gomory.[3] Another less-satisfactory approach is an examination of the final solution generated by the algorithm to determine the magnitude of setups and their total cost; this figure may then be subtracted from the indicated total contribution provided by that solution to obtain a figure representing "net-contribution." The methods for nonlinear programming cited in the footnote on page 191 of this chapter can also be used in nonlinear formulations of this type.

In concluding this section on input data requirements, we must bear in mind that seldom does any operational problem completely satisfy the requirements of the solution technique. This fact, however, does not prevent us from utilizing linear programming techniques to yield improved solutions to problems; it merely requires that we be cognizant of our input data limitations and that we analyze the solutions which are generated in light of what we know to be deficiencies or imperfections.

**Alternate optima**

In Chapter 2, we found that linear programming problems may have alternate optima. Graphically, this case occurs when the objective function is parallel to one of the constraints defining the feasible solutions area. From a managerial point of view, the identification of alternate optima is frequently important, since the manager then has the opportunity to select the one that best suits his strategy.

How are alternate optima identified in the simplex method? To identify alternate optima in the simplex method, we examine the zeros in the $C_j - Z_j$ row of the final table. If a zero appears under a variable that is *not* in the solution, then an alternate solution exists. To obtain this alternate solution, the zero is treated as if it were a positive number (or negative in a minimization problem) and the simplex computational steps are applied in the regular way.

As an example of an alternate solution, consider a product mix

---

[2] A. S. Manne, "On the Job Shop Scheduling Problem," *Cowles Commission for Research in Economics*, Contract 358(01) NR 047-066 (Washington, D.C: Office of Naval Research, 1959).

[3] R. E. Gomory, "Essentials of an Algorithm for Integer Solutions to Linear Programs," *Bulletin of the American Mathematical Society*, Vol. 64 (1958).

problem where three products must be processed through four departments. Mathematically the problem is:

Maximize $Z = \$8X_1 + \$12X_2 + \$10X_3$

Subject to:

$$4X_1 + 8X_2 + 4X_3 \leq 120 \text{ hours} \qquad \text{(Dept. 1)}$$
$$9X_1 + 4X_2 + 16X_3 \leq 240 \text{ hours} \qquad \text{(Dept. 2)}$$
$$24X_1 + 12X_2 + 16X_3 \leq 500 \text{ hours} \qquad \text{(Dept. 3)}$$
$$20X_1 + 16X_2 + 24X_3 \leq 500 \text{ hours.} \qquad \text{(Dept. 4)}$$

Using the simplex method, the optimum solution is reached after the third iteration. The third and final simplex table is shown in Figure 7-2.

FIGURE 7-2

| $C_j$ | | | $8 | $12 | $10 | $0 | $0 | $0 | $0 |
|---|---|---|---|---|---|---|---|---|---|
| | Mix | Quantity | $X_1$ | $X_2$ | $X_3$ | $S_1$ | $S_2$ | $S_3$ | $S_4$ |
| $12 | $X_2$ | $8\frac{4}{7}$ | 1/4 | 1 | 0 | 1/7 | -1/28 | 0 | 0 |
| $10 | $X_3$ | $12\frac{6}{7}$ | 1/2 | 0 | 1 | -1/28 | 1/14 | 0 | 0 |
| $0 | $S_3$ | $191\frac{3}{7}$ | 13 | 0 | 0 | -8/7 | -5/7 | 1 | 0 |
| $0 | $S_4$ | $54\frac{2}{7}$ | 4 | 0 | 0 | -10/7 | -8/7 | 0 | 1 |
| $Z_j$ | | $231\frac{3}{7}$ | 8 | 12 | 10 | 19/14 | 2/7 | 0 | 0 |
| $C_j - Z_j$ | | | 0 | 0 | 0 | -19/14 | -2/7 | 0 | 0 |

In this final simplex table, we find five zeros in the $C_j - Z_j$ row appearing under the variables $X_1$, $X_2$, $X_3$, $S_3$, and $S_4$. Of these five variables, only one, $X_1$, is not in the final solution shown in the mix column. Hence an alternate solution exists. As previously stated, to obtain the alternate solution, we treat this zero as if it were a positive number. The variable $X_1$ will enter the new solution. Applying the $\theta$ rule, we determine how many units of $X_1$ will enter the new solution:

$$8\tfrac{4}{7} \div \tfrac{1}{4} = 34\tfrac{2}{7}$$
$$12\tfrac{6}{7} \div \tfrac{1}{2} = 25\tfrac{5}{7}$$
$$191\tfrac{3}{7} \div 13 = 14\tfrac{66}{91}$$
$$54\tfrac{2}{7} \div 4 = 13\tfrac{4}{7}.$$

Thus $13\frac{4}{7}$ units of product $X_1$ will enter the next solution. Continuing the regular computational process, the alternate solution shown in Figure 7-3 is obtained.

FIGURE 7-3
Alternate Optimal Solution

| $C_j$ | | | $8 | $12 | $10 | $0 | $0 | $0 | $0 |
|---|---|---|---|---|---|---|---|---|---|
| | Mix | Quantity | $X_1$ | $X_2$ | $X_3$ | $S_1$ | $S_2$ | $S_3$ | $S_4$ |
| $12 | $X_2$ | $5\frac{5}{28}$ | 0 | 1 | 0 | $13/56$ | $1/28$ | 0 | $-1/16$ |
| $10 | $X_3$ | $6\frac{1}{14}$ | 0 | 0 | 1 | $1/7$ | $3/14$ | 0 | $-1/8$ |
| $0 | $S_3$ | $10\frac{5}{14}$ | 0 | 0 | 0 | $49/14$ | 3 | 1 | $-13/4$ |
| $8 | $X_1$ | $13\frac{4}{7}$ | 1 | 0 | 0 | $-5/14$ | $-2/7$ | 0 | $1/4$ |
| | $Z_j$ | $\$231\frac{3}{7}$ | 8 | 12 | 10 | $19/14$ | $2/7$ | 0 | 0 |
| | $C_j - Z_j$ | | 0 | 0 | 0 | $-19/14$ | $-2/7$ | 0 | 0 |

Note that the maximum expected profit ($231\frac{3}{7}$) in the alternate solution is the same as that found in the original optimum solution. The only difference is in the product mix. In the original optimum solution, only two products, $X_2$ and $X_3$, are in the mix. In the alternate solution all three products are produced. If production of product $X_1$ is necessary to achieve a balanced product line, then the manager could choose the alternate solution, without diminishing his expected maximum profit. On the other hand, if product $X_1$ is not necessary to achieve a balanced product line, he may choose the first optimum solution in order to take advantage of the savings in working time in departments 3 and 4. For example, the computation of the time involved in these two programs is as follows.

The first optimum solution:

$$
\begin{array}{lll}
4(0) + 8(8\frac{4}{7}) + 4(12\frac{6}{7}) = & 120 \text{ hours} & \text{(Dept. 1)} \\
9(0) + 4(8\frac{4}{7}) + 16(12\frac{6}{7}) = & 240 \text{ hours} & \text{(Dept. 2)} \\
24(0) + 12(8\frac{4}{7}) + 16(12\frac{6}{7}) = & 308\frac{4}{7} \text{ hours} & \text{(Dept. 3)} \\
20(0) + 16(8\frac{4}{7}) + 24(12\frac{6}{7}) = & 445\frac{5}{7} \text{ hours} & \text{(Dept. 4)} \\
\hline
\text{Total hours required} & 1,114\frac{2}{7}
\end{array}
$$

The second optimum solution:

$$
\begin{array}{lll}
4(13\frac{4}{7}) + 8(5\frac{5}{28}) + 4(6\frac{1}{4}) = & 120 \text{ hours} & \text{(Dept. 1)} \\
9(13\frac{4}{7}) + 4(5\frac{5}{28}) + 16(6\frac{1}{4}) = & 240 \text{ hours} & \text{(Dept. 2)} \\
24(13\frac{4}{7}) + 12(5\frac{5}{28}) + 16(6\frac{1}{4}) = & 489\frac{9}{14} \text{ hours} & \text{(Dept. 3)} \\
20(13\frac{4}{7}) + 16(5\frac{5}{28}) + 24(6\frac{1}{4}) = & 500 \text{ hours} & \text{(Dept. 4)} \\
\hline
\text{Total hours required} & 1,349\frac{9}{14}
\end{array}
$$

The first optimum solution yields a total saving of $235\frac{5}{14}$ hours with respect to the second optimum solution. The hours saved in departments 3 and 4 might profitably be used for some other purpose. Furthermore, in deciding which alternate solution to use, the manager may base his decision on factors that were not included in the mathematical formulation of the problem, such as customer goodwill or employee reaction.

Looking again at the $C_j - Z_j$ row of the alternate optimum solution (Figure 7–3), we find a zero under the slack variable, $S_4$, which is not included in the alternate solution. Treating this zero as a positive number and developing another table would give the original optimum solution again. This is as expected since $X_1$ replaced $S_4$ in the alternate solution.

Another question might be asked here: What would happen if we treated one of the zeros under a variable already in the solution as a positive number? The answer is that no change at all would take place in the table. An alternate optimum solution occurs only when a zero appears under a variable not already in the solution.

In large-scale linear programming problems, it is not unusual to find at least one of these zeros representing alternate optima present in the final table. In some cases, there may be several alternate optima.

### Redundant constraints

The computational time required to solve linear programming problems increases a great deal as the number of constraints and variables increases. As shown in Chapter 2, some constraints in a problem have no effect on the solution of the problem. For example, if there are two constraints, $X_1 \leq 10$ and $X_1 \leq 15$, the second constraint is redundant. The constraint stating that $X_1$ must be less than or equal to 10 eliminates the need for the restraint that $X_1$ must be less than or equal to 15.

Unfortunately, not all redundant constraints are as easily recognized as in the preceding example. Suppose that we have the following constraints in a problem:

$$11X_1 + 7X_2 \leq 77 \qquad (1)$$
$$12X_1 + 10X_2 \leq 132 \qquad (2)$$
$$7X_1 + 6X_2 \geq 42 \qquad (3)$$
$$3X_1 + 5X_2 \geq 15 \qquad (4)$$

Let us examine the first and second constraints which represent the less-than or equal-to type of inequality. By comparing the terminal points for each of these two constraints, we can determine if redundancy exists. The terminal points for constraints (1) and (2) are given below:

When

|  |  | (1) | (2) |
|---|---|---|---|
| $X_2 = 0$, | $X_1 =$ | 7 | 11 |
| $X_1 = 0$, | $X_2 =$ | 11 | 13.2 |

Recall that the values, $X_1 = 7$ and $X_2 = 11$, for constraint (1) and the values, $X_1 = 11$ and $X_2 = 13.2$, for constraint (2) represent the axis intercepts, i.e., the points at which the lines of these constraints cross the $X_1$ and $X_2$ axes. Now note that for each variable, $X_1$ and $X_2$, in constraint (2) the axis intercepts are greater than the corresponding axis intercepts of constraint (1).

|  | (2) |  | (1) |
|---|---|---|---|
| $X_1$ intercept: | 11 | > | 7 |
| $X_2$ intercept: | 13.2 | > | 11. |

This means that constraint (2) is redundant. Why? All positive values of $X_1$ and $X_2$ that satisfy constraint (1) also satisfy constraint (2). For example, the terminal points for the first constraint, (0, 11) and (7, 0), satisfy constraint (2). But the reverse is not true. The terminal points for constraint (2), (11, 0) and (0, 13.2) satisfy constraint (2) but not constraint (1). For example:

$$
\begin{array}{lll}
\text{First constraint:} & 11X_1 + 7X_2 & \leq 77 \\
(11, 0): & 11(11) + 7(0) & = 121 \\
(0, 13, 2): & 11(0) + 7(13.2) & = 92.4.
\end{array}
$$

The first constraint is more restrictive than the second; therefore, the second constraint is redundant and can be eliminated from the problem without affecting the optimum solution.

A similar situation exists between constraint (3) and constraint (4), representing the greater-than or equal-to type of inequalities. The axis intercepts of these two constraints are:

When

|  |  | (3) | (4) |
|---|---|---|---|
| $X_2 = 0$, | $X_1 =$ | 6 | 5 |

When

|  |  |  |  |
|---|---|---|---|
| $X_1 = 0$, | $X_2 =$ | 7 | 3. |

In this case, since the axis intercepts of constraint (4) are less than the corresponding axis intercepts of constraint (3), the fourth constraint is redundant. In this case, all positive values of $X_1$ and $X_2$ that satisfy constraint (3) also satisfy constraint (4). For example, the terminal points for the third constraint, (6, 0) and (0, 7), satisfy the fourth constraint. However, the terminal points of the fourth constraint, (5, 0) and (0, 3), satisfy the fourth but not the third. For example:

$$\text{Third constraint:}\quad 7X_1 + 6X_2 \geq 42$$
$$(5, 0): \quad 7(5) + 6(0) = 35$$
$$(0, 3): \quad 7(0) + 6(3) = 18.$$

This means that the third constraint is more restrictive than the fourth. Thus the fourth constraint is redundant and can be dropped from the problem.

By eliminating the redundant constraints (2) and (4), we have reduced the problem from one of four constraints to one of two constraints, thus decreasing the amount of computational work. Furthermore the two constraints,

$$11X_1 + 7X_2 \leq 77 \tag{1}$$
$$7X_1 + 6X_2 \geq 42 \tag{3}$$

together with some objective function, will have the same optimum solution as that obtained using the four constraints. This can be seen more clearly in Figure 7–4, showing the graphs of the four constraints and the feasible solutions area *ABCD* defined by constraints (1) and (3).

Since the axis intercepts of constraint (2) are greater than the corresponding axis intercepts of constraint (1), the lines do not intersect in the area of feasible solutions. Since these two constraints represent less than or equal to conditions, constraint (2) is redundant. A similar explanation applies to constraints (3) and (4) representing greater than or equal to conditions. The axis intercepts of constraint (4) are less than the corresponding axis intercepts of constraint (3). Thus constraint (4) is redundant.

In summary, the following rules may be used to test for redundancy.

1. *For less than or equal to conditions.*   Given two constraints *A* and *B*, if the axis intercepts of *A* are *greater* than the corresponding axis intercepts of *B*, then *A* is redundant.

2. *For greater than or equal to conditions.*   Given two constraints *A*

FIGURE 7-4

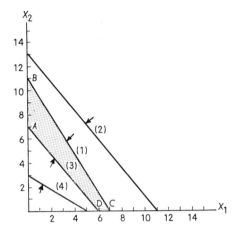

and $B$, if the axis intercepts of $A$ are *less* than the corresponding axis intercepts of $B$, then $A$ is redundant.

3. If, in either type of inequality, the axis intercepts of $A$ are *equal* to the corresponding axis intercepts of $B$, the two inequalities are identical and either is redundant

In addition to reducing the computational work, we are concerned with eliminating redundant constraints for another reason. In some cases, redundant constraints will lead to degenerate solutions. How to recognize and resolve degeneracy in the simplex method is discussed in the following section.

**Degeneracy**

Degeneracy, previously discussed with the stepping-stone method, can also be encountered in the simplex method. Recall that choosing the largest positive number (negative in minimization) in the $C_j - Z_j$ row identifies the variable *entering* the next solution. Then, by applying the $\theta$ rule and choosing the smallest nonnegative ratio, we identify the variable that is *replaced* in the next solution. In some cases, the smallest nonnegative ratios for two or more variables currently in the solution may be the same. When such a tie occurs, the problem is degenerate. Since, in this case, replacing one of the tied variables will also reduce the other tied variable(s) to zero, the question arises as to which variable to remove from the solution.

Although degeneracy does not occur too frequently, it must be recognized and resolved correctly or a great deal of work and effort can go to waste. Two things may happen if the degenerate condition is not resolved correctly. First, arbitrary removal of one of the tied variables may require a greater number of iterations to obtain the optimum solution than would be the case if some other tied variable were replaced in the solution. Second, if one of the tied variables is arbitrarily selected, the problem may begin to cycle or continue indefinitely without reaching an optimum solution. In other words, we may begin with some solution and, after several iterations, return to the same solution, so that an optimum solution may never be attained.

To demonstrate one procedure for resolving degeneracy, let us consider the following product mix problem.

Maximize

$$Z = \$20X_1 + \$30X_2 + \$21X_3$$

Subject to:

$$4X_1 + 4X_2 + 0X_3 \leq 256 \qquad \text{(Dept. 1)}$$
$$4X_1 + 2X_2 + \phantom{0}X_3 \leq 200 \qquad \text{(Dept. 2)}$$
$$2X_1 + 4X_2 + 3X_3 \leq 256 \qquad \text{(Dept. 3)}$$

The first simplex table for this problem is shown in Figure 7–5.

FIGURE 7–5
A Degenerate Problem

| $C_j$ | Mix | Quantity | $\$0$ $S_1$ | $\$0$ $S_2$ | $\$0$ $S_3$ | $\$20$ $X_1$ | $\$30$ $X_2$ | $\$21$ $X_3$ | $\theta$ Ratios |
|---|---|---|---|---|---|---|---|---|---|
| $\$0$ | $S_1$ | 256 | 1 | 0 | 0 | 4 | 4 | 0 | $256/4 = 64$ |
| $\$0$ | $S_2$ | 200 | 0 | 1 | 0 | 4 | 2 | 1 | $200/2 = 100$ |
| $\$0$ | $S_3$ | 256 | 0 | 0 | 1 | 2 | 4 | 3 | $256/4 = 64$ |
| | $Z_j$ | 0 | 0 | 0 | 0 | 0 | 0 | 0 | |
| | $C_j - Z_j$ | | $\$0$ | $\$0$ | $\$0$ | $\$20$ | $\$30$ | $\$21$ | |

The $\theta$ ratios have been computed in Figure 7–5, and we see that a tie exists between variables $S_1$ and $S_3$ ($\theta = 64$). Hence the problem is degenerate. The variable $X_2$ having the highest positive value in the $C_j - Z_j$ row will enter the next solution. The question arises as to which variable, $S_1$ or $S_3$, will be replaced in the next solution.

In this case, both departments 1 and 3 are the limiting departments. Introducing 64 units of $X_2$ at this stage will require all the time available in these two departments. This means that both $S_1$ and $S_3$ will be equal to zero in our next solution. In the problems discussed in previous chapters, we never encountered a situation in which more than one variable at a time had to be replaced from a given solution. A procedure is therefore necessary to break the tie between variables $S_1$ and $S_3$ so that only one is chosen as the replaced variable in the next solution.

Before presenting the procedure for breaking the tie (resolving the degeneracy) between variables $S_1$ and $S_2$, let us note that the first simplex table has been set up so that the slack variables appear first followed by the real product variables. Up to this point, we have used the reverse procedure in setting up the simplex table. This change in the format of the table has no effect on the computational rules or outcome of the problem. It does, however, lend itself to the application of the procedure for resolving degeneracy.

In applying the $\theta$ rule we divide each number in the quantity column by the corresponding number in the column representing the variable entering the next solution, $X_2$ in our problem. Hence, the $\theta$ ratios are:

$$\begin{array}{lll} \text{Row 1} & 256/4 = & 64 \\ \text{Row 2} & 200/2 = & 100 \\ \text{Row 3} & 256/4 = & 64. \end{array}$$

Let us refer to the divisors, 4, 2, and 4, as the *key column numbers*. The procedure for resolving degeneracy then is as follows:

1. Divide each number in the "tied" rows by its key column number.

2. Compare the ratios obtained in step 1, column by column, from left to right beginning with the first variable column. The first time the ratios are unequal, the tie is broken.

3. Select as that variable to be replaced the variable with the algebraically smaller ratio.

Applying the above procedure to our problem, we divide each number in the $S_1$ and $S_3$ rows, the tied rows or variables, by its corresponding key column number. In this case the key column number for both rows is the same, 4.

$S_1$ row   $1/4 = 1/4,\ 0/4 = 0,\ 0/4 = 0,\quad 4/4 = 1,\quad 4/4 = 1,\ 0/4 = 0$

$S_3$ row   $0/4 = 0,\quad 0/4 = 0,\ 1/4 = 1/4,\ 2/4 = 1/2,\ 4/4 = 1,\ 3/4 = 3/4$

The tie is broken with the computation of the first ratios. For the $S_1$ row, $1/4 = 1/4$ and for the $S_3$ row $0/4 = 0$. Since the smallest algebraic ratio occurs for row $S_3$, we choose variable $S_3$ as the variable to be replaced by $X_2$ in the next solution. Using the standard computational rules, we compute the second simplex table, Figure 7–6.

FIGURE 7–6
Second Simplex Table

| $C_j$ | Mix | Quantity | $0 $S_1$ | $0 $S_2$ | $0 $S_3$ | $20 $X_1$ | $30 $X_2$ | $21 $X_3$ | $\theta$ Ratios |
|---|---|---|---|---|---|---|---|---|---|
| $0 | $S_1$ | 0 | 1 | 0 | $-1$ | 2 | 0 | $-3$ | $0/2 = 0$ |
| $0 | $S_2$ | 72 | 0 | 1 | $-1/2$ | 3 | 0 | $-1/2$ | $72/3 = 24$ |
| $30 | $X_2$ | 64 | 0 | 0 | $1/4$ | $1/2$ | 1 | $3/4$ | $64/1/2 = 128$ |
| | $Z_j$ | 1,920 | 0 | 0 | $15/2$ | 15 | 30 | $22\ 1/2$ | |
| | $C_j - Z_j$ | | 0 | 0 | $-15/2$ | 5 | 0 | $-1\ 1/2$ | |

In Figure 7–6, since the largest positive number in the $C_j - Z_j$ row falls under column $X_1$, the variable $X_1$ is chosen to enter the next solution. Applying the $\theta$ rule, we find that row $S_1$ has the smallest nonnegative value. Hence, $X_1$ will replace $S_1$ in the next solution. How many units of $X_1$ can we add to the mix? Since the smallest nonnegative $\theta$ ratio is zero, we cannot really introduce any units of $X_1$. The procedure to follow at this point is to ignore this fact and carry out the usual computations to develop the third table, Figure 7-7.

FIGURE 7–7
Third Simplex Table

| $C_j$ | Mix | Quantity | 0 $S_1$ | 0 $S_2$ | 0 $S_3$ | 20 $X_1$ | 30 $X_2$ | 21 $X_3$ | $\theta$ Ratios |
|---|---|---|---|---|---|---|---|---|---|
| 20 | $X_1$ | 0 | $1/2$ | 0 | $-1/2$ | 1 | 0 | $-3/2$ | |
| 0 | $S_2$ | 72 | $-3/2$ | 1 | 1 | 0 | 0 | 4 | $72/4 = 18$ |
| 30 | $X_2$ | 64 | $-1/4$ | 0 | $1/2$ | 0 | 1 | $3/2$ | $64/\frac{3}{2} = 42\frac{2}{3}$ |
| | $Z_j$ | 1,920 | $5/2$ | 0 | 5 | 20 | 30 | 15 | |
| | $C_j - Z_j$ | | $-5/2$ | 0 | $-5$ | 0 | 0 | 6 | |

Note in the third table that we have a new solution but the profit is the same as that for the second table, namely $1,920. In those problems where degeneracy is encountered, it may be necessary to go through several such iterations, each producing a new solution but with no change in the value of the objective function. As we shall see in a moment, this is not the case in our problem.

Since only positive exchange rates need be examined in computing the $\theta$ ratios, $X_1$, with an exchange rate of $-3/2$, is not a candidate for replacement. The third table shows that $X_3$ will enter the next solution replacing $S_2$. The fourth and final table is shown in Figure 7-8.

FIGURE 7-8
Final Simplex Table

| $C_j$ | Mix | Quantity | 0 $S_1$ | 0 $S_2$ | 0 $S_3$ | 20 $X_1$ | 30 $X_2$ | 21 $X_3$ |
|---|---|---|---|---|---|---|---|---|
| 20 | $X_1$ | 27 | $-1/16$ | $3/8$ | $-1/8$ | 1 | 0 | 0 |
| 21 | $X_3$ | 18 | $-3/8$ | $1/4$ | $1/4$ | 0 | 0 | 1 |
| 30 | $X_2$ | 37 | $5/16$ | $-3/8$ | $1/8$ | 0 | 1 | 0 |
| | $Z_j$ | 2,028 | $1/4$ | $3/4$ | $3/2$ | 20 | 30 | 21 |
| | $C_j - Z_j$ | | $-1/4$ | $-3/4$ | $-3/2$ | 0 | 0 | 0 |

The procedure used in resolving the degeneracy in our problem is a general one and applies equally well, regardless of problem size, at any iteration of the problem, not only in the initial table as was the case in the above problem. It should be pointed out that in practical applications of linear programming, degeneracy is not encountered too often. This is particularly true when the problems are solved by electronic computers which can carry the computations to a sufficient number of decimals so that rounding and approximation are greatly reduced. In other words, a problem may appear degenerate when figures are rounded to a few decimals; however, if the accuracy in calculation is increased, the degeneracy may disappear.

A question quite naturally arises here: What happens if a tie occurs between two or more variables in the $C_j - Z_j$ row? The answer is that a tie between two variables in the $C_j - Z_j$ row is not a degenerate condition. Either one of the variables may be arbitrarily chosen as the variable to enter the next solution. The choice in some cases may affect the number of iterations but not the final result.

## Problems

1. A certain company produces two products (A and B). The products are both processed in two departments (1 and 2). The table below indicates the unit contribution from each product and the time requirements in each department.

|  | Product A | Product B |
|---|---|---|
| *Unit Contribution* | $10 | $5 |
| Department 1......... | 6 hours | 4 hours |
| Department 2......... | 2 hours | 1 hour |

Department 1 has 64 man-hours available each day while department 2 has 68 hours available.

A production efficiency results when more than 10 units of product A are manufactured. Unit contribution for all units over 10 increases to $11.

Set up the equations necessary to solve for the optimum product mix and find the solution using the simplex method.

2. The XYZ company is involved in metal casting. XYZ has two main products which it manufactures. Each product is initially poured in the foundry and then finished and polished in the finishing department. Six men work in the foundry and four in the finishing department. The following data reflect the time required for processing in each of the two departments.

|  | Product A | Product B |
|---|---|---|
| Foundry.............. | 10 per Man-hour | 8 per Man-hour |
| Finishing Department... | 6 per Man-hour | 5 per Man-hour |
| Contribution per unit.... | $8.00 | $6.50 |

Each man works a 40-hour week for the firm. XYZ has found that they can gain a discount on the metal used for product A if they manufacture more than 800 units of A each week. Such a discount results in a unit contribution of $8.50 per unit rather than $8.

Formulate this problem in equation form. Also, set up the initial simplex table for the equation set(s).

3. Determine the optimal solution(s) to the following problem.

$$\text{Maximize} \quad Z = 4X_1 + 6X_2 + 5X_3$$

Subject to:
$$12X_1 + 24X_2 + 12X_3 \leq 360$$
$$27X_1 + 12X_2 + 48X_3 \leq 720$$
$$72X_1 + 36X_2 + 48X_3 \leq 1,500$$
$$60X_1 + 48X_2 + 72X_3 \leq 1,500$$

4. Test the following system of equations for redundancy and check by graphing the constraints.

$$X_1 + X_2 \geq 15$$
$$5X_1 + 6X_2 \geq 100$$
$$6X_1 + 4X_2 \geq 108$$
$$25X_1 + 10X_2 \leq 425$$
$$10X_1 + 15X_2 \leq 700.$$

5. Test the following equations for redundancy and solve by the simplex method.

$$\text{Maximize} \quad Z = 14X_1 + 8X_2$$

Subject to:
$$21X_1 + 12X_2 \leq 120$$
$$7X_1 + 4X_2 \leq 36$$
$$X_1 + X_2 = 2.$$

6. Test the following equations for redundancy and solve by the simplex method.

$$\text{Maximize} \quad Z = 5X_1 + 10X_2 + 5X_3$$

Subject to:
$$X_1 + X_2 + X_3 \leq 25$$
$$5X_1 + 3X_2 + 4X_3 \geq 35$$
$$3X_1 + 5X_2 + X_3 \geq 40$$
$$12X_1 + 10X_2 + 12X_3 \leq 350.$$

7. Given the following tableau, resolve the degenerate condition and solve for the optimal solution.

| $C_j$ | Mix | Quantity | $5 $X_1$ | $6 $X_2$ | $4 $X_3$ | $0 $S_1$ | $0 $S_2$ | $0 $S_3$ |
|---|---|---|---|---|---|---|---|---|
| $5 | $X_1$ | 15 | 1 | 1/2 | 1/3 | 1/2 | 0 | 0 |
| $0 | $S_2$ | 50 | 0 | 2 | 4 | 1 | 1 | 0 |
| $0 | $S_2$ | 75 | 0 | 3 | 5 | 2 | 0 | 1 |
| | $Z_j$ | | 5 | 5/2 | 5/3 | 5/2 | 0 | 0 |
| | $C_j - Z_j$ | | 0 | 7/2 | 7/3 | -5/2 | 0 | 0 |

8. Solve the following problem by the simplex method.

$$\text{Maximize: } Z = 20X_1 + 25X_2 + 20X_3$$

Subject to:

$$3X_1 + 4X_2 + 5X_3 \leq 90$$
$$12X_1 + 12X_2 + 10X_3 \leq 240$$
$$10X_1 + 8X_2 + 5X_3 \leq 160.$$

# chapter 8

# Some economic considerations in linear programming

## Introduction

The major use of linear programming in business today is finding better methods of combining the factors of production to achieve the desired goals of an organization. We have seen examples of its use in finding the most profitable combination of products when production restraints are known; we have also seen linear programming used to determine the best method of preparing a mixture of ingredients when the costs of each ingredient and the requirements of the final mixture are known.

Aside from these two types of solutions (maximization of contribution and minimization of total cost), there are many other possible uses of linear programming. Although space will not permit enumerating all of these uses, an examination of some basic economic principles involved in linear programming will illustrate just how flexible the technique is, and will enable the reader to appreciate additional possibilities for its application in organizations today. In this chapter we shall illustrate the inherent flexibility of linear programming in solving many types of problems and ways in which management can extract and use the additional relevant information which is generated at the same time the solution to the basic problem is found. The three major concepts to be treated in this chapter are (1) the economic concept of *alternate criteria*, (2) the economic concept of the *dual* in linear programming, and (3) the case where the cost of resources changes at specific volume levels. *Alternate criteria* refers to the situation where management might want to change the economic criterion on which the solution is determined and evaluated. For example, in a product mix problem such as that illustrated first in Chapter 2, the management of a firm might well desire to determine that particular combination of possible products which produces the greatest total number of *units of output* instead of the greatest *total dollar contribution;* additionally, at a particular time, management might want to determine that combination of possible products which uses up all of the *available time* instead of that which maximizes total dollar contribution. Each of these possible alternative criteria will be discussed and examples of how to determine them given.

The second concept to be discussed in this chapter is that of the economic *dual* to a linear programming problem. The concept of the *dual* refers to another way of looking at a linear programming problem to generate additional information of use to management. For example, when a manager finds what particular combination of products maximizes the total contribution to fixed costs and profits, he might want additional information concerning how to invest capital profitably to remove those restraints to further production (and of course further profit). The use and understanding of the *dual* concept can provide this information; for that reason it is of great importance to management today.

A third concept to be covered in this chapter is the case where the prices of resources used in production change at various levels of output. This concept is often encountered in the treatment of overtime in manufacturing operations. For example, when products are produced during the regular working week (usually 40 hours) the cost of each unit produced includes an amount for wages calculated at regular wage rates. However, when the possibility of using overtime hours is considered (usually at a direct labor cost premium of 50 percent for those units produced during overtime), a special linear programming treatment must be used to ensure that the contribution from units produced during overtime hours will be reduced to reflect the increased labor cost. Another version of this same type of problem would be the use of shift work, where a small hourly premium is some-times paid to employees for work on the second and third shift. Cases such as this where the input price of certain resources changes at various volume levels can be effectively treated using the methods illustrated in this chapter.

## The concept of alternate criteria

The use of linear programming to obtain the one particular com-bination of products which maximizes the total contribution to fixed costs and profits has already been illustrated. Chapters 2, 3, and 4, presented three approaches to the same problem; in each case how-ever, the desired answer was the one particular combination of products which *maximized contribution*. In many cases, managers might want other alternative answers to the problem. For instance, in the short run, when orders have piled up, a manager might want to de-termine what particular combination of products will generate the largest total output in units, even with some sacrifice of contribution to achieve this end. In this case, he would concentrate on those products which take the least production time in order to maximize the total units of output. This would be using a different *criterion* for decision making but one which becomes important at various times in production-sales planning. Linear programming can yield the answer to this problem whenever it is desired.

Another example of alternate criteria would be the situation where the short-run objective is to use as much of the available productive capacity as is possible, again with some probable loss in contribution. When labor is paid a guaranteed wage per time period, the short-run emphasis might easily shift to using all of the available labor capacity instead of maximizing contribution. We must realize, however, that this is only a short-run objective; the long-run objective will generally always be the maximization of total contribution to fixed costs and profits. Finding optimum answers to problems involving the fullest possible use of available resources can be achieved by using linear programming. Each of these three alternative cases (1) maximum total contribution, (2) maximum production in units, and (3) minimum unused productive capacity, will be illustrated in detail using the same example.

Suppose that we have the problem illustrated in Figure 8–1.

FIGURE 8-1
Illustrative Problem for Three Alternative Criteria

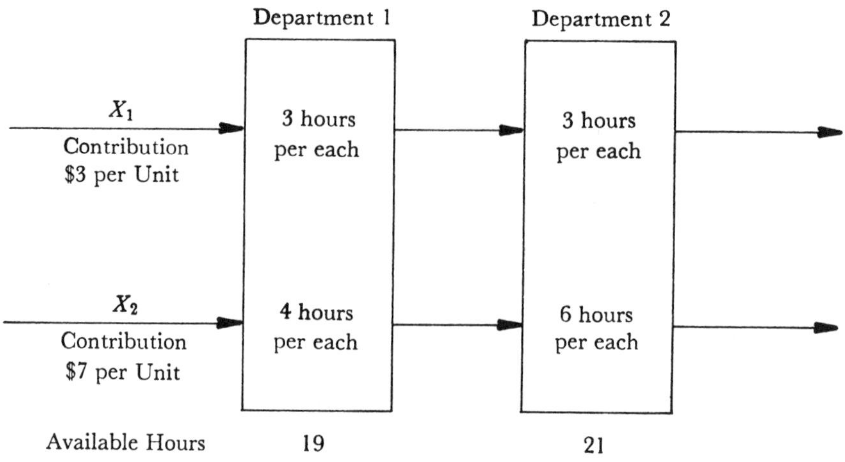

Beginning first with the mathematical statement of the relationships between the variables, and then adding appropriate slack variables according to the procedures used in Chapter 4, we have the following:

$$3X_1 + 4X_2 \leq 19 \qquad \text{Inequalities}$$
$$3X_1 + 6X_2 \leq 21$$

$$3X_1 + 4X_2 + S_1 = 19 \qquad \text{Slack Variables Added}$$
$$3X_1 + 6X_2 + S_2 = 21$$

$$3X_1 + 4X_2 + S_1 + 0S_2 = 19 \qquad \text{Balancing Variables Added}$$
$$3X_1 + 6X_2 + 0S_1 + S_2 = 21$$

Figure 8-2 illustrates the simplex solution to the problem when the criterion is maximum total contribution to fixed costs and profits. The method used is that illustrated in Chapter 4. The optimum solution for maximum total contribution is achieved in two tables; it involves production of $3\frac{1}{2}$ units of $X_2$ and zero units of $X_1$ and generates a total contribution of \$24.50. We observe from the second table of Figure 8-2 that five hours of production time in the first department, $S_1$, remain unused with this solution.

FIGURE 8-2
Maximum Contribution Solution

| $C_j$ | | | $3 | $7 | $0 | $0 | |
|---|---|---|---|---|---|---|---|
| | MIX | QTY. | $X_1$ | $X_2$ | $S_1$ | $S_2$ | |
| $0 | $S_1$ | 19 | 3 | 4 | 1 | 0 | $19/4 = 4\frac{3}{4}$ |
| $0 | $S_2$ | 21 | 3 | 6 | 0 | 1 | $21/6 = 3\frac{1}{2}$ ← OUT |
| | $Z_j$ | | $0 | $0 | $0 | $0 | $0 |
| | $C_j - Z_j$ | | $3 | $7 | $0 | $0 | |

↑ IN

| $C_j$ | | | $3 | $7 | $0 | $0 | *Optimum Solution* |
|---|---|---|---|---|---|---|---|
| | MIX | QTY. | $X_1$ | $X_2$ | $S_1$ | $S_2$ | (To maximize |
| $0 | $S_1$ | 5 | 1 | 0 | 1 | $-2/3$ | contribution) |
| $7 | $X_2$ | 3 1/2 | 1/2 | 1 | 0 | 1/6 | $3\frac{1}{2}$ $X_2$ |
| | $Z_j$ | $24\frac{1}{2}$ | $3\frac{1}{2}$ | $7 | $0 | $7/6 | 0  $X_1$ |
| | $C_j - Z_j$ | | $-1/2$ | $0 | $0 | $-7/6 | Total Contribution |

$$3\frac{1}{2} \times \$7 = \$24.50$$

## Obtaining the maximum production solution

Suppose now that management wants to determine the solution to this problem that would generate the maximum total output in units (and just how the dollar contribution would be affected by this new solution); we can procede as follows. The basic mathematical relationships must remain the same; the production we achieve must not exceed the capacity of either department. The significant difference between maximum contribution and maximum production will be in the economic values per unit we place on the two products $X_1$ and $X_2$.

When we state that we desire to achieve the maximum total production, we automatically infer that we are willing to accept some reduction in contribution if that should be a requirement in order to increase production. Thus the emphasis is now placed on *production*, not *contribution*. We logically want the simplex procedure to make decisions based on which product takes *minimum time* instead of which product generates *maximum contribution*. The easiest way to achieve this result is to assign the same dollar contribution value to both products and the simplest contribution to use is $1 per unit. Thus if we assign a contribution per unit of $1 to both of the products, we are showing *no preference* for either one of them (as far as contribution is concerned). Then, if we use the simplex maximizing procedure, it will still attempt to maximize contribution, but since both products contribute the

FIGURE 8–3
Maximum Production Solution

| $C_j$ | | | $1 | $1 | $0 | $0 | |
|---|---|---|---|---|---|---|---|
| | MIX | QTY. | $X_1$ | $X_2$ | $S_1$ | $S_2$ | |
| $0 | $S_1$ | 19 | 3 | 4 | 1 | 0 | $\theta$ $19/3 = 6\frac{1}{3}$ ◄— OUT |
| $0 | $S_2$ | 21 | 3 | 6 | 0 | 1 | $\theta$ $21/3 = 7$ |
| $Z_j$ | | $0 | 0 | 0 | 0 | 0 | |
| $C_j - Z_j$ | | | $1 | $1 | $0 | $0 | |

IN ↑

Since the $C_j - Z_j$ row involves a tie in this case, we shall let $X_1$ enter first.

| $C_j$ | | | $1 | $1 | $0 | $0 |
|---|---|---|---|---|---|---|
| | MIX | QTY. | $X_1$ | $X_2$ | $S_1$ | $S_2$ |
| $1 | $X_1$ | $6\frac{1}{3}$ | 1 | $4/3$ | $\frac{1}{3}$ | 0 |
| $0 | $S_2$ | 2 | 0 | 2 | $-1$ | 1 |
| $Z_j$ | | $19 | $1 | $4/3 | $\frac{1}{3}$ | $0 |
| $C_j - Z_j$ | | | $0 | $-\frac{1}{3}$ | $-\frac{1}{3}$ | $0 |

*Optimum Solution*                    *Total Contribution*
(To Maximize Production)

$6\frac{1}{3}$     $X_1$              $6\frac{1}{3} \times \$3 = \$19$
0       $X_2$

same per unit, it will favor that product which requires the fewest number of hours for its production. This procedure is illustrated in Figure 8–3. The reader will observe that the first table of Figure 8–3 is identical to the first table of Figure 8–2 with the exception that the contributions of both of the products are now $1.

The product mix which generates maximum production (in units) is the manufacture of $6\frac{1}{3}$ units of $X_1$ and zero units of $X_2$. Whereas this represents a significant increase in units produced ($6\frac{1}{3}$ versus $3\frac{1}{2}$) the total contribution which is generated decreases ($19 versus $24.50). We have thus gained additional production for some reduction in contribution. This maximum production solution also leaves department 2 with two production hours unused. Management need not commit themselves in advance to any one of the two alternate solutions (contribution or production) but can generate both of these solutions, notice the effect upon contribution of proposed changes in the criterion, and *then* make the decision as to whether the increased production was worth the sacrifice in contribution. The final decision would depend on a number of additional factors including customer satisfaction, etc., but with the information generated by linear programming, management would at least be in a position to know the cost of increasing production (measured in reduced contribution); their decision could then be based upon the best information available to them.

## Obtaining the minimum unused resources solution

The third criterion on which product mix decisions could be based would involve productive time available. Management might desire to determine what particular mix of possible products would most nearly use up all of the available productive time. This third criterion is often employed in inventory management. Suppose, for example, that a company has a large quantity of raw material of a semiperishable nature and desires to determine which production mix will utilize as much of this material as possible. They would then use the third criterion (minimum unused resources). Using linear programming to determine which combination most nearly utilizes all available resources, whatever their type may be, infers that management realizes that some reduction in total contribution to fixed cost and profit may result, but that in the short run at least, this policy has been determined to represent the best interests of the firm as a whole.

In these situations linear programming can offer a very effective decision-making tool.

For an example of this third criterion, we shall use the problem first illustrated in Figure 8–2 and attempt to minimize unused time in both departments. When management has decided that the emphasis must be placed on using productive resources, this must be reflected

FIGURE 8–4
Minimum Unused Time Solution

| $C_j$ | | | \$0 | \$0 | \$−1 | \$−1 | |
|---|---|---|---|---|---|---|---|
| | MIX | QTY. | $X_1$ | $X_2$ | $S_1$ | $S_2$ | |
| \$−1 | $S_1$ | 19 | 3 | 4 | 1 | 0 | $\theta\ 19/4 = 4\frac{3}{4}$ |
| \$−1 | $S_2$ | 21 | 3 | 6 | 0 | 1 | $\theta\ 21/6 = 3\frac{1}{2}$ ◄—OUT |
| | $Z_j$ | | \$−40 | \$−6 | \$−10 | \$−1 | \$−1 | |
| | $C_j - Z_j$ | | | \$6 | \$10 | \$0 | \$0 | |

↑ IN

| $C_j$ | | | \$0 | \$0 | \$−1 | \$−1 | |
|---|---|---|---|---|---|---|---|
| | MIX | QTY. | $X_1$ | $X_2$ | $S_1$ | $S_2$ | |
| \$−1 | $S_1$ | 5 | 1 | 0 | 1 | $-\frac{2}{3}$ | $\theta\ 5/1 = 5$ ◄—— OUT |
| \$0 | $X_2$ | $3\frac{1}{2}$ | $\frac{1}{2}$ | 1 | 0 | 1/6 | $\theta\ 3\frac{1}{2}/\frac{1}{2} = 7$ |
| | $Z_j$ | | \$−5 | \$−1 | \$0 | \$−1 | \$2/3 | |
| | $C_j - Z_j$ | | | \$1 | \$0 | \$0 | \$−5/3 | |

| $C_j$ | | | \$0 | \$0 | \$−1 | \$−1 |
|---|---|---|---|---|---|---|
| | MIX | QTY. | $X_1$ | $X_2$ | $S_1$ | $S_2$ |
| \$0 | $X_1$ | 5 | 1 | 0 | 1 | $-\frac{2}{3}$ |
| \$0 | $X_2$ | 1 | 0 | 1 | $-\frac{1}{2}$ | $\frac{1}{2}$ |
| | $Z_j$ | | \$0 | \$0 | \$0 | \$0 | \$0 |
| | $C_j - Z_j$ | | | \$0 | \$0 | \$−1 | \$−1 |

*Optimum Solution*
(To Minimize Unused Time)

$5X_1$
$1X_2$

*Total Contribution*

$5 \times \$3 = \$15$
$1 \times \$7 = \ \ \ 7$
$\overline{\$22}$

in the $C_j$ values we place on the variables in the problem. Since contribution is not the decision-making criterion in this case, neither of the products ($X_1$ and $X_2$) carries any contribution and their $C_j$ values are $0 as shown in Figure 8–4. This indicates that our concern has shifted away from contribution. Now that the objective is to minimize unused time, an unused hour represents an undesirable situation; thus unused hours carry a contribution value of $–1 each, in Figure 8–4. If we use the maximizing linear programming procedure with these $C_j$ values for each of the variables in the problem, it will attempt to maximize by getting rid of all of the unused time (using it in production) because even a product with a zero contribution per unit represents more contribution than an unused hour with $–1 contribution. The three simplex tables required for this solution are illustrated in Figure 8–4; the linear programming procedure used to generate the answer is that described in Chapter 4.

As an alternative approach, we could have assigned $S_1$ and $S_2$ contribution values of $ + 1 and used a minimizing simplex with the same results.

Figure 8–4 illustrates the product mix which uses all of the available time in both departments (the manufacture of five units of $X_1$ and one unit of $X_2$). This product mix generates a total contribution to fixed cost and a profit of $22, only slightly less than the maximum possible contribution of $24.50. In this case then, utilizing all of the available time in both departments reduces total contribution by $2.50; if in the mind of management this reduction is more than offset by the value of keeping both departments busy, this would represent an acceptable solution; if the reverse case is true, having unused time in one department (the solution in Figure 8–2) would still represent the best alternative open to management.

In Figure 8–5, we have illustrated the results of these three alternative solutions in tabular form. In this way the exact relationships between these three solutions can be observed, and the economic benefits which were gained (or lost) can be compared.

When management desires to maximize the profit of the firm as their operating criterion, this can best be done by maximizing the total contribution to fixed costs and profits as shown in criterion number one. When however, short-run decisions to operate under other criteria are made, the use of linear programming can tell in advance what sacrifices and what resulting benefits will obtain. When the true effects upon the firm of changes in decision-making criteria are

FIGURE 8–5
Results of Three Alternate Solutions

| Criterion | Total Dollar Contribution | Total Unit Production | Hours of Unused Time | |
|---|---|---|---|---|
| | | | Dept. 1 | Dept. 2 |
| Maximum Total Contribution.... | $24.50 | $3\frac{1}{2}$ $X_2$<br>$\underline{0}$  $X_1$<br>$3\frac{1}{2}$ | 5 | 0 |
| Maximum Unit Production...... | $19.00 | $6\frac{1}{3}$ $X_1$<br>$\underline{0}$  $X_2$<br>$6\frac{1}{3}$ | 0 | 2 |
| Minimum Unused Time......... | $22.00 | $5$  $X_1$<br>$\underline{1}$  $X_2$<br>$6$ | 0 | 0 |

known, intelligent decisions be made. In this respect linear programming can make a significant contribution to management. In the previous illustrations, all three criteria were evaluated by making changes in the objective function only.

## The dual in linear programming

The use of the term "dual" in a general sense indicates the concept of two alternatives; it can refer to a dual highway, dual controls, or any such situations where two methods are present. In a specific linear programming sense, it refers to the fact that there are *two* ways of looking at each linear programming problem we may encounter. In the simplest management illustration of the "dual," we can say that a businessman who competes in a market where selling prices of all possible products are equal *maximizes* profits by *minimizing* costs. That is, with a fixed selling price and known resources a manager who finds that product (or group of products) which *maximizes* his total contribution to fixed costs and profits (i.e., maximizes profit), is behaving in the same manner as if he found that product (or group of products) which minimized the total cost of resources used. This example is of course too elementary and involves many implicit economic assumptions, but it does illustrate the basic idea of the "dual," that is, simply another way of looking at the problem to achieve the same answer.

Each linear programming maximizing problem has its corresponding dual (a minimizing problem); by the same reasoning, each linear programming minimizing problem has its corresponding dual (a maximizing problem). An understanding of the concept of the dual will enable one to generate the desired answer either by working the original problem (called the *primal*) or by working the dual. In many cases, for reasons we shall shortly discuss, knowing how to generate the answer to the primal problem by working its corresponding dual problem will be productive of enormous savings in calculation time. Another advantage is that examination of the information contained in the dual of a product mix problem can answer many questions management might have concerning expansion of physical facilities. In the same sense, the examination of the dual to a linear programming ingredient mixture problem (such as that treated in Chapter 5) can yield useful information concerning pricing of the resulting mixture and appropriate market prices of the ingredients themselves. The dual concept is an important economic consideration for management in linear programming; from it can come answers to many questions concerning the value of alternative courses of action open to decision makers.

### An example problem (the primal)

Figure 8–6 illustrates a simple product mix problem; we shall use this as the example of the *primal*. The objective (like the other product mix problems previously explained) is, in this case, to maximize total contribution subject to limited resources. The details of the solution are illustrated in Figure 8–6.

The optimum solution to the primal problem is to produce 20/3 units of $X_1$ and 8/3 units of $X_2$; total contribution from this mix is shown to be \$58.67. Additional information concerning this problem can be observed in the $C_j - Z_j$ row of the final simplex table. The values found in this row under the $S_1$ and $S_2$ columns (\$ $- 4/3$ and \$ $- 1/9$, respectively) indicate that to remove one productive hour from each of the departments will reduce profits by these amounts. We have previously demonstrated that this information can also be interpreted as meaning that *if* additional capital were available to expand productive time in each of these two departments, the value

FIGURE 8-6
Primal Problem Solution

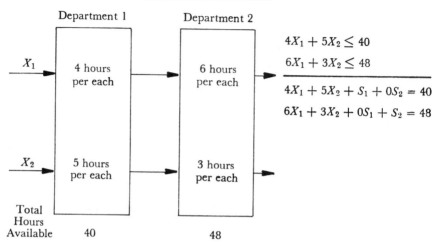

| $C_j$ | | | $6 | $7 | $0 | $0 | |
|---|---|---|---|---|---|---|---|
| | MIX | QTY. | $X_1$ | $X_2$ | $S_1$ | $S_2$ | |
| $0 | $S_1$ | 40 | 4 | 5 | 1 | 0 | $\theta\ 40/5 = 8$ ◄——— OUT |
| $0 | $S_2$ | 48 | 6 | 3 | 0 | 1 | $\theta\ 48/3 = 16$ |
| | $Z_j$ | | $0 | $0 | $0 | $0 | |
| | $C_j - Z_j$ | | $6 | $7 | $0 | $0 | |

↑ IN

| $C_j$ | | | $6 | $7 | $0 | $0 | |
|---|---|---|---|---|---|---|---|
| | MIX | QTY. | $X_1$ | $X_2$ | $S_1$ | $S_2$ | |
| $7 | $X_2$ | 8 | $4/5$ | 1 | $1/5$ | 0 | $\theta\ \dfrac{8}{4/15} = 30$ |
| $0 | $S_2$ | 24 | $18/5$ | 0 | $-3/5$ | 1 | $\theta\ \dfrac{24}{18/5} = 20/3$ ◄—OUT |
| | $Z_j$ | $56 | $28/5 | $7 | $7/5 | $0 | |
| | $C_j - Z_j$ | | $2/5 | $0 | $-7/5 | $0 | |

↑ IN

FIGURE 8-6 (*Continued*)

| $C_j$ | | | $6 | $7 | $0 | $0 |
|---|---|---|---|---|---|---|
| | MIX | QTY. | $X_1$ | $X_2$ | $S_1$ | $S_2$ |
| $7 | $X_2$ | 8/3 | 0 | 1 | 1/3 | −2/9 |
| $6 | $X_1$ | 20/3 | 1 | 0 | −1/6 | 5/18 |
| | $Z_j$ | $58 2/3 | $6 | $7 | $4/3 | $1/9 |
| | $C_j - Z_j$ | | $0 | $0 | $−4/3 | $−1/9 |

*Optimum Solution*

$\dfrac{20}{3} X_1$ at $6 = \$40.00$

$\dfrac{8}{3} X_2$ at $7 = \$18.67$

$\$58.67$

to the company (in increased production) of one more hour in each of these departments would be $4/3 and $1/9, respectively. To be quite specific about expanding the capacity, if making one more productive hour available in each department would cost the same in capital dollars spent, management would obviously spend their money in expanding department 1 since it offers the greater return. The $C_j - Z_j$ row of simplex table number 3 (Figure 8–6) contains relevant information for management decision making. We shall now demonstrate how this same information is available from a solution to the dual of this, the primal problem.

## Statement and solution of the dual problem

Whereas the primal problem was concerned with maximizing the contribution from the two products, the dual will be concerned with the cost of manufacturing these products; to be more specific, one can think of the purpose of the solution to the dual as being to minimize the expense of maintaining 40 hours available capacity in department 1 and 48 hours capacity in department 2. Since we do not know the cost of an available hour in either of the two departments (this will be the answer to the dual problem), we can let these two unknown values be $Y_1$ and $Y_2$. Thus the statement of the objective in working the dual would be to minimize:

$$40Y_1 + 48Y_2$$

where $Y_1$ and $Y_2$ represent the cost of making one productive hour available in each of the respective departments.

It becomes necessary at this point in the development of the dual problem to state the restraints under which minimization is to take place. These restraints can be developed directly from the restraints to the primal problem (repeated in Figure 8–7).

FIGURE 8–7
Restraints to the Primal Problem

|  | Contribution per Unit | |
| --- | --- | --- |
| $4X_1 + 5X_2 \leq 40$ | $X_1$ | \$6 |
| $6X_1 + 3X_2 \leq 48$ | $X_2$ | \$7 |

Management knows from looking at the restraints in Figure 8–7 that production of one unit of $X_1$ will require four hours in department 1 and six hours in department 2. Since $Y_1$ equals the cost of an hour in department 1 and $Y_2$ equals the cost of an hour in department 2, the company will have to commit $4Y_1 + 6Y_2$ dollars to produce one unit of $X_1$. The question then is: Does this expenditure of production cost equal or exceed the \$6 a finished unit of $X_1$ is worth to the company? Put in mathematical form it appears as an inequality as follows:

$$4Y_1 + 6Y_2 \geq \$6.$$

If the value of $4Y_1 + 6Y_2$ exceeds \$6, we should logically commit the resources to some other purpose; if not, the resources of the two departments can be profitably committed to the production of products $X_1$ and $X_2$.

We can reason similarly about the second restraint in the problem. Production of a unit of $X_2$ will require us to commit five hours in department 1 and three hours in department 2. The total cost of this committed time will be $5Y_1 + 3Y_2$ dollars. In exchange for these expenditures, we shall get one unit of $X_2$ worth \$7. The question we ask ourselves then is whether such commitment of expenses will produce an economic value equal to or greater than the \$7 the product is worth to us. In mathematical form this inequality is:

$$5Y_1 + 3Y_2 \geq \$7.$$

Thus to find the value of an hour of productive time in each of our departments we will solve the following linear programming minimization problem.

Minimize:

$$Z = 40Y_1 + 48Y_2$$

Subject to:

$$4Y_1 + 6Y_2 \geq \$6$$

$$5Y_1 + 3Y_2 \geq \$7.$$

Figure 8–8 illustrates first the addition of appropriate slack and artificial variables to these restraints, then the solution of the problem using the simplex minimizing method introduced in Chapter 5.

FIGURE 8-8
Statement and Solution to the Dual Problem

$$4Y_1 + 6Y_2 \geq 6$$
$$5Y_1 + 3Y_2 \geq 7$$

---

$4Y_1 + 6Y_2 - S_1 = 6$      Slack
$5Y_1 + 3Y_2 - S_2 = 7$   Variables Added

---

$4Y_1 + 6Y_2 - S_1 + A_1 = 6$      Artificial
$5Y_1 + 3Y_2 - S_2 + A_2 = 7$   Variables Added

---

$4Y_1 + 6Y_2 - S_1 + 0S_2 + A_1 + 0A_2 = 6$      Balancing
$5Y_1 + 3Y_2 + 0S_1 - S_2 + 0A_1 + A_2 = 7$   Variables Added

---

| $C_j$ | | | 40 | 48 | 0 | 0 | 100 | 100 | |
|---|---|---|---|---|---|---|---|---|---|
| | MIX | QTY. | $Y_1$ | $Y_2$ | $S_1$ | $S_2$ | $A_1$ | $A_2$ | |
| 100 | $A_1$ | 6 | 4 | 6 | −1 | 0 | 1 | 0 | $\theta\frac{6}{4} = 1.5$ |
| 100 | $A_2$ | 7 | 5 | 3 | 0 | −1 | 0 | 1 | $\theta\frac{7}{5} = 1.4$ ◄—OUT |
| | $Z_j$ | 1,300 | 900 | 900 | −100 | −100 | 100 | 100 | |
| | $C_j - Z_j$ | | −860 | −852 | 100 | 100 | 0 | 0 | |

↑ IN

FIGURE 8-8 *(Continued)*

| $C_j$ | | | 40 | 48 | 0 | 0 | 100 | 100 | |
|---|---|---|---|---|---|---|---|---|---|
| | MIX | QTY. | $Y_1$ | $Y_2$ | $S_1$ | $S_2$ | $A_1$ | $A_2$ | |
| 100 | $A_1$ | $\frac{2}{5}$ | 0 | $-\frac{18}{5}$ | $-1$ | $\frac{4}{5}$ | 1 | $-\frac{4}{5}$ | $\theta \frac{\frac{2}{5}}{\frac{18}{5}} = \frac{1}{9}$ ← OUT |
| 40 | $Y_1$ | $\frac{7}{5}$ | 1 | $\frac{3}{5}$ | 0 | $-\frac{1}{5}$ | 0 | $\frac{1}{5}$ | $\theta \frac{\frac{7}{5}}{\frac{3}{5}} = \frac{7}{3}$ |
| | $Z_j$ | 96 | 40 | 384 | $-100$ | 72 | 100 | $-72$ | |
| | $C_j - Z_j$ | | 0 | $-336$ | 100 | $-72$ | 0 | 172 | |

↑ IN

| $C_j$ | | | 40 | 48 | 0 | 0 | 100 | 100 |
|---|---|---|---|---|---|---|---|---|
| | MIX | QTY. | $Y_1$ | $Y_2$ | $S_1$ | $S_2$ | $A_1$ | $A_2$ |
| 48 | $Y_2$ | $\frac{1}{9}$ | 0 | 1 | $-\frac{5}{18}$ | $\frac{2}{9}$ | $\frac{5}{18}$ | $-\frac{2}{9}$ |
| 40 | $Y_1$ | $\frac{4}{3}$ | 1 | 0 | $\frac{1}{6}$ | $-\frac{1}{3}$ | $-\frac{1}{6}$ | $\frac{1}{3}$ |
| | $Z_j$ | $58\frac{2}{3}$ | 40 | 48 | $-\frac{20}{3}$ | $-\frac{8}{3}$ | $\frac{20}{3}$ | $\frac{8}{3}$ |
| | $C_j - Z_j$ | | 0 | 0 | $\frac{20}{3}$ | $\frac{8}{3}$ | $\frac{280}{3}$ | $\frac{292}{3}$ |

The optimum solution to the dual problem for $Y_1$ and $Y_2$ from the third simplex table of Figure 8-8 indicates that the worth to the company of a productive hour in department 1 is 4/3; this would be interpreted as meaning $1.33. The value to the company of a productive hour in department 2 is 1/9 which would be read $0.11. The total value of the objective function $40Y_1 + 48Y_2$ is seen to be $58.67, the same value observed in the solution to the primal problem. The two values in the $C_j - Z_j$ row under the slack variable columns (20/3 and 8/3) contain the solution to the primal problem, the manufacture of 20/3 units of $X_1$ and 8/3 units of $X_2$. One can reason why these two values would appear in this particular location by remembering that since we are minimizing the total cost of production expense, slack in this case would represent products *not made*.

## General remarks about the dual

All of the information which can be determined from a solution to the primal problem can also be obtained from a solution to the corresponding dual problem. Although the management information content of both of these problems is identical, there are certain cases when the solution to the dual represents far less work than a solution to the corresponding primal. For example, Figure 8–9 illustrates a problem in which two products each pass through six different departments. The inequalities for this problem appear as follows:

Maximize:

$$\$2X_1 + \$3X_2$$

Under the following restraints:

$$3X_1 + 2X_2 \leq 19 \qquad \text{(Dept. 1)}$$
$$X_1 + 4X_2 \leq 23 \qquad \text{(Dept. 2)}$$
$$5X_1 + 6X_2 \leq 18 \qquad \text{(Dept. 3)}$$
$$7X_1 + 8X_2 \leq 36 \qquad \text{(Dept. 4)}$$
$$X_1 + 9X_2 \leq 24 \qquad \text{(Dept. 5)}$$
$$4X_1 + \ X_2 \leq 27 \qquad \text{(Dept. 6)}.$$

FIGURE 8-9
First Simplex Table for Primal Problem

| $C_j$ | | | $2 | $3 | $0 | $0 | $0 | $0 | $0 | $0 |
|---|---|---|---|---|---|---|---|---|---|---|
| | MIX | QTY. | $X_1$ | $X_2$ | $S_1$ | $S_2$ | $S_3$ | $S_4$ | $S_5$ | $S_6$ |
| $0 | $S_1$ | 19 | 3 | 2 | 1 | 0 | 0 | 0 | 0 | 0 |
| $0 | $S_2$ | 23 | 1 | 4 | 0 | 1 | 0 | 0 | 0 | 0 |
| $0 | $S_3$ | 18 | 5 | 6 | 0 | 0 | 1 | 0 | 0 | 0 |
| $0 | $S_4$ | 36 | 7 | 8 | 0 | 0 | 0 | 1 | 0 | 0 |
| $0 | $S_5$ | 24 | 1 | 9 | 0 | 0 | 0 | 0 | 1 | 0 |
| $0 | $S_6$ | 27 | 4 | 1 | 0 | 0 | 0 | 0 | 0 | 1 |
| $Z_j$ | | 0 | 0 | 0 | 0 | 0 | 0 | 0 | 0 | 0 |
| $C_j - Z_j$ | | | $2 | $3 | $0 | $0 | $0 | $0 | $0 | $0 |

## FIGURE 8-10

### First Simplex Table for Dual Problem

| $C_j$ | | | | 19 | 23 | 18 | 36 | 24 | 27 | 0 | 0 | 100 | 100 |
|---|---|---|---|---|---|---|---|---|---|---|---|---|---|
| | | MIX | QTY. | $Y_1$ | $Y_2$ | $Y_3$ | $Y_4$ | $Y_5$ | $Y_6$ | $S_1$ | $S_2$ | $A_1$ | $A_2$ |
| 100 | | $A_1$ | 2 | 3 | 1 | 5 | 7 | 1 | 4 | −1 | 0 | 1 | 0 |
| 100 | | $A_2$ | 3 | 2 | 4 | 6 | 8 | 9 | 1 | 0 | −1 | 0 | 1 |
| | $Z_j$ | | | 500 | 500 | 1,100 | 1,500 | 1,000 | 500 | −100 | −100 | 100 | 100 |
| | $C_j - Z_j$ | | | −481 | −477 | −1,082 | −1,464 | −976 | −473 | 100 | 100 | 0 | 0 |

In Figure 8–10 the first simplex table for the corresponding dual problem is illustrated. The inequalities for the dual appear as follows:

Minimize:

$$19Y_1 + 23Y_2 + 18Y_3 + 36Y_4 + 24Y_5 + 27Y_6$$

Under the following restraints:

$$3Y_1 + \ Y_2 + 5Y_3 + 7Y_4 + \ Y_5 + 4Y_6 \geq 2$$
$$2Y_1 + 4Y_2 + 6Y_3 + 8Y_4 + 9Y_5 + \ Y_6 \geq 3.$$

Since the dual involves a maximum of two variables in the "mix," we know in this case that two additional simplex tables will produce the optimum solution. In the case of the primal problem (Figure 8–9), the solution may require six simplex tables beyond the original one. In cases like this where the number of slack variables is large compared with the number of real products (or other real variables) then the solution to the dual offers the best alternative in terms of time and effort.

### Changes in the prices of resources

In linear programming problems, one often encounters a situation where the per unit costs of ingredients or the per unit contribution from products changes at different levels of volume. One example of this problem is the use of overtime hours for production. During the regular time hours (usually 40 per week) wages per hour are at one level; however, when the employees work in excess of 40 hours, their wages increase by 50 percent, with a corresponding effect upon the contribution per unit of those products which are manufactured during the hours when the higher wage rates are being paid. Production beyond 48 hours brings still higher labor costs. Since production during overtime hours (even with the higher costs) may be a wise alternative, a linear programming solution must allow for such possibilities when the problem is first set up.

The data in Figure 8–11 illustrate a simple product mix problem where production during overtime hours is a possibility; the lower contributions per unit produced during these overtime hours are caused entirely by the 50 percent premium on wage rates paid for overtime work.

The linear programming solution to this problem would begin with

FIGURE 8–11
Problem Data: Overtime Work Hours

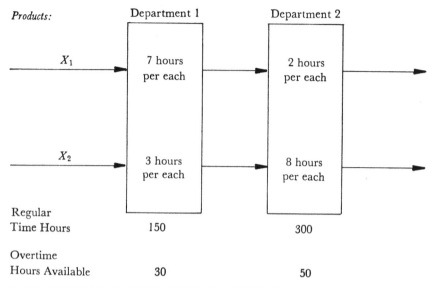

| | | Calculation of Contributions per Unit | | | | | |
|---|---|---|---|---|---|---|---|
| | | *Regular Time* | | | *Overtime* | | |
| *Product* | *Price* | *Direct Material per Unit* | *Direct Labor per Unit* | *Contribution per Unit* | *Direct Material per Unit* | *Direct Labor per Unit* | *Contribution per Unit* |
| $X_1$ | $25 | $14 | $4 | $7 | $14 | $6 | $5 |
| $X_2$ | $32 | $17 | $6 | $9 | $17 | $9 | $6 |

an algebraic statement of the regular time restraints for each department as follows:

$$7X_1 + 3X_2 \leq 150 \qquad \text{(Dept. 1, regular time)}$$

$$2X_1 + 8X_2 \leq 300 \qquad \text{(Dept. 2, regular time)}$$

Since in this case production during overtime is a legitimate alternative, we would need two additional restraints indicating that production could take place during the overtime hours available; we shall assume that it is possible for the first department to schedule overtime work equal to 20 percent of its reqular time working hours, and for the second department to schedule $16\frac{2}{3}$ percent.

To distinguish between products produced during regular time hours and the same products produced during overtime hours, we shall assign the designations $X_1'$ and $X_2'$ when we wish to refer to $X_1$ and $X_2$ produced during overtime hours. The two algebraic restraints which will limit overtime production to the hours available would then be written:

$$7X_1' + 3X_2' \leq 30 \qquad \text{(Dept. 1, overtime)}$$
$$2X_1' + 8X_2' \leq 50 \qquad \text{(Dept. 2, overtime).}$$

The four restraints involved in this problem are repeated here:

$$7X_1 + 3X_2 \leq 150$$
$$2X_1 + 8X_2 \leq 300$$
$$7X_1' + 3X_2' \leq 30$$
$$2X_1' + 8X_2' \leq 50.$$

To represent these restraints in the form of equations, appropriate slack variables will have to be added to each inequality. $S_1$ and $S_2$ represent the slack variables denoting unused regular time hours in each department, and $S_3$ and $S_4$ denote unused overtime hours in each department. The four equations which result when slack variables are added appear as follows:

$$7X_1 + 3X_2 + S_1 = 150$$
$$2X_2 + 8X_2 + S_2 = 300$$
$$7X_1' + 3X_2' + S_3 = 30$$
$$2X_1' + 8X_2' + S_4 = 50.$$

When balancing variables are added to each equation, we generate the following set of equations ready for insertion in the first simplex table:

$$7X_1 + 3X_2 + 0X_1' + 0X_2' + S_1 + 0S_2 + 0S_3 + 0S_4 = 150$$
$$2X_1 + 8X_2 + 0X_1' + 0X_2' + 0S_1 + S_2 + 0S_3 + 0S_4 = 300$$
$$0X_1 + 0X_2 + 7X_1' + 3X_2' + 0S_1 + 0S_2 + S_3 + 0S_4 = 30$$
$$0X_1 + 0X_2 + 2X_1' + 8X_2' + 0S_1 + 0S_2 + 0S_3 + S_4 = 50.$$

From the cost and contribution data in Figure 8–11, we can determine the appropriate $C_j$ values for the first simplex table for each of the variables; these values are illustrated in Figure 8–12.

FIGURE 8–12
$C_j$ Values for All Variables

| Variable | $C_j$ | Variable | $C_j$ |
|----------|-------|----------|-------|
| $X_1$............. | $7 | $S_1$............. | $0 |
| $X_2$............. | $9 | $S_2$............. | $0 |
| $X'_1$ ............ | $5 | $S_3$............. | $0 |
| $X'_2$............. | $6 | $S_4$............. | $0 |

Figure 8–13 illustrates the equations inserted in the first simplex table; the $Z_j$ and $C_j - Z_j$ rows have been completed, together with a calculation of the $\theta$ values to determine which row is replaced.

FIGURE 8–13
First Simplex Table for Overtime Problem

| $C_j$ | | | $7 | $9 | $5 | $6 | $0 | $0 | $0 | $0 |
|-------|------|------|-----|-----|------|------|-------|-------|-------|-------|
| | MIX | QTY. | $X_1$ | $X_2$ | $X'_1$ | $X'_2$ | $S_1$ | $S_2$ | $S_3$ | $S_4$ |
| $0 | $S_1$ | 150 | 7 | 3 | 0 | 0 | 1 | 0 | 0 | 0 |
| $0 | $S_2$ | 300 | 2 | 8 | 0 | 0 | 0 | 1 | 0 | 0 |
| $0 | $S_3$ | 30 | 0 | 0 | 7 | 3 | 0 | 0 | 1 | 0 |
| $0 | $S_4$ | 50 | 0 | 0 | 2 | 8 | 0 | 0 | 0 | 1 |
| $Z_j$ | | $0 | $0 | $0 | $0 | $0 | $0 | $0 | $0 | $0 |
| $C_j - Z_j$ | | | $7 | $9 | $5 | $6 | $0 | $0 | $0 | $0 |

↑ IN

$\theta S_1 = 150/3 = 50$
$\theta S_2 = 300/8 = 37\frac{1}{2}$ ◄——— OUT
$\theta S_3 = 30/0 = $ not defined
$\theta S_4 = 50/0 = $ not defined

From this point on, the solution to the problem follows the same rules first explained in Chapter 4 ("The Simplex Method of Linear Programming—Maximization). The optimum (highest total contribution) answer will indicate how many units of each product should be produced on regular time and during overtime hours. The final simplex table for this problem is illustrated in Figure 8–14; from observation of the quantity column, we can see that each of the two products is produced in both regular time and overtime hours. The final product mix uses all of the available hours in both categories. An examination of the $C_j - Z_j$ row under the slack variables indicates the cost to the company (in lost contribution) of removing a regular time or overtime hour from productive use in either department. It is interesting to note that the least valuable hour is an overtime hour in department 2, which if removed from production would result in only $27/50 or $0.54 loss; the most valuable hour to the company is a regular time production hour in department 2, which if removed from use would cost the company $21/25 or $0.84 in lost contribution.

FIGURE 8–14
Final Table for Overtime Problem

| $C_j$ | | | $7 | $9 | $5 | $6 | $0 | $0 | $0 | $0 |
|---|---|---|---|---|---|---|---|---|---|---|
| | MIX | QTY. | $X_1$ | $X_2$ | $X_1'$ | $X_5'$ | $S_1$ | $S_2$ | $S_3$ | $S_4$ |
| $7 | $X_1$ | 6 | 1 | 0 | 0 | 0 | $\frac{4}{25}$ | $-\frac{3}{50}$ | 0 | 0 |
| $9 | $X_2$ | 36 | 0 | 1 | 0 | 0 | $-\frac{1}{25}$ | $\frac{7}{50}$ | 0 | 0 |
| $5 | $X_1'$ | $\frac{9}{5}$ | 0 | 0 | 1 | 0 | 0 | 0 | $\frac{4}{25}$ | $-\frac{3}{50}$ |
| $6 | $X_2'$ | $\frac{29}{5}$ | 0 | 0 | 0 | 1 | 0 | 0 | $-\frac{1}{25}$ | $\frac{7}{50}$ |
| $Z_j$ | | $409\frac{4}{5}$ | $7 | $9 | $5 | $6 | $\frac{19}{25}$ | $\frac{21}{25}$ | $\frac{14}{25}$ | $\frac{27}{50}$ |
| $C_j - Z_j$ | | | $0 | $0 | $0 | $0 | $-\frac{19}{25}$ | $-\frac{21}{25}$ | $-\frac{14}{25}$ | $-\frac{27}{50}$ |

A careful analysis of the effects upon total contribution of proposed changes in operating hours (both regular and overtime) can be of great benefit to a company. The use of linear programming to obtain optimum work-hour schedules can ensure that all the relevant costs and profit opportunities have been explored. In particular, allowing extra variables ($X_1'$, $X_2'$, etc.) to be a part of the problem, even when overtime is not being considered as a possible alternative, will indicate whether scheduling of overtime hours can be profitable for the firm, and exactly how much each scheduled overtime hour will generate in contribution to fixed costs and profits. When the number of possible products and departments becomes quite large, linear programming probably offers the only reliable method of ensuring that all of the pertinent factors become a part of the decision.

It is a general custom for some industries to pay a small premium per hour to employees who work on the second and third shifts. Since productivity does not generally increase on these later shifts, the incurring of this extra labor cost means that the per unit contributions from products produced on the second and third shifts will be somewhat lower than those manufactured on the first shift. The method just illustrated can be used without modification to determine the profitability of second and third shift work; each of the possible products would be assigned additional designations ($X_1$, $X_1'$, $X_1''$) representing product $X_1$ produced on three different shifts. Each of the designations would carry its own $C_j$ contribution value reflecting the increased cost of labor expense on the second and third shifts.

It is also possible to adapt the overtime method just described to problems involving mixing of ingredients, such as those first discussed in Chapter 5 ("The Simplex Method of Linear Programming—Minimization"). Often in problems involving mixing ingredients, it is possible to substitute a higher priced ingredient for a lower priced one, if the stocks of the lower priced ingredient have been temporarily exhausted. In this manner, production may continue without interruption but at an additional cost. To determine just whether substitutions of this type are advantageous, and to determine exactly the additional cost which would have to be incurred by the company, if such proposed substitutions were actually made, linear programming can be effectively utilized. When the problem is first prepared for solution, the substitute ingredients with their higher per unit costs can be made a part of the problem formulation. Then if the production of the mixture can be completed by using some higher priced ingredients, the linear program will do so and indicate the exact cost of using these more costly materials. Management can then make the decision as to whether completion of the mixture at the higher cost is a worthwhile alternative, when compared to waiting for delivery of the normal (lower priced) ingredients.

In managerial decisions of this type, the usefulness of linear programming can be significant. The ability of management to bring this technique to bear on significant decisions is limited only by their ability to provide necessary input costs, contributions, etc. and by their ability to provide computer facilities for solving the problems when the number of variables rises to the level where hand computation is not feasible.

## Problems

1. Apex, Inc. manufactures two products, each of which must pass through two machine centers—assembling and finishing. Product 1 requires five hours to be assembled and one-half hour to be finished; whereas product 2 requires one hour to be assembled and one-fourth hour to be finished. Product 1 makes a $15 contribution toward fixed costs and profit and product 2 a $2 contribution. In addition there are 50 available hours in the assembly center and 10 available hours in the finishing center. Determine the various product mixes which would (*a*) maximize contribution, (*b*) maximize production, (*c*) minimize unused time.

2. Slick Refining Company has excess quantities available of heavy, medium, and light petroleum stocks. Three products can be blended from these stocks subject to the following requirements:

| | | Stock | |
| --- | --- | --- | --- |
| Product | H | M | L |
| A.......... | 5 bbl. | 3 bbl. | 0 bbl. |
| B.......... | 1 ” | 3 ” | 6 ” |
| C.......... | 2 ” | 3 ” | 3 ” |

Products A, B, and C make a contribution per barrel respectively of $150, $100, and $75.

Slick has 1,000 barrels of heavy (H) stock, 2,500 barrels of medium (M) stock, and 2,000 barrels of light (L) stock available. The company wishes to determine how much of each product to make from the available stocks so as to:
   (*a*) Maximize contribution
   (*b*) Maximize production
   (*c*) Minimize excess stock.

3. The Goodie Candy Company has 350 pounds of hard candy and 250 pounds of soft candy in stock. The company packages and sells two candy mixes: Deluxe Mix, consisting of 65 percent soft and 35 percent hard candy at $1.25 per one-pound can; and Party Mix, consisting of 75 percent hard and 25 percent soft candy at $0.75 per one-pound can. Set up the dual problem and solve for the solution that would determine the maximum amount the company could pay for additional hard and soft candy.

4. The ABC Fertilizer Company mixes two grades of fertilizer—Super and Special. The Super grade makes a contribution of $5 per 20-pound sack

and $3 per 10-pound sack. The following table gives the ingredient and labor requirements for a 10-pound sack of fertilizer.

|  | Super (pound) | Special (pound) | Available (pound) |
|---|---|---|---|
| Ingredient A......... | 4 | 5 | 4,000 |
| Ingredient B......... | 3 | 3 | 2,500 |
| Ingredient C......... | 2 | 1 | 1,200 |
| Ingredient D......... | 1 | 1 | 1,000 |
| Labor.............. | $\frac{1}{4}$ hr. | $\frac{1}{5}$ hr. | 200 hr. |

Proportional amounts of ingredients are required for 20-pound sacks, but the labor requirement is the same regardless of sack weight. Minimum and maximum expected demands for the various mixes are:

| Mix | Minimum Demand (sacks) | Maximum Demand (sacks) |
|---|---|---|
| 10-pound Super... | 10 | 100 |
| 20-pound Super... | 100 | 200 |
| 10-pound Special.. | 200 | 300 |
| 20-pound Special.. | 150 | 200 |

Set up the dual problem to solve for the maximum prices of the factors of production. Work through the problem and give a complete economic interpretation of the dual.

5. Chemical Products, Inc. markets a cleaning solution to various industrial buyers. This solvent is composed of the following ingredients:

| Ingredient | Percent of Solution | Cost per Gallon | Gallons Available |
|---|---|---|---|
| $X_1$........... | between 30 and 37 | $0.38 | 250 |
| $X_2$........... | no more than 50 | 0.25 | 750 |
| $X_3$........... | 2 | 1.38 | 18 |
| $X_4$........... | at least 10 | 0.63 | 150 |

The company uses two additional ingredients as substitutes for two of the basic ingredients. $X_5$ will substitute for $X_1$, but costs $0.51 per gallon. And $X_6$ will substitute for $X_3$ at a cost of $2.11 per gallon. Presently the firm has 150 gallons of $X_5$ and 10 gallons of $X_6$ in stock.

An order for 1,000 gallons of the cleaning solution has been received.

Set up the problem and solve for the solution which will fill the order with minimum cost to the company using only those ingredients presently on hand.

6. Carter Manufacturing Company produces two grades—Ace and Zip—of a certain consumer product. Material and labor requirements are as follows:

|  | *Ace* | *Zip* | *Availability* |
|---|---|---|---|
| Labor......... | 0.4 hr. per unit | 0.3 hr. per unit | 280 hrs. at $3 per hr. |
| High-quality material..... | 0.3 sq. ft. per unit | 0.2 sq. ft. per unit | 240 sq. ft. at $3 per sq. ft. |
| Standard material..... | 0.2 sq. ft. per unit | 0.3 sq. ft. per unit | 300 sq. ft. at $2 per sq. ft. |
| Contribution per unit..... | $6 per unit | $5 per unit | |

Overtime labor hours are available at $5 per hour up to 20 percent more hours. Due to back order, at least 300 units of each grade must be produced during the approaching production period.

As Production manager it is your responsibility to devise the schedule for this period which will enable the company to maximize contribution.

# chapter 9

# *Linear programming applications*

## Introduction

The possibilities for applying linear programming to the solution of management problems are many; to attempt even to list them is beyond the scope of this book. Instead, the authors will take the alternative in this chapter of illustrating linear programming solutions to several representative types of management problems. While this will not be anything near an exhaustive set of examples, it will at least show the varied types of problems and decision-making situations which can benefit from the use of this technique.

In order to illustrate the scope of possible applications, problems will be selected from various phases of company operations. In the order of their presentation, a solution method will be offered for these decision situations: (1) The allocation of advertising expenditures to achieve a given desired result (reach a certain audience) with limited expenditures. (2) The assignment of production of various manufactured items to different machinery when the capacities of each and the direct manufacturing costs for each product on each machine are known (in this example the objective would be to minimize total manufacturing cost). (3) The determination of the lowest cost schedule from several producing factories to several distribution warehouses (*a*) where the shipping costs from each factory to each warehouse are known; (*b*) where the needs of each warehouse and the maximum outputs of each factory are known; (*c*) where the maximum storage capacity of each warehouse is known; and (*d*) where the storage cost for items at factories and warehouses is known. The objective in this type of problem would be to determine that one particular shipping schedule which will minimize total cost of shipping and storage. (4) A problem involving several functional areas of the firm, i.e., where the decision as to product mix is influenced by production restraints, raw material restraints, and marketing restraints. (5) A problem involving production smoothing (the case where demand is not constant throughout the year and certain items must be produced and stored for sale in later periods). Linear programming in this case determines which items should be produced in each period to minimize the total yearly cost of overtime and storage. (6) A use of linear programming as an aid in the capital budgeting decision (the allocation of capital to various organizational projects so as to achieve the highest return to the assets of the firm).

## The allocation of advertising expenditures

At any one time, the expenditures a company can make for advertising purposes are limited; most companies prepare an advertising budget annually and base this budget on an anticipated advertising program which they hope will achieve certain aims in terms of stimulating sales for the organization. There are generally multiple media in which advertising can take place and one of the problems becomes

FIGURE 9–1
Readership Data for Three Magazines

|  | *Magazine 1* | *Magazine 2* | *Magazine 3* |
|---|---|---|---|
| Cost per advertising unit................ | 2,500 | $    800 | $    500 |
| Maximum units available this month....... | 14 | 35 | 20 |
| Minimum units magazine will accept....... | 2 | 0 | 4 |
| Total number of readers per unit.......... | 600,000 | 250,000 | 190,000 |
| Number of readers in geographical region 1 per unit............................. | 50,000 | 90,000 | 100,000 |
| Number of readers in geographical region 2 per unit............................. | 550,000 | 160,000 | 90,000 |
| Number of female readers between ages 21 and 35 per unit..................... | 90,000 | 70,000 | 30,000 |
| Numbers of college educated female readers per unit............................. | 200,000 | 80,000 | 100,000 |

FIGURE 9-2
Restraints for Advertising Problem

$$2,500X_1 + 800X_2 + 500X_3$$
$$X_1$$
$$X_2$$
$$X_3$$
$$X_1$$
$$X_3$$
$$50,000X_1 + 90,000X_2 + 100,000X_3$$
$$550,000X_1 + 160,000X_2 + 90,000X_3$$
$$90,000X_1 + 70,000X_2 + 30,000X_3$$
$$200,000X_1 + 80,000X_2 + 100,000X_3$$

$$2,500X_1 + 800X_2 + 500X_3 + S_1$$
$$X_1 + S_2$$
$$X_2 + S_3$$
$$X_3 + S_4$$
$$X_1 - S_5 + A_1$$
$$X_3$$
$$50,000X_1 + 90,000X_2 + 100,000X_3$$
$$550,000X_1 + 160,000X_2 + 90,000X_3$$
$$90,000X_1 + 70,000X_2 + 30,000X_3$$
$$200,000X_1 + 80,000X_2 + 100,000X_3$$

the allocation of the budgeted advertising moneys among the different media to achieve the greatest possible benefit. To help in these types of decisions, there are several research firms which collect data concerning readership of each media, i.e., the effectiveness of each of many possible magazines, for instance, in reaching a desired audience.

Let us assume that the data in Figure 9-1 represent the readership characteristics and advertising limitations of three different magazines. In these data the term "advertising unit" can be thought of as a page, a half page, a column inch or other term appropriate to a particular medium.

The company has a total advertising budget for the coming month of $56,000; they would like to allocate this money among the three magazines so that the maximum total number of readers are exposed to the ads *and* so that the following conditions are met:

a) They want to reach at least 1,500,000 readers in region 1 and at least 6,000,000 readers in geographical region 2,

b) They desire that no more than 2,000,000 female readers between ages 21 and 35 be reached by the advertising,

$$
\begin{array}{rcl}
& \leq & 56{,}000 \\
& \leq & 14 \\
& \leq & 35 \\
& \leq & 20 \quad \text{(restraints} \\
& \leq & 2 \quad \text{in} \\
& \leq & 4 \quad \text{original} \\
& \geq & 1{,}500{,}000 \quad \text{form)} \\
& \geq & 6{,}000{,}000 \\
& \leq & 2{,}000{,}000 \\
& \geq & 2{,}500{,}000
\end{array}
$$

$$
\begin{array}{rcl}
& = & 56{,}000 \\
& = & 14 \\
& = & 35 \quad \text{(slack} \\
& = & 20 \quad \text{and} \\
& = & 2 \quad \text{artificial} \\
-S_6 + A_2 & = & 4 \quad \text{variables} \\
\quad -S_7 + A_3 & = & 1{,}500{,}000 \quad \text{added)} \\
\quad\quad -S_8 + A_4 & = & 6{,}000{,}000 \\
\quad\quad\quad +S_9 & = & 2{,}000{,}000 \\
\quad\quad\quad\quad -S_{10} + A_5 & = & 2{,}500{,}000
\end{array}
$$

*c*) They desire that at least 2,500,000 college educated women be reached by the advertising.

We begin to construct the algebraic restraints for this problem with a restraint that would assure that the maximum dollar budget of $56,000 would not be exceeded. If we let $X_1$, $X_2$, and $X_3$ represent respectively an advertising unit in each of the three magazines, the restraint would appear as follows:

$$\$2{,}500X_1 + \$800X_2 + \$500X_3 \leq \$56{,}000 \quad \text{(restraint 1)}.$$

Three restraints will be required to assure that the maximum number of advertising units these magazines will accept will not be exceeded by our program; these are:

$$X_1 \leq 14 \qquad \text{(restraint 2)}$$
$$X_2 \leq 35 \qquad \text{(restraint 3)}$$
$$X_3 \leq 20 \qquad \text{(restraint 4)}.$$

And two additional restraints are needed so that our program uses at

FIGURE 9-3
First Simplex Table for Advertising Problem

| $C_j$ | | | 600,000 | 250,000 | 190,000 | 0 | 0 | 0 | 0 |
|---|---|---|---|---|---|---|---|---|---|
| | MIX | QTY. | $X_1$ | $X_2$ | $X_3$ | $S_1$ | $S_2$ | $S_3$ | $S_4$ |
| 0 | $S_1$ | 56,000 | 2,500 | 800 | 500 | 1 | 0 | 0 | 0 |
| 0 | $S_2$ | 14 | 1 | 0 | 0 | 0 | 1 | 0 | 0 |
| 0 | $S_3$ | 35 | 0 | 1 | 0 | 0 | 0 | 1 | 0 |
| 0 | $S_4$ | 20 | 0 | 0 | 1 | 0 | 0 | 0 | 1 |
| −100 | $A_1$ | 2 | 1 | 0 | 0 | 0 | 0 | 0 | 0 |
| −100 | $A_2$ | 4 | 0 | 0 | 1 | 0 | 0 | 0 | 0 |
| −100 | $A_3$ | 1,500,000 | 50,000 | 90,000 | 100,000 | 0 | 0 | 0 | 0 |
| −100 | $A_4$ | 6,000,000 | 550,000 | 160,000 | 90,000 | 0 | 0 | 0 | 0 |
| 0 | $S_9$ | 2,000,000 | 90,000 | 70,000 | 30,000 | 0 | 0 | 0 | 0 |
| −100 | $A_5$ | 2,500,000 | 200,000 | 80,000 | 100,000 | 0 | 0 | 0 | 0 |
| $Z_j$ | | | | | | | | | |
| | $C_j - Z_j$ | | | | | | | | |

least the minimum number of units each magazine requires us to utilize; these are:

$$X_1 \geq 2 \qquad \text{(restraint 5)}$$
$$X_3 \geq 4 \qquad \text{(restraint 6)}.$$

In order that the wishes of the company concerning readers in each of the two geographical areas be satisfied, we will need two additional restraints:

$$50,000X_1 + 90,000X_2 + 100,000X_3 \geq 1,500,000 \quad \text{(restraint 7; region 1)}$$
$$550,000X_1 + 160,000X_2 + 90,000X_3 \geq 6,000,000 \quad \text{(restraint 8; region 2)}.$$

To ensure that no more than 2,000,000 female readers between ages 21 and 35 be reached we would construct the following restraint:

$$90,000X_1 + 70,000X_2 + 30,000X_3 \leq 2,000,000 \quad \text{(restraint 9)}.$$

| 0 | −100 | 0 | −100 | 0 | −100 | 0 | −100 | 0 | 0 | −100 |
|---|---|---|---|---|---|---|---|---|---|---|
| $S_5$ | $A_1$ | $S_6$ | $A_2$ | $S_7$ | $A_3$ | $S_8$ | $A_4$ | $S_9$ | $S_{10}$ | $A_5$ |
| 0 | 0 | 0 | 0 | 0 | 0 | 0 | 0 | 0 | 0 | 0 |
| 0 | 0 | 0 | 0 | 0 | 0 | 0 | 0 | 0 | 0 | 0 |
| 0 | 0 | 0 | 0 | 0 | 0 | 0 | 0 | 0 | 0 | 0 |
| 0 | 0 | 0 | 0 | 0 | 0 | 0 | 0 | 0 | 0 | 0 |
| −1 | 1 | 0 | 0 | 0 | 0 | 0 | 0 | 0 | 0 | 0 |
| 0 | 0 | −1 | 1 | 0 | 0 | 0 | 0 | 0 | 0 | 0 |
| 0 | 0 | 0 | 0 | −1 | 1 | 0 | 0 | 0 | 0 | 0 |
| 0 | 0 | 0 | 0 | 0 | 0 | −1 | 1 | 0 | 0 | 0 |
| 0 | 0 | 0 | 0 | 0 | 0 | 0 | 0 | 1 | 0 | 0 |
| 0 | 0 | 0 | 0 | 0 | 0 | 0 | 0 | 0 | −1 | 1 |
|  |  |  |  |  |  |  |  |  |  |  |
|  |  |  |  |  |  |  |  |  |  |  |

And finally, to ensure that at least 2,500,000 college educated women are among the readers we would add the last restraint:

$$200,000X_1 + 80,000X_2 + 100,000X_3 \geq 2,500,000 \quad \text{(restraint 10)}.$$

Figure 9–2 illustrates all 10 restraints, shown first in their original form, then with appropriate slack and artificial variables added, ready for the first simplex table. The first simplex table for the solution to this problem appears in Figure 9–3. Since the problem requires a good bit of time and space for solution, the details of the solution are not shown here; the solution method is identical to that first introduced in Chapter 4 ("The Simplex Method of Linear Programming—Maximization"). Since the number of real variables $X_1$, $X_2$, and $X_3$ is small compared to the number of slack and artificial variables, solution of the dual in this case could well represent much less work.

Notice in Figure 9–3 that the artificial variables carry a cost of ($ – 100) since this is a *maximizing* problem.

## Machine assignment problem

Many factories have several machines which will perform the same work but at different per unit costs because of different machine efficiency. The assignment of products to various machines (or to different manufacturing plants) so as to minimize total production cost is a problem of great concern to management. For our illustrative problem, we have chosen a company which spins three sizes of cotton yarns in three plants. Whereas the machinery in each plant will produce each of the three yarns, the type of machinery in each plant produces each yarn at different speeds (pounds of yarn per spindle per three 40-hour shifts). The cost and output figures are fictitious; however, the methodology illustrated with some minor modifications is used for operational decision making in an actual yarn plant. The data in Figure 9–4 illustrate simulated production

FIGURE 9-4
Data for Spinning Plant Problem

| | | Plant 1 | | Plant 2 | | Plant 3 | |
|---|---|---|---|---|---|---|---|
| Yarn Size | Minimum Pounds Required | Pounds per Spindle in 120 hours | Cost per Pound | Pounds per Spindle in 120 hours | Cost per Pound | Pounds per Spindle in 120 hours | Cost per Pound |
| 10's | 12,000 | 6 | $0.10 | 10 | $0.12 | 12 | $0.08 |
| 16's | 15,000 | 8 | $0.20 | 5 | $0.16 | 6 | $0.25 |
| 20's | 4,000 | 3 | $0.50 | 4 | $0.40 | 2 | $0.30 |
| | Available Spindles | 1,000 | | 1,500 | | 2,000 | |

figures, costs, spindles available, and yarn requirements for a particular production period. The three different yarns are represented in the textile industry as 10's, 16's, and 20's, designating the diameter of the finished product. Since each of the possible yarn sizes (10's, 16's, and 20's) can be manufactured in each of the three spinning plants, we shall need to define our variables in a way which will show this. Figure 9–5 illustrates the method we have chosen for this purpose.

FIGURE 9-5
Designation of Variables for Spinning Plant Problem

| Yarn | Produced in Plant 1 | Produced in Plant 2 | Produced in Plant 3 |
|------|------|------|------|
| 10's........ | $X_1$ | $X_2$ | $X_3$ |
| 16's........ | $X_4$ | $X_5$ | $X_6$ |
| 20's........ | $X_7$ | $X_8$ | $X_9$ |

Our first task is to construct a set of restraints which will ensure that at least the minimum required poundage of each yarn is produced. This set will consist of three restraints as follows:

$$X_1 + X_2 + X_3 \geq 12,000 \qquad \text{(restraint 1)}$$
$$X_4 + X_5 + X_6 \geq 15,000 \qquad \text{(restraint 2)}$$
$$X_7 + X_8 + X_9 \geq 4,000 \qquad \text{(restraint 3)}$$

Having assured ourselves that the necessary poundage of required yarn will be produced, we must now ensure that the capacities of the spindles in each of the plants will not be exceeded. Looking first at plant 1 with 1,000 spindles available, we would write the restraint:

$$\frac{X_1}{6} + \frac{X_4}{8} + \frac{X_7}{3} \leq 1,000 \quad \text{(restraint 4; spindle restraint for plant 1)}$$

This restraint would be read: "the number of pounds of 10's produced in plant 1 divided by 6 pounds per spindle per 120 hours (the number of spindles used to manufacture 10's) plus the number of pounds of 16's produced in plant 1 divided by 8 pounds per spindle per 120 hours (the number of spindles used to manufacture 16's) plus the number of pounds of 20's produced in plant 1 divided by 3 pounds per spindle per 120 hours (the number of spindles used to manufacture 20's) must not exceed the 1,000 spindles available in plant 1."

In this same manner spindle restraints for plants 2 and 3, can be written:

$$\frac{X_2}{10} + \frac{X_5}{5} + \frac{X_8}{4} \leq 1,500 \quad \text{(restraint 5; spindle restraint for plant 2)}$$

$$\frac{X_3}{12} + \frac{X_6}{6} + \frac{X_9}{2} \leq 2,000 \quad \text{(restraint 6; spindle restraint for plant 3)}$$

## FIGURE 9-6
### Restraints for Yarn Spinning Problem
(Original form and with slack and artificial variables added)

Original form:

$$X_1 + X_2 + X_3 \ge 12{,}000$$
$$X_4 + X_5 + X_6 \ge 15{,}000$$
$$X_7 + X_8 + X_9 \ge 4{,}000$$
$$4X_1 + 3X_4 + 8X_7 \le 24{,}000$$
$$2X_2 + 4X_5 + 5X_8 \le 30{,}000$$
$$X_3 + 2X_6 + 6X_9 \le 24{,}000$$

With slack and artificial variables added:

$$X_1 + X_2 + X_3 - S_1 + A_1 = 12{,}000$$
$$X_4 + X_5 + X_6 - S_2 + A_2 = 15{,}000$$
$$X_7 + X_8 + X_9 - S_3 + A_3 = 4{,}000$$
$$4X_1 + 3X_4 + 8X_7 + S_4 = 24{,}000$$
$$2X_2 + 4X_5 + 5X_8 + S_5 = 30{,}000$$
$$X_3 + 2X_6 + 6X_9 + S_6 = 24{,}000$$

Restraints 4, 5, and 6 are in fractional form; they can be used *without* modification by using the decimal representation. For instance in the case of restraint 4, it can be expressed in decimal form as:

$$0.167X_1 + 0.125X_4 + 0.333X_7 \leq 1,000 \quad \text{(restraint 4 in decimal form)}.$$

To avoid changing fractional restraints into decimal form we could also find the least common denominator for the fractions in restraint 4 (24 in this case) and express it thusly:

$$4X_1 + 3X_4 + 8X_7 \leq 24,000 \quad \text{(restraint 4 in nondecimal form)}.$$

In Figure 9–6, we have illustrated the six restraints for this problem first in their original form and then with the addition of appropriate slack and artificial variables. With respect to restraints 4, 5, and 6, we have used the nondecimal form.

Figure 9–7 illustrates the first simplex table for the solution to the yarn spinning problem; since the objective in this problem is to minimize the total cost of production, the artificial variables used will take on a $C_j$ value of \$100. This will ensure that they will not appear in the final solution. The steps used in the solution of this problem once the first table has been set up are identical to those first discussed in Chapter 5, "The Simplex Method of Linear Programming—Minimization." If the company wished to consider the use of overtime in this problem, the methods described in Chapter 8 could be easily employed for this purpose. In the original problem solved by the authors from which this illustration was taken, there were 18 possible sizes and six different spinning departments; whereas the problem which resulted was much larger in size than the one we have just illustrated, the methodology used in its solution was the same.

### The transportation problem

This type of problem was first introduced in Chapter 6, "Special Purpose Algorithms." Using the methods described in that section, it is possible to work most transportation type problems; however, when the number of source points and using points becomes quite large, and storage costs enter the problem, it is often productive of time to employ the simplex method for their solution. Since computer programs for the simplex method exist, considerable timesaving can be realized in this manner.

The illustrative problem we have chosen for this section involves a

FIGURE 9-7
First Simplex Table for Yarn Spinning Problem

| $C_j$ | | | $0.10 | $0.12 | $0.08 | $0.20 | $0.16 | $0.25 | $0.50 | $0.40 | $0.30 | $0 | $100 | $0 | $100 | $0 | $100 | $0 | $0 | $0 |
|---|---|---|---|---|---|---|---|---|---|---|---|---|---|---|---|---|---|---|---|---|
| | MIX | QTY. | $X_1$ | $X_2$ | $X_3$ | $X_4$ | $X_5$ | $X_6$ | $X_7$ | $X_8$ | $X_9$ | $S_1$ | $A_1$ | $S_2$ | $A_2$ | $S_3$ | $A_3$ | $S_4$ | $S_5$ | $S_6$ |
| $100 | $A_1$ | 12,000 | 1 | 1 | 1 | 0 | 0 | 0 | 0 | 0 | 0 | −1 | 1 | 0 | 0 | 0 | 0 | 0 | 0 | 0 |
| $100 | $A_2$ | 15,000 | 0 | 0 | 0 | 1 | 1 | 1 | 0 | 0 | 0 | 0 | 0 | −1 | 1 | 0 | 0 | 0 | 0 | 0 |
| $100 | $A_3$ | 4,000 | 0 | 0 | 0 | 0 | 0 | 0 | 1 | 1 | 1 | 0 | 0 | 0 | 0 | −1 | 1 | 0 | 0 | 0 |
| $0 | $S_4$ | 24,000 | 4 | 0 | 0 | 3 | 0 | 0 | 8 | 0 | 0 | 0 | 0 | 0 | 0 | 0 | 0 | 1 | 0 | 0 |
| $0 | $S_5$ | 30,000 | 0 | 2 | 0 | 0 | 4 | 0 | 0 | 5 | 0 | 0 | 0 | 0 | 0 | 0 | 0 | 0 | 1 | 0 |
| $0 | $S_6$ | 24,000 | 0 | 0 | 1 | 0 | 0 | 2 | 0 | 0 | 6 | 0 | 0 | 0 | 0 | 0 | 0 | 0 | 0 | 1 |
| | $Z_j$ | | | | | | | | | | | | | | | | | | | |
| | $C_j - Z_j$ | | | | | | | | | | | | | | | | | | | |

firm which has two factories which supply three regional company-owned warehouses. Both factories produce identical items and the transportation costs per unit from each factory to each warehouse are known. The problem is to determine the lowest cost shipping schedule for each period. This particular problem can take several different forms, the simplest being known as the balanced case, i.e., the case where the quantities available at the factories are exactly equal to the quantities needed at the warehouses. This particular case is illustrated in Figure 9–8. The objective is to find the lowest cost shipping schedule.

FIGURE 9–8
Data for Balanced Transportation Problem

|  | Warehouse 1 | Warehouse 2 | Warehouse 3 |  |
|---|---|---|---|---|
| Factory A | $0.20 | $0.55 | $0.15 | 200 Units Available |
| Factory B | $0.40 | $0.30 | $0.60 | 90 Units Available |
| Units Required | 30 | 150 | 110 |  |

The answer to this problem will involve six quantities (the units to be shipped from each factory to each warehouse). We can let the six required answers be represented by $X$ values as illustrated in Figure 9–9.

FIGURE 9–9
Designation of Variables for Transportation Problem

|  | Warehouse 1 | Warehouse 2 | Warehouse 3 |
|---|---|---|---|
| Factory A | $X_1$ | $X_2$ | $X_3$ |
| Factory B | $X_4$ | $X_5$ | $X_6$ |

To ensure that the quantities shipped each period do not exceed those available at the factories, we can write the restraints:

$$X_1 + X_2 + X_3 \leq 200 \quad \text{(restraint 1; factory A)}$$
$$X_4 + X_5 + X_6 \leq 90 \quad \text{(restraint 2; factory B)}$$

And to ensure that the needs of each of the three warehouses are exactly met, we would write one restraint for each warehouse as follows:

$$X_1 + X_4 = \phantom{0}30 \qquad \text{(restraint 3; warehouse 1)}$$

$$X_2 + X_5 = 150 \qquad \text{(restraint 4; warehouse 2)}$$

$$X_3 + X_6 = 110 \qquad \text{(restraint 5; warehouse 3)}$$

Figure 9–10 illustrates the restraints with slack and artificial variables added, and the first simplex table for the minimum cost solution to this problem.

FIGURE 9–10

Restraints and First Simplex Table for Balanced Transportation Problem

$$
\begin{aligned}
X_1 + X_2 + X_3 \phantom{+X_4+X_5+X_6} + S_1 \phantom{+A_1+A_2+A_3} &= 200 \\
X_4 + X_5 + X_6 \phantom{+} + S_2 \phantom{+A_1+A_2+A_3} &= \phantom{0}90 \\
X_1 \phantom{+X_2+X_3} + X_4 \phantom{+X_5+X_6+S_1+S_2} + A_1 \phantom{+A_2+A_3} &= \phantom{0}30 \\
X_2 \phantom{+X_3} + X_5 \phantom{+X_6+S_1+S_2+A_1} + A_2 \phantom{+A_3} &= 150 \\
X_3 \phantom{+} + X_6 \phantom{+S_1+S_2+A_1+A_2} + A_3 &= 110
\end{aligned}
$$

| $C_j$ | | | $0.20 | $0.55 | $0.15 | $0.40 | $0.30 | $0.60 | $0 | $0 | $100 | $100 | $100 |
|---|---|---|---|---|---|---|---|---|---|---|---|---|---|
| | MIX | QTY. | $X_1$ | $X_2$ | $X_3$ | $X_4$ | $X_5$ | $X_6$ | $S_1$ | $S_2$ | $A_1$ | $A_2$ | $A_3$ |
| $0 | $S_1$ | 200 | 1 | 1 | 1 | 0 | 0 | 0 | 1 | 0 | 0 | 0 | 0 |
| $0 | $S_2$ | 90 | 0 | 0 | 0 | 1 | 1 | 1 | 0 | 1 | 0 | 0 | 0 |
| $100 | $A_1$ | 30 | 1 | 0 | 0 | 1 | 0 | 0 | 0 | 0 | 1 | 0 | 0 |
| $100 | $A_2$ | 150 | 0 | 1 | 0 | 0 | 1 | 0 | 0 | 0 | 0 | 1 | 0 |
| $100 | $A_3$ | 110 | 0 | 0 | 1 | 0 | 0 | 1 | 0 | 0 | 0 | 0 | 1 |
| $Z_j$ | | | | | | | | | | | | | |
| $C_j - Z_j$ | | | | | | | | | | | | | |

### Unbalanced cases of the transportation problem

In many cases, the quantities available at sources and the quantities required at the warehouses would not equal each other; these are referred to as unbalanced cases. The data in Figure 9–11 illustrate one unbalanced case; in this instance there are more units available than required. Before we can construct the necessary restraints we must determine where we want the excess units to remain, at the factories or at the warehouses. If, for example, we wanted the excess units to be shipped to the warehouses (at the lowest transportation cost, of course), we would write two restraints which would ensure that each factory would ship *all* its production as follows:

FIGURE 9-11
Unbalanced Case
(units available exceed units required)

| | Warehouse 1 | Warehouse 2 | Warehouse 3 | |
|---|---|---|---|---|
| Factory A | $X_1$ | $X_2$ | $X_3$ | 300 Units Available |
| Factory B | $X_4$ | $X_5$ | $X_6$ | 100 Units Available |
| Units Required | 50 | 80 | 150 | |

$$X_1 + X_2 + X_3 = 300 \qquad \text{(factory A)}$$

$$X_4 + X_5 + X_6 = 100 \qquad \text{(factory B)}$$

and three restraints ensuring that each warehouse would get *at least* its minimum requirement:

$$X_1 + X_4 \geq 50 \qquad \text{(warehouse 1)}$$

$$X_2 + X_5 \geq 80 \qquad \text{(warehouse 2)}$$

$$X_3 + X_6 \geq 150 \qquad \text{(warehouse 3)}$$

With the addition of appropriate slack and artificial variables these restraints would be ready for the first simplex table.

On the other hand, if we wanted the excess units to remain *at the factories*, we would write the first two constraints as:

$$X_1 + X_2 + X_3 \leq 300 \qquad \text{(factory A)}$$

$$X_4 + X_5 + X_6 \leq 100 \qquad \text{(factory B)}$$

And then to ensure that each warehouse received *only* its requirements, we would add three restraints like:

$$X_1 + X_4 = 50 \qquad \text{(warehouse 1)}$$

$$X_2 + X_5 = 80 \qquad \text{(warehouse 2)}$$

$$X_3 + X_6 = 150 \qquad \text{(warehouse 3)}$$

### Unbalanced transportation problem with upper warehouse limit

Often a company wishes to ship all excess units at the factories to the warehouses but finds the storage capacity of individual warehouses limited. Figure 9–12 illustrates this situation:

FIGURE 9-12
Unbalanced Case
(storage limits at warehouses)

|  | Warehouse 1 | Warehouse 2 | Warehouse 3 |  |
|---|---|---|---|---|
| Factory A | $X_1$ | $X_2$ | $X_3$ | 400 Units Available |
| Factory B | $X_4$ | $X_5$ | $X_6$ | 300 Units Available |
| Units Required | 100 | 200 | 250 |  |
| Maximum Storage Capacity | 150 | 290 | 275 |  |

In this case our first task is to write two restraints which will guarantee that each factory will ship its total production. These appear as:

$$X_1 + X_2 + X_3 = 400 \qquad \text{(factory A)}$$
$$X_4 + X_5 + X_6 = 300 \qquad \text{(factory B)}$$

To ensure that each warehouse receives the quantity it requires, three restraints are required. These appear as follows:

$$X_1 + X_4 \geq 100 \qquad \text{(warehouse 1, needs)}$$
$$X_2 + X_5 \geq 200 \qquad \text{(warehouse 2, needs)}$$
$$X_3 + X_6 \geq 250 \qquad \text{(warehouse 3, needs)}$$

And finally to ensure that the maximum storage capacity of the three warehouses is not violated, three additional restraints like the following are required:

$$X_1 + X_4 \leq 150 \qquad \text{(warehouse 1, storage limit)}$$
$$X_2 + X_5 \leq 290 \qquad \text{(warehouse 2, storage limit)}$$
$$X_3 + X_6 \leq 275 \qquad \text{(warehouse 3, storage limit)}$$

Thus eight restraints would be required in the first simplex table for this version of the unbalanced transportation problem.

## Unbalanced transportation problem with upper warehouse limits and factory limits

In some instances one encounters an unbalanced transportation problem where there are not only upper limits on the storage capacity of the warehouses but also some limits on the ability of the *factory* to store excesses. Figure 9–13 illustrates such a problem. In this instance, we can see that each factory can store *some* excess production, but only up to a certain stated level. Similar maximum storage levels have been placed on each of the warehouses.

FIGURE 9–13
Unbalanced Transportation Case
(storage limits at factories and warehouses)

| | Warehouse 1 | Warehouse 2 | Warehouse 3 | |
|---|---|---|---|---|
| Factory A | $X_1$ | $X_2$ | $X_3$ | 500 Units Available; *Must* Ship 300 of These |
| Factory B | $X_4$ | $X_5$ | $X_6$ | 600 Units Available; *Must* Ship 400 of These |
| Units Required | 150 | 160 | 300 | |
| Maximum Storage Capacity | 175 | 175 | 375 | |

To ensure that each factory does not ship more than its available units we would write two restraints:

$$X_1 + X_2 + X_3 \leq 500 \quad \text{(factory A, availability)}$$
$$X_4 + X_5 + X_6 \leq 600 \quad \text{(factory B, availability)}$$

Now, to ensure that each factory does not retain excesses beyond it storage capacity we will construct two additional restraints as follows:

$$X_1 + X_2 + X_3 \geq 300 \quad \text{(factory A, storage limit)}$$
$$X_4 + X_5 + X_6 \geq 400 \quad \text{(factory B, storage limit)}$$

Each warehouse receives its required units because of these three restraints:

$$X_1 + X_4 \geq 150 \qquad \text{(warehouse 1, needs)}$$
$$X_2 + X_5 \geq 160 \qquad \text{(warehouse 2, needs)}$$
$$X_3 + X_6 \geq 300 \qquad \text{(warehouse 3, needs)}$$

And finally, the maximum storage capacities of each of the warehouses are not exceeded because of the final three restraints:

$$X_1 + X_4 \leq 175 \quad \text{(warehouse 1, storage limit)}$$
$$X_2 + X_5 \leq 175 \quad \text{(warehouse 2, storage limit)}$$
$$X_3 + X_6 \leq 375 \quad \text{(warehouse 3, storage limit)}$$

Thus when storage limits are imposed on the factories as well as the warehouses, 10 restraints are required for this problem.

## Unbalanced transportation case with storage limits at factories and warehouses, and known storage costs per unit at either location

Often it is the case that management can calculate not only the transportation costs from each factory to each warehouse but also the storage costs *at* each factory and each warehouse for excess units. When this information is available the lowest total cost *shipping and storage* program can be determined through linear programming. For our example of this case, we shall use the same data from the previous example, with the addition, of course, of appropriate storage costs. These data appear in Figure 9–14.

FIGURE 9–14
Data for Unbalanced Transportation Problem with Storage Costs

| | Warehouse 1 | Warehouse 2 | Warehouse 3 | |
|---|---|---|---|---|
| Factory A | $X_1$ \$0.30 | $X_2$ \$0.20 | $X_3$ \$0.60 | 500 Units Available; Must Ship 300; Storage Cost is \$0.08 Unit for Remaining Units |
| Factory B | $X_4$ \$0.40 | $X_5$ \$0.18 | $X_3$ \$0.50 | 600 Units Available; Must Ship 400; Storage Cost is \$0.12 Unit for Remaining Units |
| Units Required | 150 | 160 | 300 | |
| Maximum Storage Capacity | 175 | 175 | 375 | |
| Storage Cost per Unit at Warehouse | \$0.09 | \$0.11 | \$0.13 | |

FIGURE 9-15

Restraint Equations for Unbalanced Transportation Problem
with Storage and Storage Cost

$$
\begin{array}{lllllll}
X_1 + X_2 + X_2 & & & & + S_1 & & = 500 \\
X_1 + X_2 + X_3 & X_4 + X_5 + X_6 & & & & + S_2 & = 600 \\
& & & - S_3 + A_1 & & & = 300 \\
X_1 & X_4 + X_5 + X_6 & & - S_4 + A_2 & & & = 400 \\
& + X_4 & & - S_5 + A_3 & & & = 150 \\
X_2 & + X_5 & & - S_6 + A_4 & & & = 160 \\
X_3 & + X_4 & + X_6 & - S_7 + A_5 & & & = 300 \\
X_1 & & & + S_8 & & & = 175 \\
X_2 & X_3 & + X_5 & & + S_9 & & = 175 \\
X_3 & & + X_6 & & & + S_{10} & = 375 \\
\end{array}
$$

FIGURE 9–16
First Simplex Table for Unbalanced Transportation Problem with
Storage and Storage Costs

| $C_j$ | | | $0.30 | $0.20 | $0.60 | $0.40 | $0.18 | $0.50 | $0.08 | $0.12 | $0 |
|---|---|---|---|---|---|---|---|---|---|---|---|
| | MIX | QTY. | $X_1$ | $X_2$ | $X_3$ | $X_4$ | $X_5$ | $X_6$ | $S_1$ | $S_2$ | $S_3$ |
| $0.08 | $S_1$ | 500 | 1 | 1 | 1 | 0 | 0 | 0 | 1 | 0 | 0 |
| $0.12 | $S_2$ | 600 | 0 | 0 | 0 | 1 | 1 | 1 | 0 | 1 | 0 |
| $100 | $A_1$ | 300 | 1 | 1 | 1 | 0 | 0 | 0 | 0 | 0 | −1 |
| $100 | $A_2$ | 400 | 0 | 0 | 0 | 1 | 1 | 1 | 0 | 0 | 0 |
| $100 | $A_3$ | 150 | 1 | 0 | 0 | 1 | 0 | 0 | 0 | 0 | 0 |
| $100 | $A_4$ | 160 | 0 | 1 | 0 | 0 | 1 | 0 | 0 | 0 | 0 |
| $100 | $A_5$ | 300 | 0 | 0 | 1 | 0 | 0 | 1 | 0 | 0 | 0 |
| $0 | $S_8$ | 175 | 1 | 0 | 0 | 1 | 0 | 0 | 0 | 0 | 0 |
| $8 | $S_9$ | 175 | 0 | 1 | 0 | 0 | 1 | 0 | 0 | 0 | 0 |
| $0 | $S_{10}$ | 375 | 0 | 0 | 1 | 0 | 0 | 1 | 0 | 0 | 0 |
| $Z_j$ | | | | | | | | | | | |
| $C_j - Z_j$ | | | | | | | | | | | |

The restraints in this case will be identical to those in the previous example; the only difference in the problem will be that we shall assign storage costs to units which either remain as excesses at the factories or show up as excesses at the three warehouses. Figure 9–15 illustrates the 10 restraints with appropriate slack and artificial variables added ready for the first simplex table.

Figure 9–16 is the first simplex table for the solution to this problem. The reader will notice that some of the slack variables have $C_j$ values other than zero. For example, $S_1$ and $S_2$ (the slack variables which represent quantities of units that *remain at the factories*) have $C_j$ values which were given in the problem as the storage cost per unit for factory storage. Also $S_5$, $S_6$, and $S_7$ (the slack variables which represent excess materials stored at the warehouses) have $C_j$ values

| $100 | $0 | $100 | $0.09 | $100 | $0.11 | $100 | $0.13 | $100 | $0 | $0 | $0 |
|---|---|---|---|---|---|---|---|---|---|---|---|
| $A_1$ | $S_4$ | $A_2$ | $S_5$ | $A_3$ | $S_6$ | $A_4$ | $S_7$ | $A_5$ | $S_8$ | $S_9$ | $S_{10}$ |
| 0 | 0 | 0 | 0 | 0 | 0 | 0 | 0 | 0 | 0 | 0 | 0 |
| 0 | 0 | 0 | 0 | 0 | 0 | 0 | 0 | 0 | 0 | 0 | 0 |
| 1 | 0 | 0 | 0 | 0 | 0 | 0 | 0 | 0 | 0 | 0 | 0 |
| 0 | −1 | 1 | 0 | 0 | 0 | 0 | 0 | 0 | 0 | 0 | 0 |
| 0 | 0 | 0 | −1 | 1 | 0 | 0 | 0 | 0 | 0 | 0 | 0 |
| 0 | 0 | 0 | 0 | 0 | −1 | 1 | 0 | 0 | 0 | 0 | 0 |
| 0 | 0 | 0 | 0 | 0 | 0 | 0 | −1 | 1 | 0 | 0 | 0 |
| 0 | 0 | 0 | 0 | 0 | 0 | 0 | 0 | 0 | 1 | 0 | 0 |
| 0 | 0 | 0 | 0 | 0 | 0 | 0 | 0 | 0 | 0 | 1 | 0 |
| 0 | 0 | 0 | 0 | 0 | 0 | 0 | 0 | 0 | 0 | 0 | 1 |
|  |  |  |  |  |  |  |  |  |  |  |  |
|  |  |  |  |  |  |  |  |  |  |  |  |

showing those relevant per unit storage costs. On the other hand however, $S_3$ and $S_4$ have $C_j$ values of *zero*, because these variables represent units the factories cannot store and they will show up in one of the warehouses where a cost has already been assigned ($S_5$, $S_6$, and $S_7$). Using the same reasoning, $S_8$, $S_9$, and $S_{10}$ all have $C_j$ values of zero; these variables represent quantities of units *below* the maximum limit of each warehouse (i.e., quantities not shipped to the warehouses); these will show up as being stored at one of the factories where a cost has already been assigned, ($S_1$ and $S_2$). When the transportation problem involves upper and lower limits as we have just observed, and storage costs, solutions using the "Transportation Method" illustrated in Chapter 6 are sometimes cumbersome. Use of the simplex method will generally save considerable time and effort.

## A problem involving several different areas of the firm

Managerial decisions are rarely limited to one area of the firm; most often, different functional areas of an enterprise impose certain restraints upon the decisions which are made in other areas of the same firm. For instance, production decisions concerning optimum product mix cannot really be made independent of marketing considerations as to which products will enjoy the highest demand. Marketing decisions on the other hand can hardly be made unless the current ability of the production unit to meet demand is known and made a significant part of the decision. For these reasons a problem involving several different areas of the same firm will be illustrated. A decision on quantities of each product to be produced will be made using linear programming; the specific areas from which restraints to the solution are generated are (1) production, (2) marketing, and (3) raw material supplies available.

Figure 9–17 illustrates the five possible products, each with its contribution to fixed costs and profits.

FIGURE 9-17
Possible Products and
Their Contributions

| Product | Contribution per Unit |
|---------|----------------------|
| $X_1$ | $3 |
| $X_2$ | $4 |
| $X_3$ | $5 |
| $X_4$ | $2 |
| $X_5$ | $6 |

The production restraints in the problem for each of four departments through which the products pass are given in Figure 9–18.

We shall assume in this problem that demand for the coming period for each of the five products has been estimated and that the *maximum* quantities of each product which can be sold are known. We shall also assume that there are some marketing commitments on several

FIGURE 9–18
Production Restraints

| Product | Department 1 | Department 2 | Department 3 | Department 4 |
|---------|--------------|--------------|--------------|--------------|
| $X_1$ | 3 hr. per unit | 8 hr. per unit | 2 hr. per unit | 6 hr. per unit |
| $X_2$ | 4 hr. per unit | 3 hr. per unit | 1 hr. per unit | 0 hr. per unit |
| $X_3$ | 2 hr. per unit | 2 hr. per unit | 0 hr. per unit | 2 hr. per unit |
| $X_4$ | 2 hr. per unit | 1 hr. per unit | 3 hr. per unit | 4 hr. per unit |
| $X_5$ | 5 hr. per unit | 4 hr. per unit | 4 hr. per unit | 3 hr. per unit |

Total Hours
Available:     700              600              400              900

of the products concerning *minimum* quantities which must be delivered. The data in Figure 9–19 illustrate the marketing restraints.

FIGURE 9–19
Marketing Restraints

| Product | Maximum Demand | Minimum Quantities Required |
|---------|----------------|-----------------------------|
| $X_1$ | 100 units | 30 units |
| $X_2$ | 50 units | 0 units |
| $X_3$ | 90 units | 40 units |
| $X_4$ | 70 units | 0 units |
| $X_5$ | 130 units | 35 units |

Finally, raw materials at any one time in a production operation are in limited supply; data concerning the raw material requirements of each of the five products and the total quantities of each of these raw materials currently available are given in Figure 9–20.

FIGURE 9-20
Raw Materials Required and Available

| Product | Material A | Material B | Material C | Material D | Material E |
|---------|-----------|-----------|-----------|-----------|-----------|
| $X_1$ | 4 lb. per unit | 2 lb. per unit | 0 lb. per unit | 1 lb. per unit | 3 lb. per unit |
| $X_2$ | 7 lb. per unit | 4 lb. per unit | 4 lb. per unit | 0 lb. per unit | 4 lb. per unit |
| $X_3$ | 6 lb. per unit | 2 lb. per unit | 5 lb. per unit | 7 lb. per unit | 0 lb. per unit |
| $X_4$ | 1 lb. per unit | 1 lb. per unit | 6 lb. per unit | 4 lb. per unit | 2 lb. per unit |
| $X_5$ | 3 lb. per unit | 0 lb. per unit | 2 lb. per unit | 3 lb. per unit | 4 lb. per unit |

Maximum
Pounds
Available:    600           700           300           400           1,100

Algebraic restraints for each of these areas must be written. Beginning first with the restraints on production time, we can generate four restraints, one for each department as follows:

$$3X_1 + 4X_2 + 2X_3 + 2X_4 + 5X_5 \leq 700 \quad \text{(restraint 1, dept. 1)}$$
$$8X_1 + 3X_2 + 2X_3 + \ X_4 + 4X_5 \leq 600 \quad \text{(restraint 2, dept. 2)}$$
$$2X_1 + \ X_2 + 0X_3 + 3X_4 + 4X_5 \leq 400 \quad \text{(restraint 3, dept. 3)}$$
$$6X_1 + 0X_2 + 2X_3 + 4X_4 + 3X_5 \leq 900 \quad \text{(restraint 4, dept. 4)}.$$

Eight marketing restraints would be required for the problem, five to ensure that maximum salable quantities were not exceeded, and additional restraints to ensure that minimum sales commitments are met; these appear as:

$X_1 \leq 100$    (restraint 5, maximum demand product $X_1$)

$X_2 \leq 50$    (restraint 6, maximum demand product $X_2$)

$X_3 \leq 90$    (restraint 7, maximum demand product $X_3$)

$X_4 \leq 70$    (restraint 8, maximum demand product $X_4$)

$X_5 \leq 130$    (restraint 9, maximum demand product $X_5$)

$X_1 \geq 30$    (restraint 10, required quantity product $X_1$)

$X_3 \geq 40$    (restraint 11, required quantity product $X_3$)

$X_5 \geq 35$    (restraint 12, required quantity product $X_5$)

To ensure that supplies of raw material enter the production decision as a restraint, five additional algebraic restraints must be developed; these are:

$$4X_1 + 7X_2 + 6X_3 + X_4 + 3X_5 \leq 600 \quad \text{(restraint 13, raw material A)}$$
$$2X_1 + 4X_2 + 2X_3 + X_4 + 0X_5 \leq 700 \quad \text{(restraint 14, raw material B)}$$
$$0X_1 + 4X_2 + 5X_3 + 6X_4 + 2X_5 \leq 300 \quad \text{(restraint 15, raw material C)}$$
$$X_1 + 0X_2 + 7X_3 + 4X_4 + 3X_5 \leq 400 \quad \text{(restraint 16, raw material D)}$$
$$3X_1 + 4X_2 + 0X_3 + 2X_4 + 4X_5 \leq 1{,}100 \quad \text{(restraint 17, raw material E)}.$$

Figure 9–21 illustrates all of the restraints in equality form.

In Figure 9–22, we have illustrated the first maximizing table for this problem; additional restraints could have been added for (a) capital requirements, (b) storage limitations, and (c) other pertinent decision variables. The ability of management to take into consideration all of the pertinent variables depends only upon the extent to which these variables can be quantified, and the availability of resources to perform the required calculations, either by hand methods or using a computer. We can observe here that because of the number of slack and artificial variables (20) relative to the number of real variables (5), solution of the dual instead of the primal would reduce the work considerably.

## Production smoothing problem

It is often the case in business that seasonal peaks in demand for products exceed the current ability of the production facilities in that period to supply that demand. In these cases, in order not to loes sales, production in earlier periods must be accomplished and the finished goods stored until the peak demand period. In addition to this remedy, the use of overtime hours is often employed to meet seasonal demand with, of course, a corresponding increase in labor cost. In the determination of total production plans for a yearly period, input information to the decision-making process would include (1) sales forecast by product, (2) storage cost per period for products produced in advance of sale, (3) cost of overtime if employed, and (4) maximum capacity of the production facilities by period. Determining the optimum (lowest total cost) production schedule for a year in advance is almost an impossible task unless some organized

FIGURE 9–21

Equalities for Production, Marketing, and Raw Materials

$$3X_1 + 4X_2 + 2X_3 + 2X_4 + 5X_5 + S_1$$
$$8X_1 + 3X_2 + 2X_3 + \phantom{2}X_4 + 4X_5 \phantom{+S_1} + S_2$$
$$2X_1 + \phantom{3}X_2 + 0X_3 + 3X_4 + 4X_5 \phantom{+S_1+S_2} + S_3$$
$$6X_1 + 0X_2 + 2X_3 + 4X_4 + 3X_5 \phantom{+S_1+S_2+S_3} + S_4$$
$$X_1 \phantom{+0X_2+2X_3+4X_4+3X_5+S_1+S_2+S_3} + S_5$$
$$X_2 \phantom{+0X_2+2X_3+4X_4+3X_5+S_1+S_2+S_3+S_5} + S_6$$
$$X_3 \phantom{+0X_2+2X_3+4X_4+3X_5+S_1+S_2+S_3+S_5+S_6} + S_7$$
$$X_4 \phantom{+0X_2+2X_3+4X_4+3X_5+S_1+S_2+S_3+S_5+S_6+S_7} + S_8$$
$$X_5$$
$$X_1$$
$$X_3$$
$$X_5$$
$$4X_1 + 7X_2 + 6X_3 + \phantom{2}X_4 + 3X_5$$
$$2X_1 + 4X_2 + 2X_3 + \phantom{2}X_4 + 0X_5$$
$$0X_1 + 4X_2 + 5X_3 + 6X_4 + 2X_5$$
$$X_1 + 0X_2 + 7X_3 + 4X_4 + 3X_5$$
$$3X_1 + 4X_2 + 0X_3 + 2X_4 + 4X_5$$

FIGURE 9–22

First Maximizing Table for Production, Marketing, Raw Materials Problem

| $C_j$ | | | $3 | $4 | $5 | $2 | $6 | $0 | $0 | $0 | $0 | $0 | $0 | $0 |
|---|---|---|---|---|---|---|---|---|---|---|---|---|---|---|
| | MIX | QTY. | $X_1$ | $X_2$ | $X_3$ | $X_4$ | $X_5$ | $S_1$ | $S_2$ | $S_3$ | $S_4$ | $S_5$ | $S_6$ | $S_7$ |
| $0 | $S_1$ | 700 | 3 | 4 | 2 | 2 | 5 | 1 | | | | | | |
| $0 | $S_2$ | 600 | 8 | 3 | 2 | 1 | 4 | | 1 | | | | | |
| $0 | $S_3$ | 400 | 2 | 1 | 0 | 3 | 4 | | | 1 | | | | |
| $0 | $S_4$ | 900 | 6 | 0 | 2 | 4 | 3 | | | | 1 | | | |
| $0 | $S_5$ | 100 | 1 | | | | | | | | | 1 | | |
| $0 | $S_6$ | 50 | | 1 | | | | | | | | | 1 | |
| $0 | $S_7$ | 90 | | | 1 | | | | | | | | | 1 |
| $0 | $S_8$ | 70 | | | 1 | | | | | | | | | |
| $0 | $S_9$ | 30 | | | | 1 | | | | | | | | |
| $-100 | $A_1$ | 30 | 1 | | | | | | | | | | | |
| $-100 | $A_2$ | 40 | | | 1 | | | | | | | | | |
| $-100 | $A_3$ | 35 | | | | 1 | | | | | | | | |
| $0 | $S_{13}$ | 600 | 4 | 7 | 6 | 1 | 3 | | | | | | | |
| $0 | $S_{14}$ | 700 | 2 | 4 | 2 | 1 | 0 | | | | | | | |
| $0 | $S_{15}$ | 300 | 0 | 4 | 5 | 6 | 2 | | | | | | | |
| $0 | $S_{16}$ | 400 | 1 | 0 | 7 | 4 | 3 | | | | | | | |
| $0 | $S_{17}$ | 1,100 | 3 | 4 | 0 | 2 | 4 | | | | | | | |
| $Z_j$ | | | | | | | | | | | | | | |
| $C_j - Z_j$ | | | | | | | | | | | | | | |

$$
\begin{aligned}
&= 700 \\
&= 600 \\
&= 400 \\
&= 900 \\
&= 100 \\
&= 50 \\
&= 90 \\
&= 70 \\
+\,S_9\qquad\qquad\qquad\qquad\qquad\qquad\qquad &= 30 \\
-\,S_{10} + A_1\qquad\qquad\qquad\qquad\qquad &= 30 \\
-\,S_4 + A_2\qquad\qquad\qquad\qquad &= 40 \\
-\,S_{12} + A_3\qquad\qquad\qquad &= 35 \\
+\,S_{13}\qquad\qquad\qquad &= 600 \\
+\,S_{14}\qquad\qquad &= 700 \\
+\,S_{15}\qquad &= 300 \\
+\,S_{16} &= 400 \\
+\,S_{17} &= 1{,}100
\end{aligned}
$$

| $0 | $0 | $0 | $-100 | $0 | $-100 | $0 | $-100 | $0 | $0 | $0 | $0 | $0 |
|---|---|---|---|---|---|---|---|---|---|---|---|---|
| $S_8$ | $S_9$ | $S_{10}$ | $A_1$ | $S_{11}$ | $A_2$ | $S_{12}$ | $A_3$ | $S_{13}$ | $S_{14}$ | $S_{15}$ | $S_{16}$ | $S_{17}$ |
|  |  |  |  |  |  |  |  |  |  |  |  |  |
|  |  |  |  |  |  |  |  |  |  |  |  |  |
|  |  |  |  |  |  |  |  |  |  |  |  |  |
|  |  |  |  |  |  |  |  |  |  |  |  |  |
|  |  |  |  |  |  |  |  |  |  |  |  |  |
|  |  |  |  |  |  |  |  |  |  |  |  |  |
| 1 |  |  |  |  |  |  |  |  |  |  |  |  |
|  | 1 |  |  |  |  |  |  |  |  |  |  |  |
|  |  | $-1$ | 1 |  |  |  |  |  |  |  |  |  |
|  |  |  |  | $-1$ | 1 |  |  |  |  |  |  |  |
|  |  |  |  |  |  | $-1$ | 1 |  |  |  |  |  |
|  |  |  |  |  |  |  |  | 1 |  |  |  |  |
|  |  |  |  |  |  |  |  |  | 1 |  |  |  |
|  |  |  |  |  |  |  |  |  |  | 1 |  |  |
|  |  |  |  |  |  |  |  |  |  |  | 1 |  |
|  |  |  |  |  |  |  |  |  |  |  |  | 1 |
|  |  |  |  |  |  |  |  |  |  |  |  |  |
|  |  |  |  |  |  |  |  |  |  |  |  |  |

decision-making process such as linear programming is employed. For this reason production smoothing using linear programming has found wide use in industry today.

FIGURE 9-23
Forecast Demand in Plant Hours Available
(by quarters)

| | Demand in Plant Hours | | | | Plant Hours Available | | |
|---|---|---|---|---|---|---|---|
| | Product A | Product B | Product C | Total | Regular Time Hours | Over-time Hours | Total |
| First Quarter | 50 | 60 | 70 | 180 | 280 | 80 | 360 |
| Second Quarter | 75 | 65 | 80 | 220 | 150 | 60 | 210 |
| Third Quarter | 85 | 100 | 90 | 275 | 170 | 40 | 210 |
| Fourth Quarter | 105 | 110 | 120 | 335 | 200 | 70 | 270 |
| Total | | | | 1,010 | | | 1,050 |

Figure 9–23 illustrates the forecast demand for products by quarters (converted into plant hours) and the available production capacity by quarters (illustrated in plant hours). From Figure 9–23 we observe that although the total number of plant hours available *for the year* exceeds the yearly forecast sales demand (in plant hours), the factory hours required in the last three quarters of the year exceed the hours available in those quarters. This will require us to produce certain items early in the year, store them for a certain period, and then sell them when the demand materializes.

Storage costs incurred in holding items produced in one quarter for sale in a later quarter have been estimated in terms of "cost to hold one hour's production for one quarter." This gives management considerably more flexibility because storage costs for specific products need not be calculated. Determining costs in this manner involves calculating the cost of an hour's production of each of the three products, then applying a storage rate (percent) to each of these figures. Figure 9–24 illustrates estimated storage costs for this problem.

FIGURE 9–24
Storage Costs per Quarter for One Hour's Production

| Cost to store of one hour's production of each product for one quarter | *Product A* | *Product B* | *Product C* |
|---|---|---|---|
| | $0.30 | $0.50 | $0.70 |

Finally a determination of the cost of using overtime hours as a production alternative must be made a part of the solution. This calculation is also made in terms of "the premium cost of overtime per hour of production." Here too, expressing overtime cost in this manner makes it unnecessary for management to state in advance which particular units of product will be manufactured during each period; all that is really necessary is to ensure that the total required hours of production time are available when the time comes. Figure 9–25 illustrates the extra cost of overtime per hour of production for each of the three products. The different values in Figure 9–25 reflect the different wage rates of those who work on these particular products as well as the labor intensity of each product.

FIGURE 9–25
Extra Cost of Overtime for Each of the Three Products

| The extra cost of overtime per hour of production for each of the products | *Product A* | *Product B* | *Product C* |
|---|---|---|---|
| | $0.65 | $1.05 | $1.35 |

The solution to this problem will be in terms of how many hours of regular time and overtime will be allotted during each quarter to the manufacture of each product, both for current and for future sale. Thus we shall have to designate a specific solution variable to represent the number of (*a*) regular time hours, and (*b*) overtime hours to be used in the production of products A, B, and C for (1) sale in the present quarter and (2) sale in future quarters. Since the number of such variables is quite large we have employed the table in Figure 9–26 to illustrate the designation of solution variables for this problem.

FIGURE 9–26
Designation of Solution Variables

| Production in: | | First Quarter A | B | C | Second Quarter A | B | C | Third Quarter A | B | C | Fourth Quarter A | B | C |
|---|---|---|---|---|---|---|---|---|---|---|---|---|---|
| | | For Sale in: | | | | | | | | | | | |
| First Quarter | RT | $X_1$ | $X_2$ | $X_3$ | $X_4$ | $X_5$ | $X_6$ | $X_7$ | $X_8$ | $X_9$ | $X_{10}$ | $X_{11}$ | $X_{12}$ |
| | OT | $X_{13}$ | $X_{14}$ | $X_{15}$ | $X_{16}$ | $X_{17}$ | $X_{18}$ | $X_{19}$ | $X_{20}$ | $X_{21}$ | $X_{22}$ | $X_{23}$ | $X_{24}$ |
| Second Quarter | RT | | | | $X_{25}$ | $X_{26}$ | $X_{27}$ | $X_{28}$ | $X_{29}$ | $X_{30}$ | $X_{31}$ | $X_{32}$ | $X_{33}$ |
| | OT | | | | $X_{34}$ | $X_{35}$ | $X_{36}$ | $X_{37}$ | $X_{38}$ | $X_{39}$ | $X_{40}$ | $X_{41}$ | $X_{42}$ |
| Third Quarter | RT | | | | | | | $X_{43}$ | $X_{44}$ | $X_{45}$ | $X_{46}$ | $X_{47}$ | $X_{48}$ |
| | OT | | | | | | | $X_{49}$ | $X_{50}$ | $X_{51}$ | $X_{52}$ | $X_{53}$ | $X_{54}$ |
| Fourth Quarter | RT | | | | | | | | | | $X_{55}$ | $X_{56}$ | $X_{57}$ |
| | OT | | | | | | | | | | $X_{58}$ | $X_{59}$ | $X_{60}$ |

RT—Regular Time
OT—Overtime

The blank portions of the table in Figure 9–26 indicate that production in any quarter is either for sale in *that* quarter or for sale in a *future* quarter, but never for sale in a quarter which has already passed. Each of the $X$ solution variables refers to a specific number of hours of production either regular or overtime; for example $X_{16}$ refers to the overtime which will be spent in the first quarter producing product A for sale in the second quarter. In the same manner, $X_{33}$ would refer to the regular time hours spent in the second quarter producing product C for sale in the fourth quarter.

Since the objective in the solution is to minimize the total cost of storage and overtime labor costs, we must now designate the cost which accompanies each of the 60 $X$ variables. Products made during regular time hours for sale in the current quarter incur *no* extra cost at all; products made on overtime for sale in the current quarter incur only the overtime premium. Using this same reasoning, products produced during regular time hours for sale in future periods would incur only storage costs while products produced during overtime hours for sale in future periods would incur both storage and overtime costs.

Several examples will illustrate the procedure for calculating both overtime and storage costs. Let us look first at $X_1$ (hours used in the first quarter to produce product A for sale in the first quarter). The $C_j$ cost coefficient of $X_1$ in this problem would be zero since no extra costs are involved. Observing next $X_{15}$ (overtime hours utilized in the first quarter for production of product C for sale in the first quarter) we see that the $C_j$ for this variable would be $1.35, the overtime premium; in this case no storage is involved. Using $X_{32}$ for our next example (regular time hours employed in the second quarter in the production of product B for sale in the fourth quarter) we see that the appropriate $C_j$ value would be $1, (the $0.50 per quarter required to store product B times the two quarters it would be stored). One final example will be illustrated. Let us look now at $X_{42}$ (production during overtime hours in the second quarter of product C for sale in the fourth quarter). This product would incur both overtime premium costs *and* storage costs. The appropriate $C_j$ cost for $X_{42}$ would be $1.40 for storage ($0.70 per unit of C times the two quarters it would be stored) plus $1.35 (the overtime cost for product C); thus the appropriate $C_j$ for $X_{42}$ would be $2.75. The data in Figure 9–27 illustrate the appropriate $C_j$'s for all 60 variables first shown in Figure 9–26. The authors have elected not to charge a *different* storage cost on items produced during overtime; while this might have to be done in actual practice, including it in this illustrative problem would add considerably to the calculations with little if any expositive value.

With the designation of all the variables completed and the assignment of $C_j$ values made for each of the variables, our task is now to construct the appropriate restraints for the problem. Looking at all of the $X$ variables (in Figure 9–26) representing regular time production during the first quarter we see that the sum of these hours cannot exceed 280 hours, the maximum number of regular time hours available in that quarter.

The appropriate inequality for regular time hours in the first quarter would then be:

## FIGURE 9-27
### C, Cost Value for All Variables

| | Period during Which Products Are Sold: | | | | | | | | | | | |
|---|---|---|---|---|---|---|---|---|---|---|---|---|
| | First Quarter | | | Second Quarter | | | Third Quarter | | | Fourth Quarter | | |
| Period during Which Products Are Made: | A | B | C | A | B | C | A | B | C | A | B | C |
| First Qtr. RT | $0 | $0 | $0 | $0.30 | $0.50 | $0.70 | $0.60 | $1.00 | $1.40 | $0.90 | $1.50 | $2.10 |
| OT | $0.65 | $1.05 | $1.35 | $0.95 | $1.55 | $2.05 | $1.25 | $2.05 | $2.75 | $1.55 | $2.55 | $3.45 |
| Second Qtr. RT | | | | $0 | $0 | $0 | $0.30 | $0.50 | $0.70 | $0.60 | $1.00 | $1.40 |
| OT | | | | $0.65 | $1.05 | $1.35 | $0.95 | $1.55 | $2.05 | $1.25 | $2.05 | $2.75 |
| Third Qtr. RT | | | | | | | $0 | $0 | $0 | $0.30 | $0.50 | $0.70 |
| OT | | | | | | | $0.65 | $1.05 | $1.35 | $0.95 | $1.55 | $2.05 |
| Fourth Qtr. RT | | | | | | | | | | $0 | $0 | $0 |
| OT | | | | | | | | | | $0.65 | $1.05 | $1.35 |

RT—Regular Time
OT—Overtime

Restraint 1, 1st quarter regular time:
$$X_1 + X_2 + X_3 + X_4 + X_5 + X_6 + X_7 + X_8 + X_9 + X_{10} + X_{11} + X_{12}$$
$$\leq 280$$

In the same manner, inequalities representing maximum hour limits on production in both regular time and overtime for the fourth quarter would be written:

Restraint 2, 1st quarter overtime:
$$X_{13} + X_{14} + X_{15} + X_{16} + X_{17} + X_{18} + X_{19} + X_{20} + X_{21} + X_{22} + X_{23} + X_{24}$$
$$\leq 80$$

Restraint 3, 2nd quarter regular time:
$$X_{25} + X_{26} + X_{27} + X_{28} + X_{29} + X_{30} + X_{31} + X_{32} + X_{33} \leq 150$$

Restraint 4, 2nd quarter overtime:
$$X_{34} + X_{35} + X_{36} + X_{37} + X_{38} + X_{39} + X_{40} + X_{41} + X_{42} \leq 60$$

Restraint 5, 3rd quarter regular time:
$$X_{43} + X_{44} + X_{45} + X_{46} + X_{47} + X_{48} \leq 170$$

Restraint 6, 3rd quarter overtime:
$$X_{49} + X_{50} + X_{51} + X_{52} + X_{53} + X_{54} \leq 40$$

Restraint 7, 4th quarter regular time:
$$X_{55} + X_{56} + X_{57} \leq 200$$

Restraint 8, 4th quarter overtime:
$$X_{58} + X_{59} + X_{60} \leq 70$$

These eight restraints will ensure that the maximum hours available in each quarter on both regular and overtime will not be exceeded.

In addition we will require a set of restraints to ensure that the sales forecast for each product in each future quarter will be met by the factory. Referring once again to the variables designated in Figure 9–26, we see that the first quarter production of product A will be composed of $X_1 + X_{13}$; the sum of these two values must equal the forecast of product A in the first quarter or 50 hours of production. Thus the restraint which will ensure adequate supplies of A for the first quarter is written:

Restraint 9, demand for A, 1st quarter:
$$X_1 + X_{13} = 50$$

In similar fashion, the other 11 restraints required to guarantee adequate supplies of the products for sale in all periods would be written:

Restraint 10, demand for B, 1st quarter:

$$X_2 + X_{14} = 60$$

Restraint 11, demand for C, 1st quarter:

$$X_3 + X_{15} = 70$$

Restraint 12, demand for A, 2nd quarter:

$$X_4 + X_{16} + X_{25} + X_{34} = 75$$

Restraint 13, demand for B, 2nd quarter:

$$X_5 + X_{17} + X_{26} + X_{35} = 65$$

Restraint 14, demand for C, 2nd quarter:

$$X_6 + X_{18} + X_{27} + X_{36} = 80$$

Restraint 15, demand for A, 3rd quarter:

$$X_7 + X_{19} + X_{28} + X_{37} + X_{43} + X_{49} = 85$$

Restraint 16, demand for B, 3rd quarter:

$$X_8 + X_{20} + X_{29} + X_{28} + X_{44} + X_{50} = 100$$

Restraint 17, demand for C, 3rd quarter:

$$X_9 + X_{21} + X_{30} + X_{39} + X_{45} + X_{51} = 90$$

Restraint 18, demand for A, 4th quarter:

$$X_{10} + X_{22} + X_{31} + X_{40} + X_{46} + X_{52} + X_{55} + X_{58} = 105$$

Restraint 19, demand for B, 4th quarter:

$$X_{11} + X_{23} + X_{32} + X_{41} + X_{47} + X_{53} + X_{56} + X_{59} = 110$$

Restraint 20, demand for C, 4th quarter:

$$X_{12} + X_{24} + X_{33} + X_{42} + X_{48} + X_{54} + X_{57} + X_{60} = 120$$

Figure 9–28 illustrates the 20 restraints required for this problem with appropriate slack and artificial variables added. These are now ready for insertion into the first simplex table for the solution to this problem. The first simplex table will not be represented here because it would require 83 columns; it is constructed however like any minimization table we have previously illustrated, the only difference being its size. Solution to this problem using hand calculations would

FIGURE 9-28
Equations for First Simplex Table

$$X_1 + X_2 + X_3 + X_4 + X_5 + X_6 + X_7 + X_8 + X_9 + X_{10} + X_{11} + X_{12} + S_1 = 280$$
$$X_{13} + X_{14} + X_{15} + X_{16} + X_{17} + X_{18} + X_{19} + X_{20} + X_{21} + X_{22} + X_{23} + X_{24} + S_2 = 80$$
$$X_{25} + X_{26} + X_{27} + X_{28} + X_{29} + X_{30} + X_{31} + X_{32} + X_{33} + S_3 = 150$$
$$X_{34} + X_{35} + X_{36} + X_{37} + X_{38} + X_{39} + X_{40} + X_{41} + X_{42} + S_4 = 60$$
$$X_{43} + X_{44} + X_{45} + X_{46} + X_{47} + X_{48} + S_5 = 170$$
$$X_{49} + X_{50} + X_{51} + X_{52} + X_{53} + X_{54} + S_6 = 40$$
$$X_{55} + X_{56} + X_{57} + S_7 = 200$$
$$X_{58} + X_{59} + X_{60} + S_8 = 70$$
$$X_1 + X_{13} + A_1 = 50$$
$$X_2 + X_{14} + A_2 = 60$$
$$X_3 + X_{15} + A_3 = 70$$
$$X_4 + X_{16} + X_{25} + X_{34} + A_4 = 75$$
$$X_5 + X_{17} + X_{26} + X_{35} + A_5 = 65$$
$$X_6 + X_{18} + X_{27} + X_{36} + A_6 = 80$$
$$X_7 + X_{19} + X_{28} + X_{37} + X_{43} + X_{49} + A_7 = 85$$
$$X_8 + X_{20} + X_{29} + X_{38} + X_{44} + X_{50} + A_8 = 100$$
$$X_9 + X_{21} + X_{30} + X_{39} + X_{45} + X_{51} + A_9 = 90$$
$$X_{10} + X_{22} + X_{31} + X_{40} + X_{46} + X_{52} + X_{55} + X_{58} + A_{10} = 105$$
$$X_{11} + X_{23} + X_{32} + X_{41} + X_{47} + X_{53} + X_{56} + X_{59} + A_{11} = 110$$
$$X_{12} + X_{24} + X_{33} + X_{42} + X_{48} + X_{54} + X_{57} + X_{60} + A_{12} = 120$$

involve such a substantial commitment of time that use of some electronic data processing system is the more logical alternative.

## A capital budgeting example

At any one time in the operation of a business firm, the firm usually has several different projects in which they can invest capital funds as well as some known limit on the total magnitude of capital available for investment. Usually the firm will compute some rate of return for each alternative investment (for instance, using discounted rate of return) so as to be able to rank them in terms of their desirability to the organization. If each of the alternative projects has a life of only one year and the returns from each of them are known, the problem becomes simply one of a few calculations and comparisons.

However, when the inputs of capital are not constant per year, lives of each of the projects (period over which inputs of capital and returns of savings are to be expected) differ, when the rates of return differ, and when the capital available in each of the years over which the projects will last is different, the problem of making a choice is greatly complicated because of the huge number of alternatives present. In these types of situations linear programming can be of significant help in capital budgeting. The data in Figure 9–29 describe a company which has six alternative capital projects available to it as possible investments; the present value of each of these investments together with the anticipated capital input requirements for the life of each project are illustrated. Finally the total capital investment budget for the firm for each of the future years over which the projects will require capital is given.

FIGURE 9–29
Financial Data for Capital Budgeting Decision

| | | Present Value of Required Capital Inputs in Each Year | | | | |
|---|---|---|---|---|---|---|
| Project Number | Present Value of the Returns from Each Project | Year 1 | Year 2 | Year 3 | Year 4 | Year 5 |
| $X_1$ | $ 1,000 | $ 5,000 | $ 6,000 | $ 7,000 | $ 8,000 | $ 0 |
| $X_2$ | $ 2,000 | $ 8,000 | $ 6,000 | $ 4,000 | $ 0 | $ 0 |
| $X_3$ | $ 1,500 | $ 4,000 | $ 0 | $ 0 | $ 0 | $ 0 |
| $X_4$ | $ 8,000 | $12,000 | $14,000 | $16,000 | $17,000 | $21,000 |
| $X_5$ | $15,000 | $25,000 | $30,000 | $40,000 | $ 0 | $ 0 |
| Total Capital Budget Available in Each Year | | $31,000 | $43,000 | $51,000 | $61,000 | $70,000 |

Since the capital budget for any future year (with the exception of years 4 and 5) will not allow the company to undertake all of the investment projects, some allocation of the limited budget to the most profitable projects must be made. The problem could be stated in linear programming terminology as being one of maximizing the total present value to be obtained from the projects chosen under restraints limiting the maximum capital to be spent in any one year to the amount of the capital budget available for that particular year. For example, for year 1, we could construct the following restraint:

(Year 1)
$$\$5,000X_1 + \$8,000X_2 + \$4,000X_3 + \$12,000X_4 + \$25,000X_5 \leq \$31,000.$$

This would of course ensure that the $31,000 available in that year would not be exceeded by the project chosen. In the same manner restraints covering the other four years would be constructed as follows:

(Year 2)
$$\$6,000X_1 + \$6,000X_2 + \$0X_3 + \$14,000X_4 + \$30,000X_5 \leq \$43,000$$

(Year 3)
$$\$7,000X_1 + \$4,000X_2 + \$0X_3 + \$16,000X_4 + \$40,000X_5 \leq \$51,000$$

(Year 4)
$$\$8,000X_1 + \quad \$0X_2 + \$0X_3 + \$17,000X_4 + \quad \$0X_5 \leq \$61,000$$

(Year 5)
$$\$0X_1 + \quad \$0X_2 + \$0X_3 + \$21,000X_4 + \quad \$0X_5 \leq \$70,000.$$

Since the projects we have chosen have been assumed to be single unit projects (i.e., one warehouse, one factory, one machine, etc.), we can construct additional restraints which will ensure that the projects cannot be duplicated. These can be written as follows:

$$X_1 \leq 1$$
$$X_2 \leq 1$$
$$X_3 \leq 1$$
$$X_4 \leq 1$$
$$X_5 \leq 1.$$

If on the other hand, certain of the projects could be duplicated (i.e., one or more machines of a certain type could be purchased), then we would have to allow for that when we constructed the appropriate restraints. Figure 9–30 illustrates the objective function and 10 restraint inequalities with appropriate slack variables added, assuming a limit of a single unit of any one investment project. The first simplex

FIGURE 9-30
Restraint Equalities for Capital Budgeting Problem
(Objective function: maximize $\$1,000X_1 + \$2,000X_2 + \$1,500X_3 + \$8,000X_4 + \$15,000X_5$)

$$5,000X_1 + 8,000X_2 + 4,000X_3 + 12,000X_4 + 25,000X_5 + S_1 = 31,000$$
$$6,000X_1 + 6,000X_2 + 0X_3 + 14,000X_4 + 30,000X_5 + S_2 = 43,000$$
$$7,000X_1 + 4,000X_2 + 0X_3 + 16,000X_4 + 40,000X_5 + S_3 = 51,000$$
$$8,000X_1 + 0X_2 + 0X_3 + 17,000X_4 + 0X_5 + S_4 = 61,000$$
$$0X_1 + 0X_2 + 0X_3 + 21,000X_4 + 0X_5 + S_5 = 70,000$$
$$X_1 + S_6 = 1$$
$$X_2 + S_7 = 1$$
$$X_3 + S_8 = 1$$
$$X_4 + S_9 = 1$$
$$X_5 + S_{10} = 1$$

table for the solution to this problem is illustrated in Figure 9–31. The $C_j$ values for each of the real variables ($X_1$, $X_2$, $X_3$, $X_4$, and $X_5$) are the present values for one unit of each of these investments from Figure 9–29. Using the simplex method for the solution to this prob-

FIGURE 9-31
First Simplex Maximizing Table for Capital Budgeting Problem

| $C_j$ | | | $\$1,000$ | $\$2,000$ | $\$1,500$ | $\$8,000$ | $\$15,000$ | $\$0$ | $\$0$ | $\$0$ | $\$0$ | $\$0$ | $\$0$ | $\$0$ | $\$0$ | $\$0$ | $\$0$ |
|---|---|---|---|---|---|---|---|---|---|---|---|---|---|---|---|---|---|
| | MIX | QTY. | $X_1$ | $X_2$ | $X_3$ | $X_4$ | $X_5$ | $S_1$ | $S_2$ | $S_3$ | $S_4$ | $S_5$ | $S_6$ | $S_7$ | $S_8$ | $S_9$ | $S_{10}$ |
| $\$0$ | $S_1$ | 31,000 | 5,000 | 8,000 | 4,000 | 12,000 | 25,000 | 1 | 0 | 0 | 0 | 0 | 0 | 0 | 0 | 0 | 0 |
| $\$0$ | $S_2$ | 43,000 | 6,000 | 6,000 | 0 | 14,000 | 30,000 | 0 | 1 | 0 | 0 | 0 | 0 | 0 | 0 | 0 | 0 |
| $\$0$ | $S_3$ | 51,000 | 7,000 | 4,000 | 0 | 16,000 | 40,000 | 0 | 0 | 1 | 0 | 0 | 0 | 0 | 0 | 0 | 0 |
| $\$0$ | $S_4$ | 61,000 | 8,000 | 0 | 0 | 17,000 | 0 | 0 | 0 | 0 | 1 | 0 | 0 | 0 | 0 | 0 | 0 |
| $\$0$ | $S_5$ | 70,000 | 0 | 0 | 0 | 21,000 | 0 | 0 | 0 | 0 | 0 | 1 | 0 | 0 | 0 | 0 | 0 |
| $\$0$ | $S_6$ | 1 | 1 | 0 | 0 | 0 | 0 | 0 | 0 | 0 | 0 | 0 | 1 | 0 | 0 | 0 | 0 |
| $\$0$ | $S_7$ | 1 | 0 | 1 | 0 | 0 | 0 | 0 | 0 | 0 | 0 | 0 | 0 | 1 | 0 | 0 | 0 |
| $\$0$ | $S_8$ | 1 | 0 | 0 | 1 | 0 | 0 | 0 | 0 | 0 | 0 | 0 | 0 | 0 | 1 | 0 | 0 |
| $\$0$ | $S_9$ | 1 | 0 | 0 | 0 | 1 | 0 | 0 | 0 | 0 | 0 | 0 | 0 | 0 | 0 | 1 | 0 |
| $\$0$ | $S_{10}$ | 1 | 0 | 0 | 0 | 0 | 1 | 0 | 0 | 0 | 0 | 0 | 0 | 0 | 0 | 0 | 1 |
| | $Z_j$ | | | | | | | | | | | | | | | | |
| | $C_j - Z_j$ | | | | | | | | | | | | | | | | |

lem will not guarantee that the optimum units of each of the five possible projects will be either one or zero; the answers obtained may take on fractional values; fortunately there is a method (Integer Programming) which will guarantee integer answers. While the scope of Integer Programming is beyond this book, computer programs are available which will generate integer answers to problems when such are required.

These have been only several illustrative uses of linear programming from among a large number of tested and proven applications in business and government today. The ability of management to quantify the objective and the restraints and to supply appropriate economic data represent the only practical limits to even wider use of this technique. The bibliography appearing at the end of the book will illustrate several more of the current applications of linear programming.

## Problems

1. A local firm wishes to spend $10,000 on advertising. Its goal is to reach the maximum number of potential customers with this allocated amount. The alternatives to be considered are newspaper, radio, and television advertising. The following information has been obtained and is considered to be accurate.

|  |  |  |  |
|---|---|---|---|
| Cost per advertising unit. . . . . . . . . . . . . . . | $ 250 | $ 100 | $ 2,500 |
| Number of persons reached per unit. . . . . . | 10,000 | 3,000 | 75,000 |
| Number of persons in middle and upper income brackets per unit. . . . . . . . . . . . . | 7,000 | 1,000 | 50,000 |
| Number of males above age 25 per unit. . . . | 5,000 | 500 | 25,000 |
| Maximum units available. . . . . . . . . . . . . . | — | 100 | 20 |
| Minimum units available. . . . . . . . . . . . . . | 0 | 7 | 2 |

The objectives of the firm in this advertising program are:

a) To reach at least 300,000 persons in the area,
b) At least 50 percent of those persons reached be in the middle and upper income brackets,
c) To reach at least 100,000 males above age 25.

Determine the most efficient advertising program adherent to the firm's goals and limitations.

2. Cascade Manufacturing Company produces three products *X*, *Y*, and *Z*. The company has three type A machines all of which perform the same function but at different speeds to complete the function. Likewise, Cascade has two type B machines both of which do the same work. Each product must be processed on one type A machine and also on one type B machine. The following table gives machine time (in minutes per unit) and machine requirements for each product.

| | | Machine | | | |
| Product | $A_1$ | $A_2$ | $A_3$ | $B_1$ | $B_2$ |
|---|---|---|---|---|---|
| X................. | 4 | 5 | 6 | 4 | 6 |
| Y................. | 8 | – | 7 | 6 | – |
| Z................. | – | – | 9 | – | 10 |
| Total time available (in minutes)...... | 7,000 | 4,000 | 9,000 | 6,000 | 7,000 |

Machine cost is directly proportional to operating time. All other costs, being approximately the same, can be ignored. Machine operating costs per minute are as follows:

| Machine | Cost per Minute |
|---|---|
| $A_1$................. | $0.06 |
| $A_2$................. | $0.05 |
| $A_3$................. | $0.45 |
| $B_1$................. | $0.08 |
| $B_2$................. | $0.10 |

The minimum sales demands below were forecast for the given time period.

| Product | Minimum Demand |
|---|---|
| X................. | 750 |
| Y................. | 500 |
| Z................. | 250 |

You are to determine a production schedule which will minimize costs.

3. As a management consultant to Prospect Industries, Inc., you are presented the following information:

| Sources | | Users | |
|---|---|---|---|
| Location | Available Quantity | Location | Quantity Required |
| Factory A.... | 200 units | Warehouse X.... | 160 units |
| Factory B.... | 350 units | Warehouse Y.... | 100 units |
| | | Warehouse Z.... | 140 units |

| *Shipping Cost per Unit* | | *Storage Cost per Unit* | |
|---|---|---|---|
| Factory A to warehouse $X$.... | $0.10 | at factory A.... | $0.07 |
| Factory A to warehouse $Y$.... | 0.13 | at factory B.... | 0.06 |
| Factory A to warehouse $Z$.... | 0.12 | at warehouse $X$. | 0.04 |
| Factory B to warehouse $X$.... | 0.14 | at warehouse $Y$. | 0.07 |
| Factory B to warehouse $Y$.... | 0.11 | at warehouse $Z$. | 0.05 |
| Factory B to warehouse $Z$.... | 0.19 | | |

In addition, factory B has built up excess inventory and must ship out at least 250 units. The capacities (in excess of actual needs) of warehouses $X$, $Y$, and $Z$ are; respectively, 200, 200, and none. You are assigned the task of determining that particular shipping schedule which will minimize the total cost of shipping and storage.

What would be the value to the company of building a 100-unit warehouse at warehouse $Z$?

4. During a given time period an automobile production plant can manufacture combinations of these three models:

| Model | Contribution per Unit |
|---|---|
| Convertible.......... | $300 |
| Sweptback.......... | $250 |
| Squareback........ | $220 |

Each model must pass through four machine centers enroute to completion of finished product. Individual model requirements in terms of hours are as follows:

| Product | Center 1 | Center 2 | Center 3 | Center 4 |
|---|---|---|---|---|
| Convertible........... | 3 hours per unit | 4 hours per unit | 1 hour per unit | 3 hours per unit |
| Sweptback........... | 2 hours per unit | 3 hours per unit | 2 hours per unit | 4 hours per unit |
| Squareback........... | 2 hours per unit | 2 hours per unit | 3 hours per unit | 2 hours per unit |
| Available hours per center............. | 600 | 700 | 500 | 700 |

Maximum anticipated sales for the time period are shown below along with minimum demands for certain models due to unfilled backorders.

| Model | Maximum Demand | Minimum Demand |
|---|---|---|
| Convertible........... | 150 | 60 |
| Sweptback............ | 100 | 0 |
| Squareback.......... | 75 | 35 |

Four basic materials are required in this production process. The table below sets forth the per unit requirements for each model and the availability of each material for the time period.

| Model | Material A | Material B | Material C | Material D |
|-------|-----------|-----------|-----------|-----------|
| Convertible........ | 1½ tons per unit | 100 pounds per unit | 350 pounds per unit | 25 pounds per unit |
| Sweptback......... | 1¼ tons per unit | 80 pounds per unit | 325 pounds per unit | 30 pounds per unit |
| Squareback........ | ¾ tons per unit | 50 pounds per unit | 150 pounds per unit | 30 pounds per unit |
| Total available...... | 400 tons | 12 tons | 30 tons | 7,000 pounds |

Determine the optimum manufacturing schedule for the time period if the basic criterion of the company is to maximize contribution to fixed cost and profit.

What would the company pay per hour for extra supplies of material C?

5. As production manager of Apex, Inc. you have the task of determining the production schedule for next year given the following information:

| | Demand in Plant Hours | | | Plant Hours Available | | |
|---|---|---|---|---|---|---|
| | Product X | Product Y | Total | Regular Time Hours | Overtime Hours | Total |
| 1st Quarter | 60 | 60 | 120 | 200 | 70 | 270 |
| 2nd Quarter | 70 | 100 | 170 | 140 | 40 | 180 |
| 3rd Quarter | 120 | 110 | 230 | 140 | 50 | 190 |
| 4th Quarter | 120 | 160 | 280 | 140 | 70 | 210 |
| Total | 370 | 330 | 800 | 620 | 230 | 850 |

The accounting department has computed the premium cost of overtime per hour of production. These costs for products $X$ and $Y$ are, respectively: $1.20 and $0.80. The same department also supplies you with the cost to hold one hour's production for one quarter for product $X$ and $Y$. These are, respectively: $0.40 and $0.70.

Set up the primal linear programming problem and solve for the production scheduling solution which will minimize total cost.

6. The Longview Corporation is faced with the following alternative investment projects:

| Type Project | Present Value of Returns from Project | Present Value of Required Capital Expenditures Each Year | | | | |
|---|---|---|---|---|---|---|
| | | Year 1 | Year 2 | Year 3 | Year 4 | Year 5 |
| A...... | $15,000 | $ 5,000 | $10,000 | $15,000 | 0 | $ 5,000 |
| B...... | $ 1,000 | $ 5,000 | 0 | $ 5,000 | 0 | $ 5,000 |
| C...... | $ 4,000 | $ 1,000 | $ 5,000 | $ 9,000 | 0 | 0 |
| D...... | $ 9,000 | $ 5,000 | $10,000 | $15,000 | $20,000 | $25,000 |
| E...... | $25,000 | $50,000 | $40,000 | $30,000 | $20,000 | $10,000 |

Sixty thousand dollars will be available each year for investment. Noninteger solutions are feasible because all of these projects are open to the investor in small increments.

The company wishes to limit its investment on these type A projects to 30 percent of its total investment.

In addition the firm desires that at least 40 percent of its investment be in projects of types D and E.

Allocate the budget to those projects that will result in the highest total yield.

# chapter 10

# Linear programming and electronic computers

To a large extent, the success of linear programming in both its theoretical development and its application is due to the development of the electronic computer. This valuable tool has made it possible to attack large-scale problems, which otherwise would have been impossible or economically impractical to solve.

There is ample evidence to indicate that the development of linear programming has paralleled the development of the electronic computer. The first truly electronic computer, in terms of its internal operation, was the Electronic Numerical Integrator and Computer (ENIAC). Completed in 1946 by the Moore School of Electrical Engineering at the University of Pennsylvania, the ENIAC contained 18,000 vacuum tubes and was used primarily for solving problems of trajectory for the Ballistics Research Laboratories at the Aberdeen Proving Grounds. In 1947, Dantzig developed and successfully applied the general linear programming problem for the Department of the Air Force. The first successful solution of a linear programming problem on an electronic computer took place in January, 1952, at the National Bureau of Standards.

With the development of the transistor, the second generation of computers was born. Transistorized computers became available commercially in 1959. Today all modern computers use solid state and very few first generation computers are operational. The third generation of computers using microelectronics is currently in advanced stages of development. At the end of 1954 fewer than 10 electronic computers were in use. At the present time there are over 20,000 domestic installations involving more than 100 types of general purpose electronic computers.

In this chapter, we will not be concerned with the intricate details of computer programming or computer construction. However, since the computer, used in conjunction with linear programming methods, represents an ideal instrument for the solution of problems, it would be helpful to have some knowledge of the general working characteristics of computers in much the same way that it is helpful for the automobile driver to know something of the general working characteristics of his car. Furthermore, we want to discuss the use and availability of special computer programs, sometimes referred to as canned programs, which have been written specifically to solve linear programming problems. Since no attempt will be made to cover these topics in depth, a special list of references will be found at the end of this chapter.

## The computer and its basic units

The term electronic computer is applicable to two basically different types of machines, digital and analog computers. The digital computer operates on numbers (digits) performing the arithmetic operations (addition, subtraction, multiplication, and division) in a manner similar to the desk calculator. On the other hand, rather than computing directly with numbers, the analog computer manipulates some physical quantity, such as voltage or length or frequency of an electric current, which represents the numbers that are being computed. The slide rule, for example, operates by the analog principle—multiplying by combining two lengths. We shall concentrate on digital computers, since most linear programming problems are solved on digital computers, rather than analog computers.

## Basic computer units

Although digital computers vary a great deal in size, speed and operational details, most of them have the same basic logical structure. The functional relationships that exist between the basic sections of any digital computer are shown in Figure 10–1. The solid lines in Figure 10–1 indicate information flow and the broken lines represent implementation of the control function.

The computer has five basic units: input, memory or storage, arithmetic, output, and control. Let us consider the function of each unit.

FIGURE 10–1
Basic Computer Units

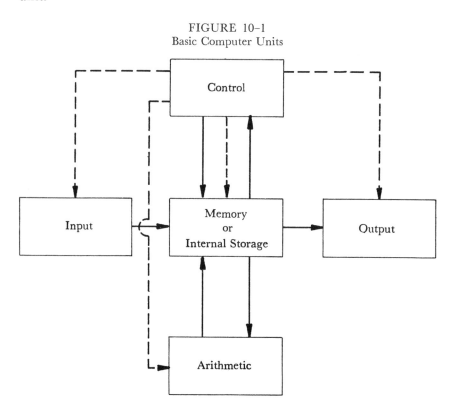

### Input

All information is usually entered into the computer through the input unit and placed directly in the storage unit. A number of input devices exist to convert the information to a form that the computer can utilize, for example, punched cards, punched paper tape, magnetic tape and magnetic-ink characters. One or more of these devices may be used to enter information into a computer at various speeds depending on the input device used. For example, one high-speed magnetic tape unit has a speed of 100,000 characters per second. The average typist can type about 60 words per minute or five characters per second, a word being defined as five characters. One of these tape units, therefore is roughly equivalent in speed to 20,000 typists. The information entering the computer is either a set of instructions which tell the computer what to do, or it represents the raw data to be processed.

## *Memory*

From the input device or devices, the information is transmitted to the memory or storage unit. In addition to receiving the raw data and computer instructions from an input device, the memory unit exchanges data with and supplies instructions to the arithmetic unit, and provides data to the output unit.

The memory unit of a computer is divided into locations, and each of these locations is identified by a number called the address of that location. Thus its arrangement is similar to a group of numbered mailboxes in a post office. Each location holds a specific unit of information. In order to insert, remove, or recall information, the address of the location must be known. In computer terminology a location is referred to as a word. A computer's memory capacity is usually measured in words. A word is a group of characters or digits that may be processed by the computer at one time. For example, the UNIVAC 1108 has a memory capacity of 32,768 to 131,072 words. The amount of information that a word or address can hold varies depending upon the type of computer.

The time required to locate and transfer information to or from a single memory location is known as access time. Several different concepts have been used to provide memory with rapid access, including magnetic drums and thin film. From the standpoint of the user of the machine, the major difference between the memory devices is their speed. The average access time for the magnetic drum is measured in thousandths of a second (milliseconds) and ranges from 1 to 20 milliseconds; the average access time for the magnetic core is measured in millionths of a second (microseconds) and varies between 1 and 50 microseconds; and the film memory has an average access time measured in billionths of seconds (nanoseconds). Finally, the size and complexity of problems and the time required to process them are determined by the capacity and speed of the memory unit.

### Arithmetic

After information has been entered into the computer and placed in specific memory locations, processing can begin. The arithmetic unit performs the operations of addition, subtraction, multiplication, division, shifting, and sorting. In addition the arithmetic unit can perform logical operations which distinguishes the computer from all other computation devices. For example, in comparing two numbers, say $X$ and $Y$, there are three possible outcomes: $X$ is equal to $Y$; $X$ is smaller than $Y$; $X$ is larger than $Y$. With each possible outcome, there is associated a set of instructions. After the arithmetic unit has compared the two numbers, it will follow a given set of instructions depending upon the desired outcome of the comparison. An example of a logical operation in the simplex method would be the comparison of the numbers in the $C_j - Z_j$ row to determine if any improvement is possible. Here the computer would follow a given path of instructions depending upon the outcome. In a maximization problem one outcome might show that all the numbers are zero or negative indicating that the optimum solution had been obtained. The computer might then be instructed to print out the final solution. If some of the numbers were positive, then the computer would follow another given path of instructions.

The speed of the arithmetic unit will range from 100 operations per second to over 1,000,000 operations per second depending upon the size and cost of the machine. An even more vivid example of speed is given by Eckert and Jones **5**. Consider the multiplication of two 10-digit numbers. If we had to perform a thousand such multiplications, the time required by various methods would be approximately as follows:

> By hand........................ 1 week
> Using a desk calculator............. 1 day
> With a small electronic computer..... 1 minute
> With a very large computer.......... 1 second

### Output

The output unit provides the means for transmitting the results of the processing to the outside world. Conventionally used output devices are: magnetic tape, paper tape, punched cards, on-line printers, plotting machines, and various types of optical devices. The punched cards, punched paper tape, and magnetic tape can be processed further on auxiliary equipment (high-speed printers) to present the user with a report in a form convenient for him as well as understandable. This usually means that the output is printed on paper as numbers, letters, or words. High-speed printers vary in speed from about 150 lines per minute to 1,000 lines per minute or more. In some cases, the output may be left on cards or tape to be re-entered into the computer for further processing.

## Control

The control unit directs the operation of the entire computer system. All other units are dependent upon the truly amazing ability of the control unit. It is in the control section that the various computer instructions are interpreted into action, specifying exactly what each part of the computer system is to do and exactly when each operation is to begin. This involves directing the input unit to enter information into the memory unit; instructing memory where to place this information; regulating the operations in the arithmetic unit; and finally transferring the proper information to the correct output device. All of this is accomplished by means of a stored program.

## The stored program

A computer program is a set of instructions that directs the computer to produce a desired result. The writing of these instructions is called programming. Essentially, computer programming requires that the problem be reduced to a sequence of elementary computational steps or machine operations before it can be solved. Hence, each instruction defines a basic operation to be performed and identifies the device necessary to carry out the operation. The set of instructions that the computer must carry out is stored in the memory of the computer, hence, the term stored program.

A general purpose computer can be compared to a carpenter's lathe which is a tool designed to perform many different tasks. The immediate task that the lathe will perform depends upon how the lathe operator sets up the machine. Once the lathe is cutting the wood it is executing the instructions the operator commanded it to perform. With one major exception the computer operates in much the same way as the lathe. The stored program is the operator that sets up the computer to perform a specific task. Once the computer is processing data, it is executing the instructions that the program commanded it to perform. The computer, however, has one major advantage over the lathe. It can modify its sequence of instructions during execution. For example, a lathe cannot be instructed to cut around a knot of wood whenever it encounters one. The lathe opera-

FIGURE 10-2
Basic Block Diagram for the Simplex Method

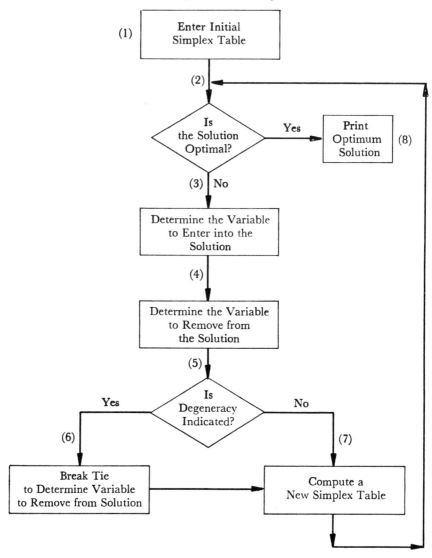

tor must intervene. The computer, however, can be set up (programmed) to disrupt its normal sequence of processing depending upon some designated yes-or-no condition. These so-called branching instructions decide on the basis of the answer to a specific question where in memory to go for the next instruction. Through this branching ability, the computer can handle data processing situations in which exceptions occur.

To illustrate the yes-or-no conditions in the solution to a linear programming problem, we have diagrammed in Figure 10–2 the basic simplex procedure.

The diagrammatic representation in Figure 10–2 is referred to as a block diagram or flow chart. The first step in programming a problem is to construct a basic flow chart to provide the programmer with a means of describing the sequence in which logical and arithmetic operations should take place, and the relationship between one part of the program and another. Before actually writing the computer program, the programmer would probably construct a detailed flow chart for each of the blocks in Figure 10–2. Our primary concern is to give an example of the yes-or-no conditions that occur in the basic block diagram of the simplex method. These take place first in examining the $C_j - Z_j$ row to determine whether the optimum solution has been obtained (step 2 in diagram), and, second, in testing the solution for degeneracy (step 5 in diagram). At each of these points the computer would be programmed to follow a given path of instructions depending upon the yes-or-no condition that occurred.

## Linear programming codes

As pointed out earlier, it is not necessary to know the intricate details of electronic computers or computer programming in order to solve a linear programming problem on a computer. Computer manufacturers have devoted a great deal of time to the development of program packages for certain rather specialized applications such as linear programming. These linear programming packages, often referred to as linear programming codes or canned programs, have been standardized and tested for use in solving linear programming problems. The fact that linear programming codes have been written and are available for use on almost every type of computer presently being operated indicates the importance of the linear programming technique. From the users' standpoint, this results in a substantial savings in planning and programming costs, since all that is required is to convert the raw data to punched cards, magnetic tape, or other suitable input devices to the given computer.

Although the computer manufacturer is the primary source of these specialized programs, the users of a particular type of computer have, in some cases, formed an organization for the general dissemination of information concerning applications and techniques common to their computer needs. These organizations have large cooperative libraries of programs available to members. One of the largest of these is the IBM "SHARE" organization (the Society to Help Avoid Redundant Effort).

### A sample of linear programming codes

In order to appreciate the size and scope of linear programming codes, a sample of the codes, available for various types of computers will be examined. For a more complete and detailed discussion of available codes the reader should consult reference 7 in listing at the end of this chapter. Since data of this type do not remain up-to-date for any length of time, the current status of the codes available for any given computer should be obtained from the manufacturer or user organization.

As a basis for comparing different computers and their linear programming capabilities, three arbitrary classifications of computer systems have been selected: small-scale, medium-scale, and large-scale. Typical systems under each classification and average monthly rentals are given in Figure 10–3 and reference 4.

Each linear programming code is designed to handle problems of various dimensions. Hence, computer manufacturers' information concerning the codes available for their computers includes the number of constraints or equations (designated by the letter $m$) and the number of variables or columns ($n$) that can be processed at one time. With regard to those codes available to solve the transportation problem, the number of sources, $m$, and the number of destinations, $n$, are given for each code. Also included is information concerning the technique employed in solving the problem. For example, a transportation problem may be solved using either the stepping-stone method or the MODI method. Many of the codes available for solving the transportation problem use the MODI method since it is computationally more efficient than the stepping-stone technique.

FIGURE 10-3

| | Large-Scale Systems | |
| *Over $100,000* | *$50,000 to $75,000* | *$30,000 to $50,000* |
|---|---|---|
| IBM 360/92 | IBM 7090, 7094 | IBM 360/60 |
| Control Data 6800 | Control Data 3800, 3600 | Control Data 1604 |
| UNIVAC LARC | UNIVAC 1108 | UNIVAC 1107 |

| | Medium-Scale Systems | |
| *$20,000 to $30,000* | *$12,000 to $20,000* | *$8,000 to $12,000* |
|---|---|---|
| IBM 360/50 | Burroughs B5000 | IBM 360/40 |
| Control Data 3400 | GE 210 | Control Data 924 |
| RCA 3301 | IBM 7040 | NCR 315 |

| | Small-Scale Systems | |
| *$4,000 to $8,000* | *$2,000 to $4,000* | *Under $2,000* |
|---|---|---|
| IBM 360/30 | Control Data 160A | IBM 1620 |
| Control Data 3100 | IBM 650 | UNIVAC 1004 |
| Honeywell 400 | SDS 920 | Control Data 160 |
| GE 425 | ASI 2100 | NCR 390 |

Likewise there are variations of the standard simplex method which are used in linear programming codes because of their computational efficiency. The revised simplex method is one such variation that is often used. For a detailed discussion of the variations of the simplex method, the reader is referred to Cutler and Wolfe **2**.

A sample of available codes is given below for both linear programming and transportation problems. Each code listed gives the type of computer, the code identification number, the technique used, and dimensions (size of problem that can be handled with the given code).

*Linear programming simplex codes*
1. Computer:      IBM 740
   Identification: RS M1
   Technique:      Revised Simplex Method
   Dimensions:     $m \leq 97$ (rows or constraints)
                   $n \leq 299$ (columns or variables)
                   $mn \leq 2,499$ (number of nonzero entries in table)

2. Computer:       IBM 7090
   Identification: LP/90 (CEIR, Inc.)
   Technique:      Revised Simplex Method
   Dimensions:     $m \leq 512$
                   $n$   unlimited

3. Computer:       UNIVAC 1108
   Identification: UNIVAC 1108 L.P.
   Technique:      Staged-Pivot-Product-Form Algorithm, a variation of standard simplex method
   Dimensions:     $m \leq 4,094$
                   $n \leq 99,000$

4. Computer:       Control Data 1604
   Identification: CDM3/LP Publication Number 526
   Technique:      Revised Simplex Method
   Dimensions:     $m \leq 400$
                   $n \leq 999$

5. Computer:       IBM 650
   Identification: LP 10.1001
   Technique:      Standard Simplex Method
   Dimensions:     $m \leq 30$
                   $n \leq 59$
                   $m(n+1) \leq 1,400$

6. Computer:       Burroughs Datatron
   Identification: Datatron L.P.
   Technique:      Standard Simplex Method
   Dimensions:     $m \leq 40$
                   $n \leq 200$
                   $mn \leq 3,000$

*Transportation codes*

1. Computer:       IBM 704
   Identification: SDA 3225
   Technique:      Stepping-Stone Method
   Dimensions:     $m$ (sources) $+ n$ (destinations) $\leq 318$

2. Computer:       IBM 704
   Identification: The Transportation Problem NYRT1
   Dimensions:     $n \leq 800$
                   $m + n \leq 5,500$
                   $mn \leq 700,000$

3. Computer:       IBM 704
   Identification: IBTFL
   Technique:      Hungarian Method
   Dimensions:     $n \leq 600$
                   no restriction on $m$

## Using the codes

### *Formulating the problem*

Particularly important when solving linear programming problems on the computer is the correct formulation of the problem. All variables and restraints must be clearly defined, as well as the objective function. Errors in setting up the problem may lead to degeneracy. On computers that rent for over $800 per hour, these errors obviously can be very costly.

### *Choosing the code*

Having formulated the problem, it is necessary to investigate the available computers and linear programming codes. The choice of a given code depends on the size of the problem, the speed of the code, and rental charges for the computer. As shown in the sample of codes, the size of the problem that can be handled is given for each particular code. On the other hand, computation time for a given problem may be difficult to estimate. In many cases, write-ups of linear programming codes usually include an estimate of computation time for an example problem; but, for an entirely different size problem, this may be of little value in estimating computation time. Also, the type of computer used is an important factor with regard to both computation time and computation cost. In a problem solved by Naylor and Byrne **11**, 30 hours of computer time were required using an IBM 650 with an hourly rental rate of $50 per hour. The same problem was solved in slightly more than one hour using the IBM 709 with an hourly rental rate of $700. Clearly, the IBM 709 provided the least cost alternative.

For relatively small problems, an attempt should be made to compare the time necessary to solve the problem using hand calculations with the computer time required to solve the problem; computer time in this case would include the time required to prepare the data for input into a computer. In some cases, the computational cost of a linear programming solution may be greater than the saving that it produces. Thus, as with all techniques used in operations research, one should attempt to apply the cost-versus-benefit criterion.

### Preparing the unit

For most linear programming simplex codes, it is necessary to set up the initial simplex table. This table is then entered into the computer from punched cards, magnetic tape, or punched paper tape. Only the nonzero elements of the initial table are read into the computer, since zeros are usually stored in all locations of the computer memory prior to entering the nonzero elements. Finally, the costs assigned to the artificial variables should be large enough relative to other costs to force the artificial variables out of the final solution.

### Output

Most linear programming codes provide the following types of information on the print-out. After each iteration, the code will (1) identify the variable entering the solution, (2) give the value of the objective function, and (3) provide a count of the number of iterations. Finally, when the optimum solution has been obtained, the code will provide a complete print out of the final simplex table and the total number of iterations required.

We have included in Appendix A of this chapter a relatively simple linear programming code written in FORTRAN IV which will solve small linear programming problems. This program prints each simplex table in its entirety after each iteration so that the student can follow the iterative process as it moves toward the optimal solution.

### Computer applications of linear programming problems

With the development of the high-speed computer the solution of large-scale linear programming problems has become economically feasible. For example, the solution of a problem with 38 equations and 41 variables (excluding slack and artificial variables) required six seconds, computation time, on a Philco S-2000. The same problem would require several hours per iteration, using a desk calculator. A transportation problem involving 15 sources and 488 destinations took 20 minutes on a UNIVAC II.

The solution to these problems and to a linear programming problem of any size and complexity involves hundreds of thousands of simple repetitive calculations which would be impractical without a computer. This point is well illustrated by the following example from Martin **9**.

. . . it takes about an hour on an IBM 7094 computer to do the equivalent of a million man-hours of desk calculator work. At an hourly rate of $575 for rental of the computer, it costs just one cent for the equivalent of three man-days of desk calculator effort. One dollar buys as much calculating as a man could do in a year!

Large-scale linear programming problems are indeed prevalent in business. The Dupont Company, for example, has solved problems involving over 800 constraints and 2,500 variables. Many large-scale applications can also be found in the petroleum industry. The value of linear programming to this industry has been estimated at $50,000,000 per year compared to an estimate of $3,000,000 for computer rental costs **10**.

The relationship between computers and linear programming applications is a reciprocal one; the nature of the equipment and programming methods influences the applications and the needs of the applications influence the development of computer technology and programming methods. Given the rapid development of computer technology and computationally efficient methods, we can only conclude that the number and size of applications of linear programming in industry will continue to increase.

## Selected references

1. Charnes, A., and Cooper, W. W. *Management Models and Industrial Applications of Linear Programming*, Vol. 1 (New York: John Wiley & Sons, Inc., 1961).
2. Cutler, L., and Wolfe, P. "Experiments in Linear Programming," *Rand Report*, RM-3402-PR (Santa Monica, Calif.: RAND Corporation, February, 1963).
3. Dantzig, G. B., "Computational Algorithm of the Revised Simplex Method." *Rand Report*, RM-1266 (Santa Monica, Calif.: RAND Corporation, 1953).

4. Davis, B. D., *An Introduction to Electronic Computers* (New York: McGraw-Hill Book Co., 1965).

5. Eckert, W. J., and Jones, R., *Faster, Faster* (International Business Machines Corporation, 1955).

6. Elliot, C. O., and Wasley, R., *Business Information Processing Systems* (Homewood, Ill.: Richard D. Irwin, Inc., 1965).

7. Gass, S. I., "Recent Developments in Linear Programming." *Advances in Computers*, ed. F. L. Alt (New York: Academic Press, Inc., 1961), pp. 296–366.

8. Graves, R. L., and Wolfe Phillip (eds.). *Recent Advances in Mathematical Programming* New York: McGraw-Hill Book Co., 1963).

9. Martin, E. W., *Electronic Data Processing* (Homewood, Ill.: Richard D. Irwin, Inc., 1965).

10. McKeague, G. C., "The Value of Linear Programming to the Petroleum Industry," *Computer Applications—1962*, ed. M. M. Gutterman and R. S. Hollitch (London: Cleaver-Hume Press, 1964), pp. 169–76.

11. Naylor, T. H., and Byrne, E. T., *Linear Programming* (Belmont, Calif.: Wadsworth Publishing Company, Inc., 1963).

12. Withington, F. G., *The Use of Computers in Business Organizations* (Reading, Mass.: Addison-Wesley Publishing Co., 1966).

# *Appendix*

In this Appendix we have included a relatively simple simplex algorithm written in FORTRAN IV which will solve small linear programming problems. The output section of the program prints each tableau in its entirety so that the student can follow the logical development of the iterative process as it seeks the optimal solution. This program is dimensioned to handle problems that have as many as 50 rows and 100 columns including all the slack and artificial variables. However, since the program uses a step-by-step process to calculate the entries in each table and does not contain a test for degeneracy, it is recommended as a pedagogical tool only.

The user must add all the slack and artificial variables to the objective function and the constraint-equations following the procedures outlined in Chapters 4 and 5.

### Structuring a problem for solution

The problem below will provide an example of the procedure to be followed in structuring a problem for solution by this program. The problem is the example used as an illustration in Chapter 5. (Note—the user can alter the format specifications to suit his purpose. The formating used in this program is specifically tailored for the solution to problems in this text.)

$$\text{Min.} \quad Z = 4X_1 + 5X_2 + 3X_3$$

Subject to:

$$X_1 \leq 30$$
$$X_2 \geq 20$$
$$X_3 \leq 40$$
$$X_1 + X_2 + X_3 = 100$$

**Step I.** Convert constraint inequations to equations.

$$1X_1 + 0X_2 + 0X_3 + 1X_4 + 0X_5 + 0X_6 + 0X_7 + 0X_8 = 30$$
$$0X_1 + 1X_2 + 0X_3 + 0X_4 - 1X_5 + 1X_6 + 0X_7 + 0X_8 = 20$$
$$0X_1 + 0X_2 + 1X_3 + 0X_4 + 0X_5 + 0X_6 + 1X_7 + 0X_8 = 40$$
$$1X_1 + 1X_2 + 1X_3 + 0X_4 + 0X_5 + 0X_6 + 0X_7 + 1X_8 = 100$$

where in our problem $X_4$, $X_5$, and $X_7$ are slack variables and where $X_6$ and $X_8$ are artificial variables.

**Step II.** Revise objective function to include artificial and slack variables.

Min. $Z = 4X_1 + 5X_2 + 3X_3 + 0X_4 + 0X_5 + 1,000X_6 + 0X_7 + 1,000X_8.$

**Step III.** Rearrange constraint-equations with identity matrix first followed by the real variables and then the remaining slack and artificial variables.

$$1X_4 + 0X_6 + 0X_7 + 0X_8 + 1X_1 + 0X_2 + 0X_3 + 0X_5 = 30$$
$$0X_4 + 1X_6 + 0X_7 + 0X_8 + 0X_1 + 1X_2 + 0X_3 - 1X_5 = 20$$
$$0X_4 + 0X_6 + 1X_7 + 0X_8 + 0X_1 + 0X_2 + 1X_3 + 0X_5 = 40$$
$$0X_4 + 0X_6 + 0X_7 + 1X_8 + 1X_1 + 1X_2 + 1X_3 + 0X_5 = 100.$$

**Step IV.** Rearrange objective function into the same column order as revised constraint equations.

Min. $Z = 0X_4 + 1000X_6 + 0X_7 + 1000X_8 + 4X_1 + 5X_2 + 3X_3 + 0X_5.$

**Step V.** Prepare data cards.

### Preparing individual cards

An explanation of the methods used to prepare the individual cards is given below, followed by a listing of the data set for this problem. (Note—letters are used to aid in identifying cards for explanation and are not part of the data set.)

### Title and control card (A)

| | | |
|---|---|---|
| Columns 1–6 | Alphameric problem label | (Example) |
| Columns 11–13 | Number of rows in initial solution | (4) |
| Columns 14–16 | Total number of variables in problem | (8) |
| Column 19 | An integer (one) must appear here at all times | (1) |

Subscript values of the variables in the initial solution (B)

List in row order the subscript values of the variables in the initial solution. In our example, the subscript values of the variable in the initial solution are 4, 6, 7, and 8. Maximum of 26 values per card in integer fields of I 3. Do not use columns 79 or 80.

Constraint constant column (C)

Values of the right-hand side of the constraint equations. Maximum of 7 values per card in floating point fields of F 11.3. Do not use columns 78, 79, or 80.

Coefficients of variables in the objective function (D, E)

The values assigned to the variables in the objective function in column orders as determined in the revised objective function. Maximum of 7 values per card in floating point fields of F 11.3. Do not use columns 78, 79, or 80.

Column subscripts (F)

*Subscripts* of variables in column order as determined in revised constraint equations. Maximum of 26 values per card in integer fields of I 3. Do not use columns 79 or 80.

Tableau entries (G–N)

Tableau entries are loaded by row and column with a maximum of 7 values per card in floating point fields of F 11.3, excluding columns 78, 79, or 80. Note that each new row must begin on a new card.

### EXAMPLE PROBLEM DATA SET

| | | | | | | | | |
|---|---|---|---|---|---|---|---|---|
| A. | EXAMPLE | 4 | 8 | 1 | | | | |
| B. | 4 6 7 8 | | | | | | | |
| C. | 30. | 20. | 40. | 100. | | | |
| D. | 0. | 1000. | 0. | 1000. | 4. | 5. | 3. |
| E. | 0. | | | | | | |
| F. | 4 6 7 8 1 2 3 5 | | | | | | | |
| G. | 1. | 0. | 0. | 0. | 1. | 0. | 0. |
| H. | 0. | | | | | | |

| | | | | | | | |
|---|---|---|---|---|---|---|---|
| I. | 0. | 1. | 0. | 0. | 0. | 1. | 0. |
| J. | 1. | | | | | | |
| K. | 0. | 0. | 1. | 0. | 0. | 0. | 1. |
| L. | 0. | | | | | | |
| M. | 0. | 0. | 0. | 1. | 1. | 1. | 1. |
| N. | 0. | | | | | | |

The number of data cards will vary with each problem selected for solution, however by following the structure outlined on the previous page, the user can prepare acceptable data decks for any size problem. In addition, the user can process multiple data sets by stacking data sets behind each other. The program will operate on each set until all the data have been exhausted.

**Maximization case**

The procedure for solving problems of the maximization type are the same as for the minimization type with two notable exceptions. The objective function must be multiplied by $-1$ after the introduction of the slack and artificial variables in Step II of the procedure outlined on the previous pages. Secondly, since the coefficients of the real variables in the objective function are all negative, the optimal solution will have a negative value for the total profit of the variables in the product mix. To adjust this, the user must multiply this figure by $-1$ converting it to a positive and economically meaningful quantity after the optimal solution has been found.

The following is a print out of the solution to the example problem on the previous page obtained from an IBM 7094.

```
$DATA
PROBLEM EXAMPL        ITERATION  0

                                  0.        1000.000        0.        1000.000      4.000
                               X( 4)      X( 6)        X( 7)      X( 8)      X( 1)
       0.     X( 4)    30.000   1.000      0.          0.         C.         1.000
 10C0.000   X( 6)    20.000   0.         1.000       0.         0.         0.
       0.     X( 7)    40.000   0.         0.          1.000      0.         0.
 1000.000   X( 8)   100.0C0   0.         0.          C.         1.000      1.000

              120000.00C       0.       1000.000     C.       1000.000   1000.000
                               0.          0.          0.          0.       996.000


                                  5.000        3.000        0.
                               X( 2)      X( 3)        X( 5)      X(
       0.     X( 4)    30.0C0   C.         0.          C.
 10C0.000   X( 6)    20.000   1.000      0.         -1.000
       0.     X( 7)    40.0C0   0.         1.000       0.
 10C0.000   X( 8)   100.0C0   1.00C      1.C00       0.

              120000.000     2000.000   1000.000  -1C00.C00
                             1995.000    997.000  -1000.000

PROBLEM EXAMPL        ITERATICN  1

                                  0.        1000.000        0.        1000.0C0      4.000
                               X( 4)      X( 6)        X( 7)      X( 8)      X( 1)
       0.     X( 4)    30.000   1.000     -0.         -0.        -0.         1.000
   5.000   X( 2)    20.000   0.         1.000       C.         0.         0.
       0.     X( 7)    40.000  -0.        -0.          1.000     -C.        -0.
 1000.000   X( 8)    80.000  -0.        -1.000      -0.         1.0CC      1.000

              80100.00C      -0.        -995.000     -0.       1000.000   1000.CC0
                             -0.       -1995.000     -0.         0.       996.CCC


                                  5.C00        3.000        C.
                               X( 2)      X( 3)        X( 5)      X(
       0.     X( 4)    30.0C0  -0.        -0.          C.
   5.000   X( 2)    20.000   1.000      0.         -1.CCC
       0.     X( 7)    40.000  -C.        1.C00       C.
 10C0.000   X( 8)    80.000  -C.        1.000       1.CCC

              80100.000       5.000   1000.000     995.0C0
                             0.        997.C00     995.CC0

PROBLEM EXAMPL        ITERATICN  2

                                  0.        1000.000        0.        1000.000      4.CCC
                               X( 4)      X( 6)        X( 7)      X( 8)      X( 1)
       0.     X( 4)    30.0C0   1.000     -0.          C.        -0.         1.000
   5.000   X( 2)    20.000   0.         1.000       -0.        0.         0.
   3.000   X( 3)    40.0C0  -0.        -0.          1.000     -0.        -0.
 10C0.0C0   X( 8)    40.0C0   0.        -1.C00       -1.000      1.000      1.000




              40220.00C       0.        -995.000    -997.000   1000.000   1000.CCC
                             0.       -1995.000    -SS7.000     0.       SS6.CCC


                                  5.000        3.000        C.
                               X( 2)      X( 3)        X( 5)      X(
       0.     X( 4)    30.0C0  -C.        0.          C.
   5.000   X( 2)    20.0C0   1.00C     -0.         -1.CCC
   3.000   X( 3)    40.0C0  -C.        1.C00       C.
 1000.000   X( 8)    40.000   0.        -0.          1.000

              40220.00C       5.000      3.000      SS5.000
                             0.          0.        SS5.000
```

PROBLEM EXAMPL          ITERATICN  3

|  |  |  | 0. | 1000.000 | 0. | 1000.000 | 4.000 |
|---|---|---|---|---|---|---|---|
|  |  |  | X( 4) | X( 6) | X( 7) | X( 8) | X( 1) |
| 4.000 | X( 1) | 30.000 | 1.000 | -0. | 0. | -0. | 1.000 |
| 5.000 | X( 2) | 20.000 | -0. | 1.000 | -0. | 0. | -0. |
| 3.000 | X( 3) | 40.000 | 0. | -0. | 1.000 | -0. | 0. |
| 1000.000 | X( 8) | 10.000 | -1.000 | -1.000 | -1.000 | 1.000 | -0. |
|  |  | 10340.000 | -996.000 | -995.000 | -997.000 | 1000.000 | 4.000 |
|  |  |  | -996.000 | -1995.000 | -997.000 | 0. | 0. |

|  |  |  | 5.000 | 3.000 | 0. |  |
|---|---|---|---|---|---|---|
|  |  |  | X( 2) | X( 3) | X( 5) | X( |
| 4.000 | X( 1) | 30.000 | -0. | 0. | C. |  |
| 5.000 | X( 2) | 20.000 | 1.000 | -0. | -1.000 |  |
| 3.000 | X( 3) | 40.000 | -0. | 1.000 | 0. |  |
| 1000.000 | X( 8) | 10.000 | 0. | -0. | 1.000 |  |
|  |  | 10340.000 | 5.000 | 3.000 | 995.000 |  |
|  |  |  | 0. | 0. | 995.000 |  |

PROBLEM EXAMPL          ITERATICN  4

|  |  |  | 0. | 1000.000 | 0. | 1000.000 | 4.000 |
|---|---|---|---|---|---|---|---|
|  |  |  | X( 4) | X( 6) | X( 7) | X( 8) | X( 1) |
| 4.000 | X( 1) | 30.000 | 1.000 | 0. | 0. | -0. | 1.000 |
| 5.000 | X( 2) | 30.000 | -1.000 | -0. | -1.000 | 1.000 | -0. |
| 3.000 | X( 3) | 40.000 | 0. | 0. | 1.000 | -0. | 0. |
| 0. | X( 5) | 10.000 | -1.000 | -1.000 | -1.000 | 1.000 | -0. |
|  |  | 390.00C | -1.000 | -0. | -2.000 | 5.000 | 4.000 |
|  |  |  | -1.000 | -1000.000 | -2.000 | -995.000 | 0. |

|  |  |  | 5.000 | 3.000 | 0. |  |
|---|---|---|---|---|---|---|
|  |  |  | X( 2) | X( 3) | X( 5) | X( |
| 4.000 | X( 1) | 30.000 | -C. | 0. | -0. |  |
| 5.000 | X( 2) | 30.000 | 1.000 | -0. | 0. |  |
| 3.000 | X( 3) | 40.000 | -0. | 1.000 | -0. |  |
| 0. | X( 5) | 10.000 | 0. | -0. | 1.000 |  |
|  |  | 390.000 | 5.000 | 3.000 | 0. |  |
|  |  |  | 0. | 0. | 0. |  |

OPTIMAL SOLUTION FOUND

```
C
C        SIMPLEX ALGORITHM ( INPUT VARIABLE DICTIONARY )
C
C           PROB   -ALPHAMERIC PROBLEM LABEL ( UP TO 6 CHARACTERS )
C
C           NXI(I)-NUMBERS ( SUBSCRIPTS ) OF VARIABLES IN INITIAL
C                    SOLUTION IN ROW ORDER
C
C           B(I)   -RIGHT-HAND SIDE VALUES FOR INITIAL SOLUTION
C                    IN ROW ORDER
C
C           CJ(J)  -COSTS OF VARIABLES ( PROGRAM MINIMIZES OBJECTIVE
C                    FUNCTION SO THAT MAXIMIZATION REQUIRES THAT
C                    OBJECTIVE FUNCTION BE MULTIPLIED BY -1. )
C
C           NXJ(J)-NUMBERS ( SUBSCRIPTS ) OF ALL VARIABLES IN
C                    COLUMN ORDER
C
C           A(I,J)-TABLEAU ENTRIES ( BY ROW AND COLUMN )
C
C
C
C        SIMPLEX ALGORITHM  (BEGIN)
C
         DIMENSION CI(50),NXI(50),B(50),CJ(100),NXJ(100),
        1    A(50,100), Z(100), ZC(100)
C
C        READ DATA.
C
       1 READ(5,61) PROB,M,N,KODE
         READ(5,62)(NXI(I),I=1,M)
         READ(5,63)(B(I),I=1,M)
         READ(5,63)(CJ(J),J=1,N)
         READ(5,62)(NXJ(J),J=1,N)
         DO 7 I=1,M
       7 READ(5,63)(A(I,J), J=1,N)
C
C        SETUP CI.
C
         DO 15 I=1,M
         DO 15 J=1,N
         IF (NXI(I)-NXJ(J)) 15,14,15
      14 CI(I)=CJ(J)
      15 CONTINUE
         ITER = 0
C
C        COMPUTE Z AND ZC.
C
      21 DO 25 J=1, N
         Z(J) =0.0
         DO 24 I=1,M
      24 Z(J) = Z(J)+CI(I)*A(I,J)
      25 ZC(J) = Z(J)-CJ(J)
         OBJ = 0.0
         DO 28 I=1,M
      28 OBJ = OBJ+CI(I)*B(I)
C
C        PRINT TABLEAU.
C
```

```
      WRITE(6,64)PROB,ITER
      N1 = 1
      N2 = 5
   43 IF (N2-N) 45,45,44
   44 N2 = N
   45 WRITE(6,65)(CJ(J),J=N1,N2)
      WRITE(6,66)(NXJ(J),J=N1,N2)
      DO 48 I=1,M
   48 WRITE(6,67)CI(I),NXI(I),B(I),(A (I,J),J=N1,N2)
      WRITE(6,68)OBJ,(Z(J),J=N1,N2)
      WRITE(6,69)(ZC(J),J=N1,N2)
      IF (N2-N) 52,55,55
   52 N1 = N1+5
      N2 = N2+5
      GO TO 43
   55 WRITE(6,70)
      ITER = ITER+1
C
C     DETERMINE PIVOT COLUMN.
C
      ZCM = ZC(1)
      JM = 1
      DO 109  J=2,N
      IF (KODE) 106,105,106
  105 IF (ZC(J)-ZCM) 107,109,109
  106 IF (ZC(J)-ZCM) 109,109,107
  107 ZCM = ZC(J)
      JM = J
  109 CONTINUE
C
C     CHECK FOR OPTIMAL.
C
      IF (KODE) 122,121,122
  121 IF (ZCM)   131,123,123
  122 IF (ZCM)   123,123,131
  123 WRITE(6,71)
      GO TO 1
C
C     DETERMINE PIVOT ROW.
C
  131 XM = 1.0E38
      IM = 0
      DO 139 I=1,M
      IF (A(I,JM)) 139,139,135
  135 XX = B(I)/A(I,JM)
      IF (XX-XM) 137,139,139
  137 XM = XX
      IM = I
  139 CONTINUE
      IF (IM) 141,141,151
  141 WRITE(6,72)
      GO TO 1
C
C     PERFORM PIVOT OPERATION.
C
  151 XX = A(IM,JM)
      B(IM) = B(IM)/XX
      DO 154 J=1,N
  154 A(IM,J) = A(IM,J)/XX

      DO 161 I=1,M
      IF (I-IM) 157,161,157
  157 XX = A(I,JM)
      B(I) = B(I)-XX * B(IM)
      DO 160 J=1,N
  160 A(I,J) = A(I,J)-XX * A(IM,J)
  161 CONTINUE
      CI(IM) = CJ(JM)
      NXI(IM) = NXJ(JM)
      GO TO 21
C
   61 FORMAT (A6,4X,3I3)
   62 FORMAT (26I3,2X)
   63 FORMAT (7F11.3,3X)
   64 FORMAT (9H PROBLEM A6, 8X,9HITERATION I3//)
   65 FORMAT (28X,5F11.3)
   66 FORMAT (28X,5(6H   X(I2,2H)   )  )
   67 FORMAT (1X, F9.3,  3H X(I2,1H), F10.3, 1X, 5F10.3)
   68 FORMAT (/15X,F10.3,3X,5F10.3)
   69 FORMAT (28X,5F10.3////)
   70 FORMAT (79X,1H-)
   71 FORMAT (23H OPTIMAL SOLUTION FO ND/79X,1H-)
   72 FORMAT (19H UNBOUNDED SOLUTION/ 9X,1H-)
      END
$DATA
```

# Bibliography

## Books

ARROW, KENNETH J., HURWICZ, LEONID, and UZAWA, HIROFUMI, *Studies in Linear and Non-Linear Programming*. Stanford, Calif.: Stanford University Press, 1958.

BENNION, EDWARD G. *Element Mathematics of Linear Programming and Game Theory*. East Lansing, Mich.: Michigan State University Press, 1960.

BOULDING, KENNETH EWART. *Linear Programming and the Theory of the Firm*. New York: The Macmillan Company, 1960.

BRISTOL, JAMES D. *An Introduction to Linear Programming*. Boston: D. C. Heath & Co., Boston, 1963.

CHARNES, ABRAHAM, and COOPER, W. W. *Management Models and Industrial Applications of Linear Programming*. New York: John Wiley & Sons, Inc. 1961.

CHENG, DAVID K. *Analysis of Linear Systems*. Reading, Mass.: Addison-Wesley Publishing Co., Inc., 1959.

CHUNG, AN-MIN. *Linear Programming*. Columbus, Ohio: Charles E. Merrill Books, Inc., 1963.

CONFERENCE ON RESEARCH IN INCOME AND WEALTH. *Input-Output Analysis, an Appraisal*. Princeton, N. J.: Princeton University Press, 1955.

COOPER, W. W., and HENDERSON, A. *Introduction to Linear Programming*. New York: John Wiley & Sons, Inc., 1953.

CRAM, DAVID. *Explaining "Teaching Machines" and Programming*. San Francisco: Fearon Publishers, Inc., 1961.

CROWELL, RICHARD H., and WILLIAMSON, R. E.: *Calculus of Vector Functions*. Englewood Cliffs, N. J.: Prentice-Hall, Inc., 1962.

CURTIS, CHARLES W. *Linear Algebra, an Introductory Approach*. Boston: Allyn & Bacon, Inc., 1963.

DANG, SVEN. *Linear Programming in Industry*. Vienna: Springer Publishers, 1960.

DANTZIG, GEORGE BERNARD. *Linear Programming and Extensions.* Princeton, N. J.: Princeton University Press, 1963.

DICKSON, LEONARD EUGENE. *Linear Algebra.* New York: Hafner Publishing Co., Inc., 1960.

DORFMAN, ROBERT, SAMUELSON, PAUL A., and SOLOW, ROBERT M. *Linear Programming and Economic Analysis.* New York: McGraw-Hill Book Co., 1958.

FERGUSON, ROBERT O., and SARGENT, LAUREN F. *Linear Programming; Fundamentals and Applications.* New York: McGraw-Hill Book Co., 1958.

FICKEN, FREDERICK ARTHUR. *The Simplex Method of Linear Programming.* New York: Holt, Rinehart, & Winston, Inc., 1961.

FORD, L. R., JR., and FULKERSON, D. R. *Flows in Networks.* Princeton, N.J.: Princeton University Press, 1962.

GALE, DAVID. *The Theory of Linear Economic Models.* New York: McGraw-Hill Book Co., 1960.

GARVIN, WALTER W. *Introduction to Linear Programming.* New York: McGraw-Hill Book Co., 1960.

GASS, SAUL I. *Linear Programming; Methods and Applications.* New York: McGraw-Hill Book Co., 1964.

GEARY, ROBERT CHARLES, and MCCARTHY, M. D. *Elements of Linear Programming with Economic Applications.* New York: Hafner Publishing Co., Inc., 1964.

GLICKSMAN, ABRAHAM M. *An Introduction to Linear Programming and the Theory of Games.* New York: John Wiley & Sons, Inc., 1963.

GRAVES, ROBERT L., and WOLFE, PHILIP (eds.). *Recent Advances in Mathematical Programming.* New York: McGraw-Hill Book Co., 1963.

GRAYBILL, FRANKLIN A. *An Introduction to Linear Statistical Models.* New York: McGraw-Hill Book Co., 1961.

GREENWALD, DAKOTA ULRICH. *Linear Programming.* New York: The Ronald Press Co., 1957.

HADLEY, GEORGE. *Linear Algebra.* Reading, Mass.: Addison-Wesley Publishing Co., 1961.

———. *Linear Programming.* Reading, Mass.: Addison-Wesley Publishing Co., 1962.

HAMMOND, PERCIVAL HUDSON. *Feedback Theory and Its Applications.* New York: The Macmillan Co., 1958.

HEADY, EARL O., and CANDLER, WILFRED. *Linear Programming Methods.* Ames, Ia.: State College Press, 1958.

HENDERSON, JAMES M. *The Efficiency of the Coal Industry; An Application of Linear Programming.* Cambridge, Mass.: Harvard University Press, 1958.

KARLIN, SAMUEL. *Mathematical Methods and Theory in Games, Programming, and Economics.* Reading, Mass.: Addison-Wesley Publishing Co., 1959.

LLEWELLYN, ROBERT W. *Linear Programming.* New York: Holt, Rinehart, & Winston, Inc., 1964.

LOOMBA, N. PAUL. *Linear Programming, an Introductory Analysis.* New York: McGraw-Hill Book Co., 1964.

MATHEWS, JEROLD C., and LANGENHOP, CARL E. *Discrete and Continuous Methods in Applied Mathematics.* New York: John Wiley & Sons, Inc., 1966.

MEISELS, KURT. *A Primer in Linear Programming.* New York: New York University Press, 1962.

METZGER, ROBERT W. *Elementary Mathematical Programming.* New York: John Wiley & Sons, Inc., 1958.

MILLER, RONALD E. *Domestic Airline Efficiency; An Application of Linear Programming.* Cambridge, Mass.: The M.I.T. Press, 1963.

MIRSKY, LEONID. *An Introduction to Linear Algebra.* Oxford: Clarendon Press, 1955.

MORGENSTERN, OSKAR (ed.). *Economic Activity Analysis.* New York: John Wiley & Sons, Inc., 1954.

MORISHIMA, MICHIO. *Equilibrium, Stability, and Growth; A Multi-Sectoral Analysis.* Oxford: Clarendon Press, 1964.

NERING, EVAR D. *Linear Algebra and Matrix Theory.* New York: John Wiley & Sons, Inc., 1963.

REINFELD, NYLES V., and VOGEL, WILLIAM R. *Mathematical Programming.* Englewood Cliffs, N. J.: Prentice-Hall, Inc., 1960.

RILEY, VERA, and GASS, SAUL I. *Linear Programming and Associated Techniques.* Baltimore: The Johns Hopkins Press, 1958.

SIMONNARD, MICHEL. *Linear Programming.* Englewood Cliffs, N. J.: Prentice-Hall, Inc., 1966.

SPIVEY, W. ALLEN. *Linear Programming, An Introduction.* New York: The Macmillan Co., 1963.

STEWART, FRANK MOORE. *Introduction to Linear Algebra.* Princeton, N. J.: D. Van Nostrand Co., Inc., 1963.

STOLL, ROBERT ROTH. *Linear Algebra and Matrix Theory.* New York: McGraw-Hill Book Co., 1952.

SYMONDS, GIFFORD H. *Linear Programming; The Solution of Refinery Problems.* New York: Esso Standard Oil Company, 1955.

VAJDA, STEVEN. *An Introduction to Linear Programming and the Theory of Games.* New York: John Wiley & Sons, Inc., 1960.

———. *Readings in Mathematical Programming.* New York: John Wiley & Sons, Inc., 1962.

————. *Readings in Linear Programming.* New York: John Wiley & Sons, Inc., 1958.

VAZSONYI, ANDREW. *Scientific Programming in Business and Industry.* New York: John Wiley & Sons, 1958.

WEINGARTNER, H. MARTIN. *Mathematical Programming and the Analysis of Capital Budgeting Problems.* Englewood Cliffs, N.J.: Prentice-Hall, Inc., 1963.

WEISS, LIONEL. *Statistical Decision Theory.* New York: McGraw-Hill Book Co., 1961.

ZAANEN, ADRIAAN COR ELIS. *Linear Analysis.* New York: Interscience Publishers, 1953.

## Articles

ARONOFSKY, J. S. "Linear Programming; Problem Solving Tool for Petroleum Industry Management," *Journal of Petroleum Technology,* Vol. 14 (July, 1962), pp. 729–36.

BABBAR, M. M. "Distributions of Solutions of a Set of Linear Equations (with an Application to Linear Programming)," *Journal of the American Statistical Association,* Vol. 50, No. 271 (September, 1955), pp. 854–69.

BARANKIN, EDWARD W. "On Systems of Linear Equations, with Applications to Linear Programming—and the Theory of Tests of Statistical Hypotheses," *University of California Publications in Statistics,* Vol. 1, No. 8 (1951), pp. 161–214.

BAUMOL, W. J., and WOLFE, P. "Warehouse-Location Problem," *Operations Research,* Vol. 6 (March, 1958), pp. 252–63.

BEALE, E. M. L. "Cycling in the Dual Simplex Algorithm," *Naval Research Logistics Quarterly,* Vol. 2, No. 4 (December, 1955), pp. 269–76.

BOAS, A. H. "Optimizing via Linear and Dynamic Programming," *Chemical Engineering,* Vol. 70 (April, 1963), pp. 85–88.

BOLES, JAMES N. "Short Cuts in Programming Computations," *Journal of Farm Economics,* Vol. 38, No. 4 (November, 1956), pp. 981–90.

BOWMAN, E. H. "Schedule—Sequencing Problem," *Operations Research,* Vol. 7 (September, 1959), pp. 621, 4.
*Operations Research,* Vol. 8 (January, 1960), pp. 101–11.

CHENEVEY, J. E. "What Is Linear Programming and How Do You Put It to Work?" *Oil and Gas Journal,* Vol. 58 (March, 1960), pp. 113–16.

CONSTANT, P. C., JR. "Matrix Computation Methods," *Electro-Technology,* Vol. 72 (November, 1963), pp. 68–73.

COURTILLOT, M. "Varying All the Parameters in a Linear Programming Problem," *Operations Research*, Vol. 10 (July, 1962), pp. 471–75.

CROES, G. A. "Method for Solving Traveling Salesman Problems," *Operations Research*, Vol. 6 (November, 1958), pp. 791–812.

DANTZIG, GEORGE B. "The Central Mathematical Problem," The RAND Corporation, p. 892., July 9, 1956.

DANTZIG, G. B., *et al.* "Linear Programming, Combinatorial Approach to the Traveling-Salesman Problem," *Operations Research*, Vol. 7 (January, 1959), pp. 58–66.

DANTZIG, G. B., and WOLFE, P. "Decomposition Principle for Linear Programs," *Operations Research*, Vol. 8 (January, 1960), pp. 101–11.

DENNIS, J. B. "High-Speed Computer Technique for the Transportation Problem; Stepping-Stone Method," *Journal of the Association for Computing Machinery*, Vol. 5 (April, 1958), pp. 132–53.

DULMAGE, A. L., and MENDELSOHN, N. S. "Matrices Associated with the Hitchcock Problem," *Journal of the Association for Computing Machinery*, Vol. 9 (October, 1962), pp. 409–18.

EARLE, E. P., "Economic Decisions and Scheduling for the Small Plant," *Chemical Engineering*, Vol. 69 (June, 1962), pp. 118–20.

EISEMANN, K. "Primac-Dual Method for Bounded Variables," *Operations Research*, Vol. 12 (January, 1964), pp. 110–21.

ELMAGHRABY, S. E. "Approach to Linear Programming under Uncertainty," *Operations Research*, Vol. 7 (March, 1959), pp. 208–16.

ENRICK, N. L. "Improve Your Profit Picture," *Textile Industries*, Vol. 128 (April, 1964), pp. 111–15.

———. "Modern Textile Management; Linear Programming, New Management Tool, Helps Match Production and Sales," *Textile Industries*, Vol. 125 (March, 1961), pp. 71–73.

FEGLEY, K. A. "Designing Sampled-Data Control Systems by Linear Programming," *IEEE Transactions on Applications and Industry*, Vol. 83 (May, 1964), pp. 198–200.

GILMORE, P. C. and GOMORY, R. E. "Linear Programming Approach to the Cutting Stock Problem," *Operations Research*, Vol. 11 (November, 1963), pp. 863–88.

GOLDMAN, ALAN J., and TUCKER, ALBERT W. "Theory of Linear Programming," *Annals of Mathematics Studies*, No. 38, Princeton University Press, Princeton, N.J., 1956, p. 53–97.

HADLEY, G. F. "Linear Programming Can Be Easy Math," *Product Engineering*, Vol. 29 (March, 1958), pp. 55–58.

HALEY, K. B. "Solid Transportation Problem," *Operations Research*, Vol. 10 (July, 1962), pp. 448–63.

HAYWARD, A. P., *et al.* "Minimization of Fuel Costs by the Technique of Linear Programming," *Power Apparatus and Systems*, February, 1959, pp. 1288–93.

HEAD, R. V. "Seven Configurations for Real-Time Computer Systems," *Control Engineering*, Vol. 11 (June, 1964), pp. 104–08.

HEALY, W. C., JR. "Multiple Choice Programming," *Operations Research*, *Vol.* 12 (January, 1964), pp. 122–38.

HERTZ, D. B., and OLSON, N. O. "Profitable Control of Production and Transportation through Operations Research," *Mining Congress Journal* Vol. 47 (October, 1961), pp. 47–50.

HILTY, D. C., *et al.* "Predicting Minimum Materials Cost for Stainless Steels," *Journal of Metals*, Vol. 11 (July, 1959), pp. 458–64.

INSTRUMENTS AND CONTROL SYSTEMS, "Solving Simultaneous Linear Equations with an Iterative Computer," Vol. 38 (January, 1965).

JEWELL, W. S. "Classroom Example of Linear Programming," *Operations Research*, Vol. 8 (July, 1960), pp. 565–70.

KARUSH, W. and MOODY, L. A. "Determination of Feasible Shipping Schedules for a Job Shop," *Operations Research*, Vol. 6 (January, 1958), pp. 35–55.

KAWARATANI, T. K., *et al.* "Computing Tetraethyl-Lead Requirements in a Linear-Programming Format," *Operations Research*, Vol. 8 (January, 1960), pp. 24–29.

KILLIN, E. L. "Highway-Traffic Estimation by Linear Programming," *Proceedings of the American Society of Civil Engineers*, Vol. 85 (January, 1959), pp. 17–33.

KLAHR, C. N. "Multiple Objectives in Mathematical Programming," *Operations Research*, Vol. 6 (November, 1958), pp. 849–55.

KNIGHT, U. G. W. "Logical Design of Electrical Networks Using Linear Programming Methods," *Proceedings of the Institute of Electrical Engineering*, Vol. 107 (June, 1960), pp. 306–14.

KURTZBERG, J. M. "Approximation Methods for the Assignment Problem," *Journal of the Association for Computing Machinery*, Vol. 9 (October, 1962), pp. 419–39.

LANDES, R. "Optimizing Refinery Operations with a Digital Computer," *ISA Journal*, Vol. 6 (January, 1959), pp. 66–69.

LANDSLY, G. L. "Linear Programming Tells You How to Run Several Refineries the Best Way," *Petroleum Refiner*, Vol. 38 (February, 1959), pp. 139–41.

LEE, A. S., and ARONOFSKY, J. S. "Linear Programming Model for Scheduling Crude Oil Production," *Journal of Petroleum Technology*, Vol. 10 (July, 1958), pp. 51–54.

MACHOL, R. E. "Application of the Assignment Problem," *Operations Research*, Vol. 9 (July, 1961), pp. 585–86.

MADANSKY, A. "Methods of Solution of Linear Programs under Uncertainty," *Operations Research*, Vol. 10 (July, 1962), pp. 463–71.

MAGEE, F. H. "Planning Your Distribution," *Modern Materials Handling*, Vol. 13 (April, 1958), pp. 110–13.

MANNE, A. S. "On the Job-Shop Scheduling Problem," *Operations Research*, Vol. 8 (March, 1960), pp. 219–23.

MARTINO, R. L. "How to Calculate Best Product Mix," *Canadian Chemical Processing*, Vol. 48 (October, 1964), pp. 76.

McCLUSKEY, E. J., JR. "Error-Correcting Codes; Linear Programming Approach," *Bell System Technical Journal*, Vol. 38 (November, 1959), pp. 1485–1512

McINTIRE, R. L. "What Is Linear Programming?" *Oil and Gas Journal*, Vol. 55 (November 25, 1957), p. 121.

————. "How to Solve Those Linear Programming Problems," *Oil and Gas Journal*, Vol. 55 (December, 1957), p. 135.

MOORE, J. C., and VANDEGRIFT, J. B. "Programming Technique Assigns Work to Machines," *Machinery*, Vol. 66 (January, 1960), pp. 103–06.

NICHOLS, C. R. "How to Formulate a Linear-Programming Model for Refinery Simulation," *Oil and Gas Journal*, Vol. 57 (February, 1959), pp. 101–06.

PEARSON, CARL E. "Note on Linear Programming, *Quarterly of Applied Mathematics*, Vol. 14, No. 2 (July, 1956), pp. 205–06.

PEART, R. M., *et al.* "Optimizing Systems When Components Have Discontinuous Cost Functions," *Operations Research*, Vol. 9 (July, 1961), pp. 468–78.

PINKHAM, R. "Approach to Linear Inventory-Production Rules," *Operations Research*, Vol. 6 (March, 1958), pp. 185–89.

POLLACK, M., and WIEBENSON, W. "Solutions of the Shortest Route Problem," *Operations Research*, Vol. 9 (January, 1961), pp. 129–32.

RAM, V. B., *et al.* "Take the Guesswork out of Blending with Linear Programming," *Textile Industries*, Vol. 128 (February, 1964), pp. 75–77.

RITTER, J. B., and SHAEFFER, L. R. "Blending Natural Earth Deposits for Least Cost; Applicability of Linear Programming," *Proceedings of the American Society of Civil Engineers*, Vol. 87 (March, 1961), pp. 39–61.

ROTHMAN, H. and REILLY, P. "Computer Systems for Matrix Operations," *Proceeding from the American Society of Civil Engineers*, Vol. 90 (June, 1964), pp. 125–46.

SAATY, T. L. "Coefficient Perturbation of a Constrained Extremum," *Operations Research*, Vol. 7 (May, 1959), pp. 294–302.

————. "Conjecture Concerning the Smallest Bound on the Iterations in Linear Programming," *Operations Research*, Vol. 11 (January, 1963), pp. 151–53.

SCHOOMER, B. A. "Incorporation of Step Functions and Ramp Functions into a Linear Programming Model," *Operations Research*, Vol. 12 (September, 1964), pp. 773–77.

SHETTY, C. M. "Solution to the Transportation Problem with Nonlinear Costs," *Operations Research*, Vol. 7 (September, 1959), pp. 571–80.

SIMPSON, K. F., JR. "Theory of Allocation of Stocks to Warehouses," *Operations Research*, Vol. 7 (November, 1959), pp. 797–805.

SINDEN, F. W. "Mechanisms for Linear Programs," *Operations Research*, Vol. 7 (November, 1959), pp. 728–39.

SPIEGELMAN, S. "Linear Programming, Tool for Small Business," *American Machinist*, Vol. 102 (June 16, 1958), pp. 110–12.

THEILER, T. C. "Linear Programming and Optimal Cutting Policies," *Paper Industry*, Vol. 41 (September, 1959), pp. 384–86.

TORNG, H. C. "Optimization of Discrete Control Systems through Linear Programming," *Journal of the Franklin Institute*, Vol. 278 (July, 1964), pp. 28–44.

TOTSCHEK, R., and WOOD, R. C. "Investigation of Real-Time Solution of the Transportation Problem," *Journal of the Association for Computing Machinery*, Vol. 8 (April, 1961), pp. 230–39.

VAN DUYNE, R. W. "Linear Programming and the Paper Industry," *Tappi*, Vol. 44 (May, 1961), pp. 189A–93A.

WAGNER, H. M. "Simplex Method for Beginners," *Operations Research*, Vol. 6 (March, 1958), pp. 190–99.

————. "Practical Guide to the Dual Theorem," *Operations Research*, Vol. 6 (May, 1958), pp. 364–84.

WEBB, K. W. "Some Aspects of the Saaty Linear Programming Sensitivity Equation," *Operations Research*, Vol. 10 (March, 1962), pp. 266–67.

WILDE, D. J. "Production Planning of Large Systems," *Chemical Engineering Progress*, Vol. 59 (January, 1963), pp. 46–61.

WOLFE, P. "Some Simplex-Like Non-Linear Programming Procedures," *Operations Research*, Vol. 10 (July, 1962), pp. 438–47.

————, and DANTZIG, G. B. "Linear Programming in a Markov Chain," *Operations Research*, Vol. 10 (September, 1962), pp. 702–10.

ZABORSZKY, J., and DIESEL, J. W. "Design for Minimum Probabilistic Error of Continuous Linear Control Systems Subject to Constraints," *Applications and Industry*, May, 1960, pp. 44–54.

# Index

*This book has been set in 11 and 10 point Baskerville, leaded 2 points. Chapter numbers are in 14 point Baskerville Bold; chapter titles are in 24 point Bulmer italic. The size of the type page is 27 x 45 picas.*